RĂZVAN PETRESCU
SMALL CHANGES IN ATTITUDE

Translated by James Christian Brown

Featured Artist
Daniel Bălănescu

University of Plymouth Press

20 ROMANIAN WRITERS SERIES

Răzvan Petrescu's *Small Changes in Attitude* is the twelfth title to be published in the series 20 Romanian Writers by the University of Plymouth Press. The series is one aspect of the University of Plymouth's ongoing commitment to introduce Romania's vibrant artistic culture to other nations. In addition to the literature, the University of Plymouth is hosting a series of exhibitions and performances of Romania's visual and musical arts over five years to coincide with the publications. The following supplement features one of Romania's leading contemporary artists.

Featured Artist

DANIEL BĂLĂNESCU

Daniel Bălănescu (born 1967) studied at the University of Fine Arts, Faculty of Decorative Arts and Design, Bucharest, Romania with Professor Olga Birman-Sabău. Bălănescu's work is inspired by human nature and the turmoil of our times. After the isolation and restrictions of the Ceauşescu years, new freedoms and ideas from the West were not what he expected. Petrescu's stories, like Bălănescu's work, are faithful renditions of scenes framed in visions, and thoughts in a dark zone, which eventually open up into pools of light.

Personal exhibitions by Bălănescu include *Atittudes* at Cărtureşti, Bucharest, 2007, and *25 Years of Metro*, Brussels, 2001. Group exhibitions have included *Blaue Stunde* at Gallery 11, Cologne, and *Artists for Peace* at Dolmabahçe Gallery, Istanbul, Turkey, both in 2009. Other group exhibitions Balkanart, Čačak, Serbia, 2007, and *Make Friends, Not War* at Ripustus Art Gallery, Hämeenlinna, Finland, 2005, illustrate Bălănescu's concerns. His work has also appeared in movies and stage design.

MAD

LEAVING

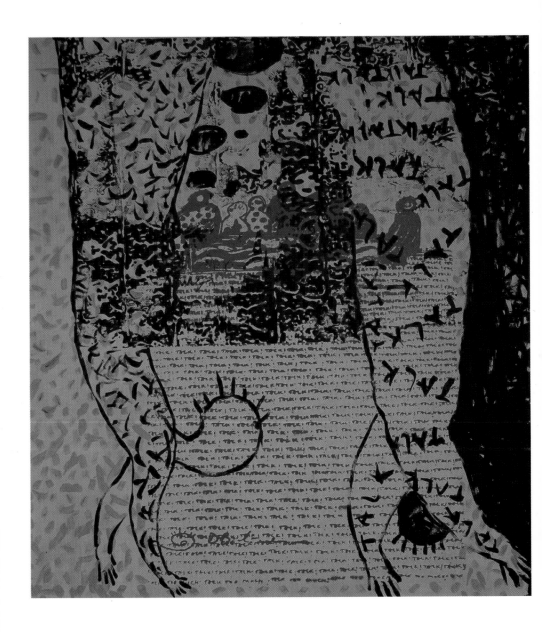

ANGELS

TALK! TALK! TALK! TALK! TALK! TALK! TALK! TALK! TALK! TALK!
TALK! TALK! TALK! TALK! TALK! TALK! TALK! TALK! TALK! TALK!
TALK! TALK! TALK! TALK! TALK! TALK! TALK! TALK! TALK! TALK!
TALK! TALK! TALK! TALK! TALK! TALK! TALK! TALK! TALK! TALK!
TALK! TALK! TALK! TALK! TALK! TALK! TALK! TALK! TALK! TALK!
TALK! TALK! TALK! TALK! TALK! TALK! TALK! TALK! TALK! TALK!
TALK! TALK! TALK! TALK! TALK! TALK! TALK! TALK! TALK! TALK!
TALK! TALK! TALK! TALK! TALK! TALK! TALK! TALK! TALK! TALK!
TALK! TALK! TALK! TALK! TALK! TALK! TALK! TALK! TALK! TALK!
TALK! TALK! TALK! TALK! TALK! TALK! TALK! TALK! TALK! TALK!
TALK! TALK! TALK! TALK! TALK! TALK! TALK! TALK! TALK! TALK!
TALK! TALK! TALK! TALK! TALK! TALK! TALK! TALK! TALK! TALK!
TALK! TALK! TALK! TALK! TALK! TALK! TALK! TALK! TALK! TALK!
TALK! TALK! TALK! TALK! TALK! TALK! TALK! TALK! TALK! TALK!
TALK! TALK! TALK! TALK! TALK! TALK! TALK! TALK! TALK! TALK!
TALK! TALK! TALK! TALK! TALK! TALK! TALK! TALK! TALK! TALK!
TALK! TALK! TALK! TALK! TALK! TALK! TALK! TALK! TALK! TALK!
TALK! TALK! TALK! TALK! TALK! TALK! TALK! TALK! TALK! TALK!
TALK! TALK! TALK! TALK! TALK! TALK! TALK! TALK! TALK! TALK!
TALK! TALK! TALK! TALK! TALK! TALK! TALK! TALK! TALK! TALK!
TALK! TALK! TALK! TALK! TALK! TALK! TALK! TALK! TALK! TALK!
TALK! TALK! TALK! TALK! TALK! TALK! TALK! TALK! TALK! TALK!
TALK! TALK! TALK! TALK! TALK! TALK! TALK! TALK! TALK! TALK!
TALK! TALK! TALK! TALK! TALK! TALK! TALK! TALK! TALK! TALK!
TALK! TALK! TALK! TALK! TALK! TALK! TALK! TALK! TALK! TALK!
TALK! TALK! TALK! TALK! TALK! TALK! TALK! TALK! TALK! TALK!
TALK! TALK! TALK! TALK! TALK! TALK! TALK! TALK! TALK! TALK!
TALK! TALK! TALK! TALK! TALK! TALK! TALK! TALK! TALK! TALK!
TALK! TALK! TALK! TALK! TALK! TALK! TALK! TALK! TALK! TALK!

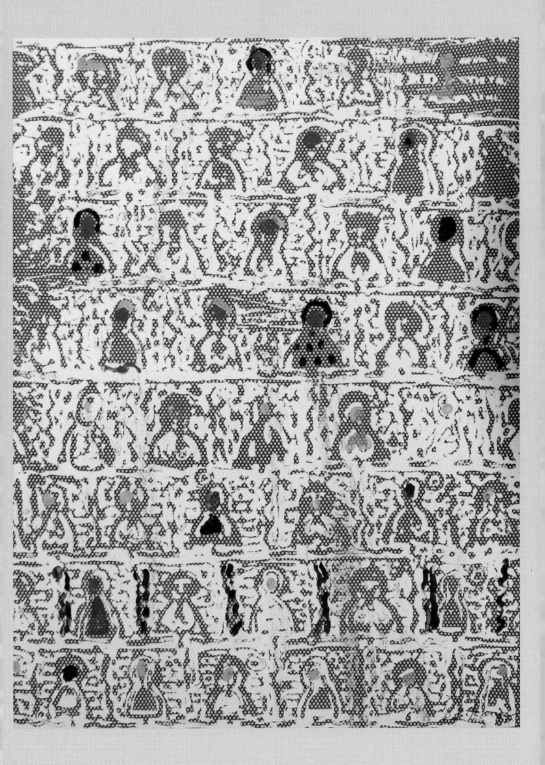

PEOPLE

ÉTRANGER! ÉTRANGER! ÉTRANGER!
ÉTRANGER! ÉTRANGER! ÉTRANGER!
FOREIGNER! ÉTRANGER!
ÉTRANGER! ÉTRANGER! ÉTRANGER!
BLUE!
BUM! BUM! BUM!
ETRANGER

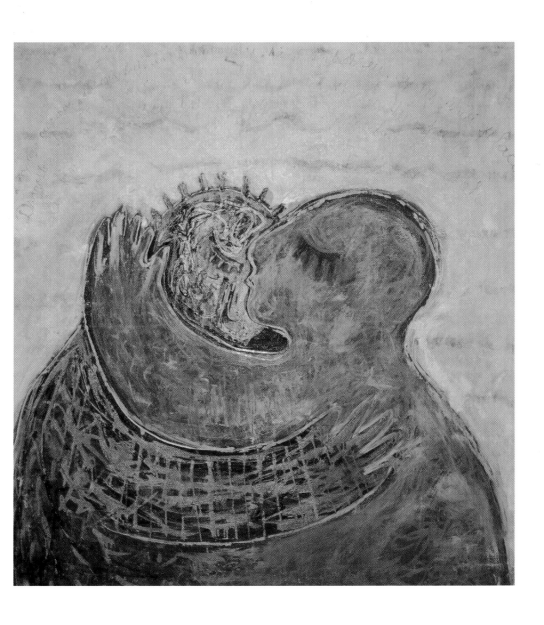

LOVERS

I TAKE CARE OF YOU

NO ANGELS

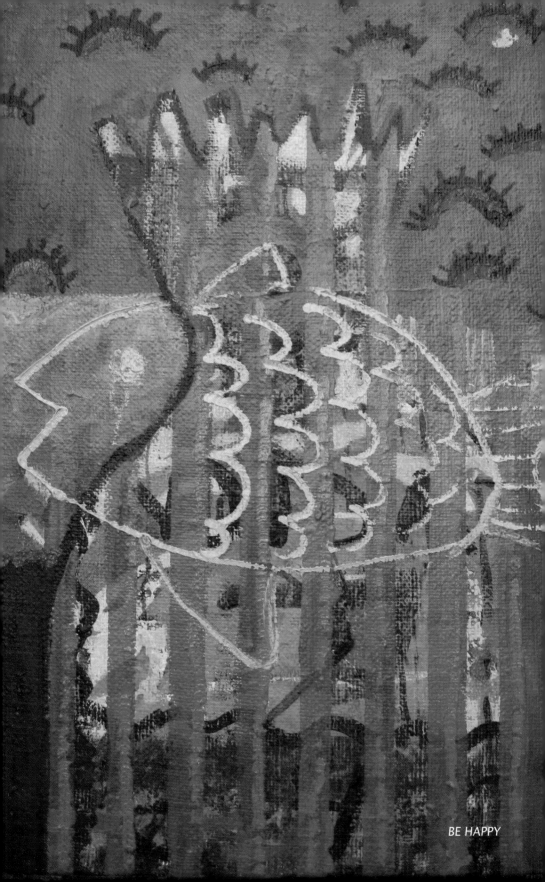

BE HAPPY

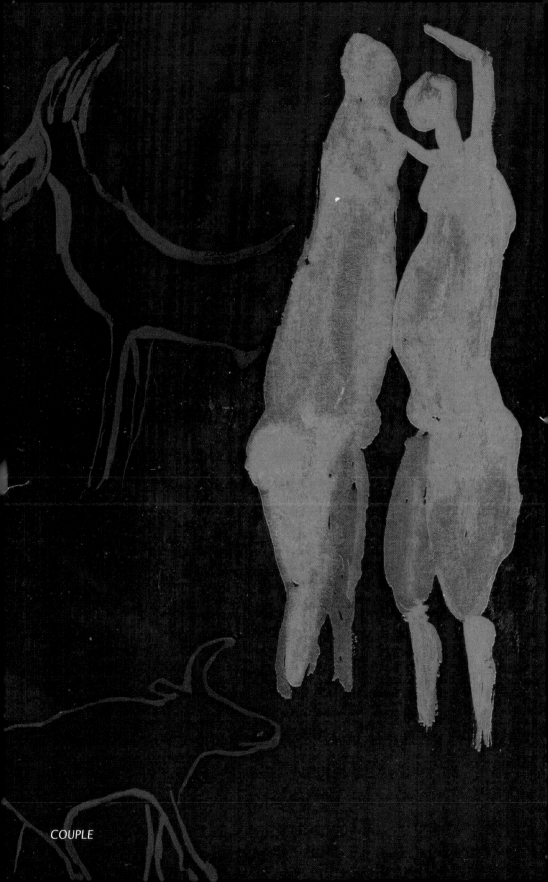

COUPLE

RĂZVAN PETRESCU
SMALL CHANGES IN ATTITUDE

Translated by James Christian Brown

Contents

James Christian Brown

Introducing
Răzvan Petrescu

Răzvan Petrescu was born in 1956, and brought up in Bucharest. As a teenager he became fascinated by literature and music. He went on to study at the Medical University in Bucharest, while continuing to pursue his literary interests as a member of an influential writers' workshop organised by the distinguished critic and literary scholar Mircea Martin. After graduating in General Medicine in 1982, Petrescu was posted to Dîmboviţa county, northwest of Bucharest, where he worked for five difficult years in rural clinics, before finally giving up medicine to devote himself to writing. His first book of short stories, *The Summer Garden*, appeared in 1989. Since 1990, he has worked as an editor for a number of literary periodicals and publishing houses, and was for a time, in the early 1990s, employed by the Romanian Ministry of Culture. His second book of short stories, *Eclipse*, was published in 1993, followed by two plays, *The Joke* and *Springtime at the Bar*, developed from stories in *Eclipse*, and his third, *One Friday Afternoon*, in 1997. He currently works for the publisher Curtea Veche, and is a frequent contributor to Romanian literary and cultural periodicals. His latest book, *Foxtrot XX*, was published in 2008.

Petrescu's writing has met with widespread critical acclaim and has attracted numerous literary awards: the Liviu Rebreanu Prize for *The Summer Garden*; the City of Târgovişte Prize for best prose work of the year for *Eclipse*; the UNITER (Romanian Theatre Union) Prize for best play of the year for *The Joke*; the Grand Prize of the Camil Petrescu National Stage Writing Competition, and Best Play award of the Writers' Union of Romania for *Springtime at the Bar*; the Book of the Year prize at the National Book Salon, the ASPRO (Romanian Professional Writers' Association) Prize for the best prose work of the year, and the Bucharest Writers' Association Prize for *One Friday Afternoon*; and the Radio România Cultural prize for *Foxtrot XX*.

The stories gathered here were originally published in Petrescu's first three collections: 'The Crystal Globe', 'Chance' and 'At the Bar' in *The Summer Garden* (1989); 'The Door', 'The Joke', 'Black Encephalitis', 'Diary of a Flat-dweller' and 'Rubato' in *Eclipse* (1993); and the remaining stories in *One Friday Afternoon* (1997).

The reader coming to Petrescu's writing for the first time will find a body of stories in which a sometimes dizzying diversity of narrative strategy, perspective and style is brought to bear on a range of themes in which the fundamental tragic issues of failure, guilt and death are never far away.

Sharply observed social and psychological realism (more than one critic has described Petrescu as writing with a scalpel – an obvious conceit, given his medical background, but nevertheless an apt one) blend seamlessly with forays into the surreal and fantastic. A playful and infectious delight in the joy of writing, an ironic detachment and an absurd sense of humour overlie a profound sense of anguish at the tragedy of human existence. The world of Petrescu's stories is a dark one, full of disappointed hopes, minds driven to insanity, bodies subjected to torture, disease, decay and dissection. The dispassionate technical vocabulary of the doctor's surgery and the anatomy room is a characteristic part of the texture of his writing. But equally characteristic are the many references to favourite pieces of music, which at times, most obviously but not only in 'Jazz', almost amount to a soundtrack to the stories. And there is love too, affirmed at times in surprising ways, as in the conclusion of 'Wedding Photographs', as well as in the lyricism of 'October Letter'.

Though some of Petrescu's earlier stories, those that draw most directly on his experience as a country doctor, have been seen as original contributions to the rich Romanian tradition of literature about village life, the dominant setting in *One Friday Afternoon* is Bucharest, the city where the author has spent most of his life. Names of districts, streets, parks and Metro stations anchor the events in the environment of the Romanian capital. The characters, like most urban Romanians, live in blocks of flats, each with its paid caretaker, its management committee and residents' meetings. Thin walls and ceilings transmit sound easily from one flat to another, amplifying the sense of forced proximity. The exclusively intellectual community in 'Diary of a Flat-dweller' is unusual. More commonly (as we see in the 'The Crystal Globe' or 'Flash'), habits and prejudices moulded by a tradition of city dwelling share space uneasily with the very different cultural norms of the only half-urbanised rural population brought in from the countryside by the hurried industrialisation of the communist period.

The range and distinctive character of Petrescu's writing are already apparent in the three stories from his first collection that are included in the present volume. 'The Crystal Globe' consists almost entirely of an extended interior monologue, constantly drifting from the gradual recollection of the significant details of a life apparently now ending in personal and professional failure into passages of dreamlike fantasy of sometimes lyrical intensity. The protagonist, like several of Petrescu's principal characters, is an individual of exceptional talents whose early promise has ended in frustration and despair, in this case starting from his refusal to comply with the demands of ideological conformity (the vagueness of the setting in time and place, and as regards what precisely the university authorities find wrong with his teaching, are reminders that the story was published before the fall of the communist regime). In 'Chance' and 'At the Bar', on the other hand, quite unexceptional characters, limited in their vision and in their capacity to articulate their experiences, are confronted with extraordinary situations. In these two stories, Petrescu makes use of one of his characteristic storytelling techniques, presenting the reader with a continuous stream of direct speech, mixed with occasional interventions from an external narrator, in which one voice follows another, without any form of quotation marks and often leaving the reader to guess at the identity of the speakers. Petrescu's remarkable ability to capture vernacular speech, with all its rough edges, ambiguities and suggestive power (an aspect of his writing that unfortunately can only be hinted at in translation), recalls a Romanian tradition going back to the great nineteenth-century dramatist Ion Luca Caragiale, whose satires of social and political life still resonate in the Romanian language. It should come as no surprise that the post-revolution sequel to 'At the Bar', 'Springtime at the Bar' (not included in this selection), in which a similar group of drinkers discuss the events of the first months of 1990 in the nation and the village, was subsequently adapted by the author into an award-winning play.

'The Door', from *Eclipse*, like 'The Crystal Globe', deals with the lonely transition from life to death, this time in the understated manner of a sketch from hospital life. In 'Black Encephalitis' (written in the 1980s, though not published until 1993), the solemnly sustained parody of a clinical description and the tragicomic case study offer an original slant on the theme of the gifted and idealistic individual at odds with his surroundings, and raise disturbing questions about a society in which illness can be redefined as normality. In 'The Joke', another story that subsequently developed into a play, Petrescu reworks the biblical story of Cain and Abel, shifting from playful evocation of the narrator's unique family background to the menace of an absurd trial and its dark conclusion.

Other stories, particularly those from the third volume, *One Friday Afternoon*, take the form of monologues, in which a succession of narrators tell their life stories, revisit memories, or record extraordinary experiences.

The title story of Petrescu's third collection, 'One Friday Afternoon', looks back into dark memories of the communist past, and the unacknowledged guilt that continues to haunt Romania. (It is difficult to read of the 'seaside' to which the narrator's father is said to have sent his victims without recalling the labour camps on the Danube–Black Sea Canal, where tens of thousands of political prisoners were sent, many of them to their deaths, in the early years of the communist regime.) Elsewhere, the setting is the 'transitional' world of post-communist Romania, perhaps most strikingly evoked through its television. The daily two hours of largely propaganda broadcasting on a single state channel, to which Romanians had become accustomed in the 1980s, rapidly gave way in the 1990s to a plurality of voices from state and private broadcasters, and a massive influx of foreign TV channels distributed by cable networks. It is from television that the female speaker in 'Where are You, Eleonora?' has stocked her vivid imagination, and from the horrifying bombardment of television, more than from her disability itself, that the bedridden woman in 'Playing Jesus' needs to be released.

The attentive reader will notice that Petrescu's characters have a tendency to migrate between stories; several of them make more than one appearance in *One Friday Afternoon*, for example. It has, indeed, been suggested that the sequence of stories in this third collection might be read as a single work, a jazz-like progression through a succession of themes and improvisations. And in fact such cross-referencing of characters (and also objects: the hammer, the piano…) occurs frequently enough in Petrescu's work to give at times the feeling that we are reading fragments of one large open-ended and many-voiced novel – a multi-faceted human tragicomedy. And yet seen from another perspective, many of the stories have themselves something of the character of tightly compressed novels – novels reduced to their essence, as it were. (In a recent magazine interview, Petrescu playfully recommends the short story as good value for money in a time of economic crisis, on the grounds that a well-written book of short stories will offer the essence, free of literary ballast, of 10 or 15 novels.) In offering this translation from a representative selection of Răzvan Petrescu's short fiction, it is my pleasure to introduce English-speaking readers to one of the most distinctive voices in contemporary Romanian literature – indeed some would say Romania's finest living writer of short stories – and to invite them to share in a reading experience that may be challenging and at times disturbing, but will, I hope, also prove to be highly entertaining and rewarding.

SMALL CHANGES IN ATTITUDE

The Crystal Globe

The doctor gets into his sterile coat, then pulls on his gloves. He looks over his shoulder. Sometimes it seems to me that only two or three minutes have passed, at the most. The instruments shine, arranged in order on the metal table. The nurse raises the lever of the spotlight, adjusting the beam. At other times I have the impression that months have passed while I've been lying here. When I say *here* it's just a manner of speaking, because I haven't the faintest idea where I am. Someone fills a syringe with serum. With his left hand, the doctor palpates the swollen abdomen. He presses here, there. It will be a difficult one, he says. Set up the drip, please. My head aches terribly. As if an immense weight were pressing on my skull. I am so crushed that I probably wouldn't even fill a fist, if someone were to collect the pieces. Leaning over, out of curiosity at first, to look at me. Touching what's left of me with his hand. What could this be? he would ask, scrutinising me under the light, running me slowly through his fingers. A fantasy, it is well known that death has its fantasies too. Once again I am scattered on the sand, crushed by shoes with studded soles, drenched by waves. Time passes, in all directions. Sometimes it stands still. I have the sensation of being in the middle of a sea of people who are waiting for something. Nobody blinks, not the slightest noise can be heard. I struggle in vain among them, endeavouring to make a sign from among the crowd. It is as if I were trying to get out of a photograph. Old, chipped colours. The effort wears me out. Now it seems to me that it is morning, because I can make out the dreams of long ago, drying on a string of blue light, like clothes on the line. They become lighter, flap gently in the wind, disappear. The green emperor, the money in the piggy bank with which I am going to buy myself a filing cabinet, a horse with wooden wings, my new scooter, a bilious but decent head teacher, the classmate who won't let me catch her in the corridor, then does, under the bust of Julius Caesar and the lists of resits, patricians who give me thunderous applause, legions who idolise me, a glittering professional career, the steps of glory, a better house, a better classmate, marriage, money in the Savings Bank and interviews in the great newspapers of the world, Damocles drunk, Napoleon under his tricorne, in the mausoleum, a dentist red in the face, who strains with his pliers at my molar, I'm just a child, I howl and look out of the window, a sunrise, very white dead people made into paper boats that float on the ocean until they reach islands with palm trees, women wearing no underwear and flats without doors, my mother's face, Jung, a bridge, and the sound of the alarm clock, like the chiming of a bell. How nice it would be if you could call the man who carries the night in his boat, to carry it faster, so that you could wake up just once with a great quantity of morning in your blood, even if it is raining, the bed sags, someone has just left you and the new day is identical to the last one. Disordered details come into my mind, out of which something may eventually emerge. Perhaps a sun, or a firefly. Lighting my way home. A limping consciousness drags itself through the darkness, holding my hand, leading me by all sorts of twisting paths, seeking to remake the road to the mush that I have become. The railway. Step by step, the map takes shape. A little flag, a broken dream. There are a whole lot of veils to be pushed aside. I lose myself in their grassy rustle, the sleepers disappear as I advance and the station turns into an echo.

Up to the present moment I have managed to reconstitute very few things. One: I can move. More precisely I can curl myself up, and that in a space that is narrow and completely unknown. Two: I can feel. My whole body hurts. Even the place where pain becomes conscious hurts. Three, I have found out who I am. My name is Radu G., I am 52 years old, I think, and I practise the trade of shoe seller. At one time I was also a university teacher of history. I am absolutely sure, because by an intense effort of memory I have seen again the Degree that I keep hanging above the chest of drawers. In fact my wife keeps it there. It has a photograph. Things are starting to get clearer, as in a bath of developer fluid. I also worked as a radio and TV repairer. I dealt with photography too. And nothing came out of all that. I was always short of money. I went to endless trouble to falsify the photographs so that everyone would look beautiful, intelligent and of noble descent. I came up against similar difficulties when I had to make the apparatus work to suit the clients' wishes. They were never satisfied. They wanted to catch channels with voices from the cosmos, to see unusual, lubricious images, which, after all the valves had been replaced, then the transistors and finally the integrated circuits, the screws, the scale and the aerial, became absolutely impossible. I received a pile of complaints and in a short time I was thrown out of both jobs. A pity, I liked them.

To stay in the dark and not even be able to find your cigarette lighter. No match flame, no candle, nothing. Where are my fingers? So that I can put them on my temples, on my abdomen, I don't know, where it hurts worst of all. To calm myself. To make a little order in my mind. But I can't find the ring finger. And not even the index finger, to indicate with, look, the ants are coming, the waves, the band, the rainbow or whatever that is over there, the building with frosted windows out of which people keep coming wearing boots, imported ballet pumps and ladies' shoes in imitation leather. Because at last I managed to find myself a job in a shoe shop. The only one, in an undistinguished small provincial town. A closed community, generating confidences, reminding you not to kill mockingbirds. Thirty thousand inhabitants, zero mockingbirds, a lot of intimate dust and a view over a field to one side. I bought myself a sofa bed, a few art books, a chandelier, a canary, a radio, and I got married. I was always on time with the rent. I said hello to everybody. After a while we moved into a bigger house, then, one after the other, came two little boys and a Pobeda. One is now 14, the other 11. I struggled hard to succeed, especially where the car was concerned. And, I can say with due modesty, I managed. It's true that as regards the aesthetic side, both the car and the children leave rather a lot to be desired, like all things obtained too late, but they run well. A year ago, Bogdan, my elder son, almost finished his class with a mention.

I have had an accident. And I can't remember what I did with the wallet in which I kept my wages and Mariana's photo. When I left, I had it in my back pocket, I presume. I have no way of checking. I can't touch my back, due also to some extent to these rhythmic shocks of unknown origin. It's as if I were in a train in which the lights have gone out, the doors are blocked and restless people are crowding against me in the corridor. I really must remember what I did with the photo and the money. If they didn't somehow fall out of the train. Things of mine have always been falling out of trains. Ever since the first railway journeys where you were blinded by the steam, frozen by the air coming in through the broken windows and suffocated under tons of luggage, journeys and words. The time when I commuted to work. After I gave up travelling, I started to be successful as a shoe seller. I set out to be honest, helpful, silent. It wasn't hard. One of my father's brothers had been an illusionist in his youth and I had picked up all sorts of tricks from him. Like the one with the dove that comes out of the hat. When the moment came, all I did was change the hat for a shoe, and sales rocketed. I speculated on the moment of glory for all it was worth and invested my takings in the things I have already mentioned. I was entering the ranks of humanity with my head held high.

After a while, however, it dawned on everyone that the dove wasn't able to get out of the shoe at the client's home too, then it happened that the bird got sick and didn't want to show itself even in the shop, a real disaster. The manager cut my wages accordingly. A few months went by. A year, then another. People started to look at me with a wide grin. Some pretended not to notice me, others encouraged me. Patted me on the back. I knew that at the hairdresser's, in parks, at the chemist's, in the queue, at street corners, in endless lovers' confabs, they were talking about me. They were making bets. I had no option but to keep my cool and my job especially after a New Year's Eve that left us with nothing to eat for almost two whole days. On which occasion Mariana made some rather unkind allusions to the hardships of life in general. I couldn't give up, and apart from that I had got rather tired of continually looking for work. I was, at that time, 38 years old.

I don't know exactly how old I am now, but I do know that someone or something is hard at work grinding me down and mixing me into a sort of sticky dough. With a little vinegar. Springing from my pores which are dilated with fear. The agony is so great that I imagine it is impossible for it to be mine. In that case, the only one I could hurt is Mother, she is the only one I could make to stay with teeth clenched, eyes closed and fingers tearing at the bed cover, perhaps waiting to give birth to me again. And especially at the beginning of this nightmare, I had the impression that a lot of people were coming to stare at her or at me-who-had-not-yet-come, all full of wonder, advice, interjections and head-shaking, seemingly I was in breech position, I was going to come out feet first, jostling one another, shaking handkerchiefs and phials of medicine, nose drops, antibiotics, vociferating, clicking their tongues, breaking the odd glass and smelling overpoweringly of perfume, but I admit it was reassuring. It's a relief that the show is not free. But for a few hours, no one has come any more. I am as alone as a cuckoo in the dark.

I have had such periods before, without necessarily having been hit on the head. When I was a student, I only knew three people in the whole capital, two gynaecologists with whom I sometimes went out for a beer, and Monica. What a time we had together, in her double studio flat on the eighth floor, on Saturday evenings. We ate chips, she didn't know how to cook anything else, drank wine and complained to each other. That the horizon could no longer be seen in its proper place, in the morning, the same with the line of life, that phone books couldn't be found any more. That we had no money. Over the last glass, Monica would suddenly get into a poetic mood and tell me she loved me with lips sweet with Grasa de Cotnari, kept in the fridge for moments of truth. As well as her weekend solitudes, she had, my beloved of the time, incredible buttocks, they darkened the room when they appeared at the window from under her skirt. The bed, on the other hand, was small, narrow, and pressed against the radiator at one end, so that I regularly banged myself on the pipes. On Sunday mornings I would go home with a devastatingly bitter taste in my mouth and a sharp pain in my toes. I had to put compresses on all week. Monica had blue eyes. Everything about her, even her smile, was blue, especially by the light of the lamp with Lake Baikal painted on its shade. I sank so many times through that colour that one day my breathing stopped. The bends. I was pulled up in time, then forced to go further on in the boat where I was given first aid, by another Monica. When the waves lifted us up, I could make out the beach, far away, among the fallen clouds.

My head pushed down against my thorax, my torso bent double, my knees against my mouth, like a foetus in its antechamber, that's how I have been lying for who knows how long, all the time thinking to myself that I can't understand exactly what is happening to me. Indeed I have never understood, but now I really ought to be a bit more alert in my mind. If only because I am urged to be so by this damp, heavy something that is crawling on my back. Perhaps a turtle. Away with it! Let the others keep pulling on the oars. Looking for a sunny beach on which to lay its eggs.

I was heading for home that night. Quite fast, it's true. I had drunk a bottle of cheap brandy with the lads, to celebrate Petrache's birthday. The cashier. Still as far as I recall I wasn't any more sad or tipsy than any other time. It had been raining the night before and the road was shining like a mirror. I don't remember very much. All I know is that I wondered in that fraction of a second what she could be doing there, alone, in her white suit. She just appeared in front of me all of a sudden, right after the bend. I braked, twisting the steering-wheel sharply to the left. The headlight beams swept the motorway and leapt in the air, striking the parapet, then the car tilted, swung for a moment, and then headed down into the valley with scraping, banging and landscape. After a while, there came the cold of the water. Slowly swallowing the front of the car, the bonnet, the windscreen, gushing in powerful jets from under the doors. That was about it.

Again my temporal bones are hurting. Parietal. Occipital. And what is between them. In fact the migraine hasn't let up for a moment. They hurt the same way then, on the bridge, when I arrived in town for the first time. I felt as if my eyes were going to jump out of their sockets. The bridge was full of people. Mothers with children, fleshless children, battered lorries, gloomy cyclists, Gypsy women with baskets full of gaudy flowers ready to foretell that you would become a great man, but you had a problem, a whirlpool of soot, suits, carts, blonde girls, dubious papers. I had stopped beside the parapet, with my temples throbbing. A tall chap, chestnut-haired, with an unattractive face and a baseball cap slanted laddishly over one eyebrow asked me if I needed a room. I answered that right at that moment I desperately needed an aspirin. He immediately offered me one. His pockets were full of them. I took a tablet and swallowed it with water from the drinking fountain, Then we introduced ourselves, we wondered at the possible coincidence of names, discussed this and that, went to a restaurant, ate and became friends. That afternoon he found me an acceptable room, at a ridiculously low rent. The days of the week took to going by in their natural order, at last, after so long. Overpowered by our chaotic enthusiasm. We usually met at his place, chatted, smoked and dreamed without a care in the world, we drank tankfuls of brandy, people came to listen to us under the window, we didn't pay any attention, playing jazz records, 'meditating' to the solos of Lester Young, with the evening curling up in saxophone sonorities at our feet, that's the way he put it.

My unexpected friend was an engineer, he had studied aerospace engineering and dreamt of building an object that would be extremely small, but would fly; for the time being he made paper aeroplanes in an office, where he wrote poems on the walls. He was always on at me to leave together. He could invent a rocket any time, a twin-engine, a module, a gondola. He would have liked to go away anywhere, France, Alaska, a warm country, a plant. We'll meet in a petunia, he would say, to be contented with little. With the infinite. I would agree with him, crush the odd jet-propelled mosquito on my cheek, and send my gaze into the unfathomable distance. Time went by. We didn't bother that much, we were busy, we were debating the existential rhythm in Johnette's drum accompaniment, without neglecting the tonal clarity, sharing cigarettes, philosophies and accidental lovers for scientific, harmonic purposes, seeking and making each other promises of liberation. From this fog. From the great confusion that reigned in our heads. Until, one Thursday, my sole and debatable alter ego disappeared. I looked for him everywhere, for days on end, weeks, months. He had fallen ill, he had run away to France, into a vegetable, he had found another bridge, he had fallen in the water, I don't know. All I know for sure is that he told me absolutely nothing, never gave me any warning and left me high and dry, to make my own way forward through the obscurities, asking myself more and more muted questions, trying to distinguish the cursed bridgehead, underneath the muddy water. Shoe toes before my eyes, first the right, then the left, exams, shadows round the eyes and trades that I practised conscientiously, one after the other. I might believe that it was all nothing but a stupid dream, if it wasn't for the headache, like a mouth chewing me in slow motion, voluptuously, with dental plaque. Now I have some strange, vague sensations. Like the feeling that I have wet myself. Otherwise, emptiness, the cosmos. I have urinated in the cosmos. Nothing has happened, the quarks are not wet, they haven't blown up, but how curious everything is like this, without margins, without any news about the world. Giving you the aquatic feeling that you are swimming in a drop of CFC on the back of this huge inconsolable monster, the world, which has died or is still sleeping. Let's not waken it!

At my request, Mariana used to curl up and press her burning body against mine. She was as hot as a cake. I met her at a party at the club. Music, shouts of joy, confetti. She was sitting on a chair by the wall, she was nibbling a biscuit and no one was inviting her to dance. Because of the sharp look in her eyes I think more than for any other reason. Like her long dress with mauve polka dots for example. Although I had drunk about six glasses of liqueur, I recognised her immediately. It was destiny. Without a doubt. I was just trying to make my way towards her in order to unburden myself of this remarkable thought, when she lifted her eyes towards me. A master-stroke! She held me fixed like a butterfly in the air behind me, which had suddenly become solid. I stopped for a few seconds with my mouth slightly open. She had been my student, in the only year that I had taught history. A mediocre student, as far as I recalled, but look at her now, splendid, with her dress lifted slightly over her knees. And a compound look, she had chosen specially for me the deepest eyes she was capable of, so deep that it was possible to see in their aquarium green the sloping road to her bed, right on the other side of town. What are *you* doing here, sir? I wanted to answer that I was selling shoes, and everything would have been fine, but I didn't have the courage, so I invited her to dance. A tango, then another one, a bit closer together, we made a date in the botanic gardens, I supported her on an oak, the sort of tree that has a broad crown, durable wood, and whose fruit is the acorn, together we saw the Milky Way and a few war films, we held hands, we made love in my room, we liked it, and we got married. However I knew from the first moment that she had got it into her head to save me, to rescue me from the swamp, because a teacher, not to mention one as talented as me, had no business to be selling shoes, she wanted to rehabilitate me, a large-scale mission, which of course she considered herself capable of carrying through to a conclusion, so that we would live in plenty surrounded by general respect and correcting doctoral theses by the dozen, together, in the living-room, preferably in the living-room of a three-storey villa situated right in the centre of town. She held on to this belief for almost 12 years. She didn't look after herself. She gave me two children too, although it was clear that it harmed her figure. She was always on the go. She bore without a murmur the first wrinkles, a few white hairs also appeared, and still she believed. I looked at her in wonder that there could be such strength in her. She was extremely beautiful, at least at the beginning. Tall, lithe, gracious and with very warm eyes when she wanted something, a perfume for example, with breasts like two little boats and a pair of thighs as smooth as a car driver's day-dream. In bed, all this was gathered together into a sort of bomb that exploded right in your face. Leaving you blind until the clock sounded and you had to go to work. Over time her eyes became cooler, her skin lost its tautness, her breasts began to retain water, only her height remained unchanged, and that was so that she could dominate me. At this point I need to confess that between us there was (or still is) a difference in height of 12 centimetres, which I thought, I don't know why, would lessen in time. I was wrong, indeed the difference I have mentioned tended to become more accentuated. I can't condemn her. Seeing year by year how my height diminished, it was only natural that she should try to make me subject. It is all part of human nature, little by little she took everything from me, even the house keys. If it sometimes happened that I stayed out late with the lads at some party, I would be left in the street. I tried not to be late. I sought to keep her happy, one day I caught myself polishing her shoes. All to no effect. She continued to tell me that I had disillusioned her. That I had taken advantage of my experience, meaning my age, to betray her most burning hopes. And, consequently, I should expect something similar from her side. So I was waiting for some sort of lover to show up in our unsettled family life, when this thing happened that has knocked me out of the race. Petrache warned me. Leave the old banger, mate. It's raining, and you've had one too many. Take the bus. It's safer, believe me. Yes, just that I had been shopping, I had three packages in the boot and I didn't feel up to holding them in my arms in the packed bus at that hour. They were 10 oranges, some pastries, a cake, and three pairs of Italian shoes. The symbol of my trade.

Perhaps they are waiting for me with dinner. All three. In the living-room, looking sometimes at the food, sometimes at the TV. Supposing it all took place no more than a few minutes ago, today is Wednesday. And if it's still eight o'clock too, then *Telecinemateca* should be on. A film with Bogart. But why doesn't Dad hurry up and come? Bogdănel would ask. Mariana would shrug her shoulders, intently watching the shooting in *Dead End*. Mihai would yawn demonstratively, and surreptitiously take a gulp of the rice pudding. Mum, look what Mihai's doing, he's stealing some of the rice! Leave him alone. Quiet. And come on, let's eat too! They would start to eat. Who knows where he may be wandering. Where Dad may have got to.

All the same I think they're at the hospital. The smell, the noises. Although, it's just an opinion, it might equally well be that I am still in the car or in the bed in my old room or in any other bed or not even in any object of that sort, but actually inside one of those crystal globes I had as a child, which you turned upside down and they made it look as if it was snowing in your palm, no matter how many times you turned them over, snow falling slowly, tremulously, without the smallest flake ever going missing, and so without ever finishing, like a toy winter.

My packages have probably turned into a sort of soup if they didn't take them out of the car, when they took me out. If they have taken me out. Because I am no longer sure of anything. I felt so good that night, at the wheel, eating up kilometre after kilometre, with Ben Webster on the radio and my foot pressing the accelerator pedal down to the floor. Not that you should imagine that I was going at any great speed. Even revved up to the maximum, my Podeba doesn't make 80 kph. My thoughts are dissolving, giving me the impression that I can understand them. In that hissing darkness by the windows I thought of the surprise I was going to give them. Through the windscreen I imagined their joy. And even if they wouldn't have been over-the-top with joy, I would still have been left with the pleasure. I feel an immense pleasure when I give them little presents from time to time. On which occasion they also take note of the fact that I exist. Because as a rule the boys don't take much notice of me, to put it mildly. Always seem awkward in my presence. I appear to them, I think, like a biological necessity, a fat man getting on a bit, bound in some obscure way to their mother. They are even a little embarrassed when they have to mention me in school questionnaires, in the box marked *Father*. I feel fragile in front of them and they know it very well. And thus I was content to gravitate like a dwarf star, kept in orbit by the irresistible force of attraction of these bright and cruel stellar bodies, trying to approach them, to kiss them, only when they were asleep.

One day, I couldn't manage to work out a mathematics problem for Mihai. I could feel him looking at me. The result isn't coming out, Mihai. Maybe there's a mistake in the book, I said finally, with a guilty look on my face. Not only are you the oldest father in the whole school, you can't even solve a lousy problem with taps. I remained silent, and carried on scribbling enigmatic figures. You don't know anything, he went on, getting up from his chair. That's why nobody loves you! I slapped him and of course he ran straight to his mother, howling at the top of his voice. At dinner I was given a dressing-down in front of the children, as was only right and fitting, and I was almost starting to think that I wouldn't get any dessert. I did get it, but I ate it with a lump in my throat. Then I took my hat and walked out. It was a cool night, quiet, with no moon. I wandered the streets for a long time, kicking out at the odd apple core, it was the season for apples, under the street lights flew the core, will, goal, inflexibility, paternity, well-being, sometimes it hit some drunk passer-by, I apologised, so did he, and we both thought as we parted that if we had managed to obtain anything up until that moment, it had been nothing but everyone's contempt. Getting used to it gradually, in fact it's not that hard. I returned home around four in the morning. The house was immersed in darkness and for a moment I felt a pang in my heart, but it was a false alarm, the door was unlocked. I let the handle return gently to its place, took off my shoes, ah, shoes, and, after infinite precautions, I stretched out on the bed, on top of the covers. My wife was breathing softly, almost imperceptibly. I shut my eyes too but I couldn't sleep, because the canary had started to sing. At which point Mariana's dream became heavier than usual, taking the form of a size 45 climbing boot that set about methodically trampling my sea shells from the last beach of hope in a better world, one by one, transforming them into a marine paste. I got up, went to the bar and drank a whole bottle of brandy all by myself, in memory of my French friend, then in memory of myself, trying to sing along to the creaking of furniture that portended nothing good, until seven o'clock, when the children left for school. I said goodbye to them sadly and they didn't reply. Consequently, I decided that it didn't matter any more what I drank, what mattered was not to give up.

How awful I feel. Then, now, for all time. Creangă. I couldn't go to work on the morning in question. I would have liked never to go again. It didn't work. The make-up artist was signalling to me desperately. I had to go back on stage and muddle on with my role. Powdered, and with spots of red paint on my cheeks. But they suit you very well, madam, I assure you! Perhaps a larger size?... Wait a moment, I'll be right back. On tiptoe. Seeking, freezing. Look, I've found them! Something special for you. Cheap, of course. And sir? Galoshes? Yes, we have. Oh, I'm terribly sorry, not in brown, we'll have them in next week. I rub my hands to give myself the air of a professional but also because it is very cold. The customers don't care. They keep coming, one after the other, it's as if they are catapulted, and not even in reality, but there's nothing else for it. I have to serve them. A pair of boots? I understand, to match your overcoat. Clink, clink, goes the drawer of the till. How I long to get home. On the way, greenish clouds fall on my windscreen, I start the wipers. Mum, look what I've found, cries Mihai, waving an empty wine bottle. Put it back, at once! And don't let your Dad find out. It's just us two that know, all right? All right, Mum, says Mihai, disappointed. But everybody knows, anyway.

What was I to do? I was never what you would call a drinker. But from time to time, or very often, I felt an absolute need to get tight. I didn't hide my bottles, and it wasn't my fault that they always maintained that I hid them. Basically I was just trying not to upset anyone. I was really making an effort. And I still am, trying to adapt to this strange space around me, which I can push with my hands. It's as if I were in a soap bubble. A tiny liquid universe. And there goes a red fish, with blue stripes, passing two fingers' breadth from my nose. I feel really nauseous, this darkness throws me, I hiccup. Non-existent lights continually flicker and flash, it means I've gone mad. I can see masses of coral, nebulas, a red giant and a white dwarf, sea horses, organ-pipes of coral with a pulsar in the centre, Cats-eyes swimming this way and that, idly, the principal with his hand raised, you are dismissed, shipwrecks, deep-sea asteroids, among which I dive towards solar systems and ships eaten by the stillness of the waters, veritable explosions of black lichen at whose heart lie astronauts and purple octopuses, chests full of silver, I rummage through crypts of rotten timber and the craters of comets at rest, frozen, and I fill my hands with bubbles of air, up and down exist at the same time, compact, I keep seeking and never find the words of gold that, if we are to judge by ancient manuscripts and maps, somebody flung to the bottom of the galaxy of the ocean, a long time ago, I do my utmost, I, Radu G., shoe seller by profession, want at all cost to bring them up from the depths and scatter them through the air. No one can believe that you trouble your head with this sort of thing. And yet I have sought, I have scrabbled, I have drunk strengthening syrup, I have scraped until I could no longer grasp anything, not even the soup-spoon.

When I emerged once more at the surface, the bridge was deserted. Only the wind passed that way, chasing long wisps of snow over the tarmac. I began to walk. Walking, the simple philosophy of the normal world. The only certainty. I wonder if I didn't perhaps take the wrong direction. I remember a photograph that caused me a lot of headache. Mariana and the boys, shouting at the tops of their voices on one of the highest mountain peaks in the country. A magnificent landscape, clouds all around, a little yellow sunlight, reddish vegetation, only that on paper nothing came out, not a single colour, nothing could be seen but an overpowering granulated grey. Dad, I need a poo, the boys were calling, while I was tormenting myself in the darkroom I had improvised in the bathroom, trying to bring out at least their rosy cheeks, making use of all my knowledge as an ex-professional, listening to *The Tempest* on the radio and splashing myself liberally with developer. Dad, open up, I can't wait any more! In the end I had to open for them, thus turning my best proof black. After the whole family had used the toilet, the electricity went off. Probably Mihai had been improvising something on the fuse-box. A new fuse.

The next day I came back late from work, it had been a stocktaking day, I was worn out, I had been unable to account for two pairs of sandals, then time passed again without my realising it, and now I can understand even less than I could guess then about what happened to that photo. On the other hand all sorts of profound thoughts about death seem to be coming into my mind. About the billions of people who walk indifferently on their little paths, years on end, only to wake up some ordinary day reduced to a miserable little heap of frightened looks, and arteries through which nothing flows but a single viscous drop, a single and endless horror. Revolting with all their strength, then. Trying to drive off death with their hands, with a stick, with the soles of their feet, with high-pitched cries. Diving under the blankets or throwing in its face fistfuls of pills, bottles of spirit, eiderdowns, hernia bandages, bank-books, thermometers, anything, if it will only go away! A poor sweeper, there, in the doorway. Rather horrible, it's true, but only cleaning up, clearing away the remains. The rubbish. More inoffensive, you might think, than the mincing machine in which we shove our heads from the moment we're born. So that it's pointless making a fuss when the time comes.

I no longer remember where I read, a long time ago anyway, a law of accommodation, Pajot's law, which I have tried to apply whenever I had the occasion. It goes something like this: "If the *Container* is the seat of alternative phases of movement and repose and if the surfaces are slippery, the *Content* will tend to adapt its form and dimensions to the form and dimensions of the *Container*." I think it was in a treatise of gynaecology. But that is of no importance, the formulation is very clear. As a linguistic alternative, and not only that, to the feminine nouns for life and death, the neuter 'container' strikes me as an expressive word. Indeed, so much fuss just so that you can adapt yourself to the slippery surfaces of the day. But you have no choice. And if you have to do it anyway, it's better to do it scientifically. Pajot for ever! As far as the end is concerned, it is much easier, given that you are accommodating yourself for the last time, diminuendo. It also takes less time. And it is preferable to expiate discreetly, calmly, with a contented look, even if you are torn to pieces or who knows what, to give a single sigh, short, with dignity and with a candle at your head, putting your memories in order and even smiling condescendingly while the others weep like fools around you, assuming that there are others around you. If not, that's no more than one more little irritation, the last. They say that that is how you should behave, elegantly, humbly and with detachment, even if sometimes these seem irreconcilable, conciliate them, now all that is expected of you is that you get used to the bag of soil that is starting to be pulled over your head, With a little patience you can also pass decently over the fact that you can hardly breathe any more, over the life that you feel you are just losing now, hissing away like a cracked oxygen tube, when in fact you have lost it anyway, from the very start, over the smell of death and the silent explosions in your eyes. In fact everything is exploding, you might say that the journey is starting, here, among the last knots of barbed wire that wrench from you whole lumps of memory and skin, and yet everything is starting in quite a curious way, to say the least, not at all as I expected, with energetic contractions, almost voluptuous, gigantic, that envelop the bed and the night. And, believe me, I am capable of giving a lyrical, precise, even naturalistic description of what is happening. Because I am lyrical.

Everyone knows that there is an uneasy, slightly perverse pleasure, when you are sick in bed. People talk in whispers, your slightest wish is carried out, you are admired for everything, you are forgiven everything. That's not the case with me, of course, I am speaking in general. I am also speaking in order to forget that I have a sort of sea urchin in my belly. Or in my brain. It never stops pricking and pinching me, probably it's doing its duty. I tried to do mine too. But I always missed what was essential. And you have no chance, if you just busy yourself with details. You screw up. You even screw up your past. There are few things that I recall with pleasure. One of them is my history class. They were very attentive, those students. They didn't interrupt my exposition, and at the end they assaulted me with a barrage of questions. I tried to make them understand the true mission of this science that is never an art. I was happy. Perhaps I gave them something to think about. Perhaps that's why the committee was convoked. I gave them something to think about too. I was informed just five minutes before. I only had time to run a comb twice through my hair and to splash my face with a little water. When I entered the staff room, it was pervaded by a relaxed atmosphere, like a courtroom. I didn't sit down on a chair, because the principal looked at me as at a man who had no right to sit down on a chair.

The meeting was short. I wasn't invited to speak. To cut it all short, it was established that I could no longer practise the profession of teacher and it was proposed that I should be hospitalised at the university's expense. I refused politely. However I could not refuse the termination of my employment contract, which involved a precise statement of the nature of the nervous illness that I undoubtedly suffered from. The four members of the committee looked at each other, nodded their approval, and added their signatures. They had Pelikan fountain-pens. One of them murmured what a pity, a man who seemed destined for a brilliant career. I looked at them sympathetically. Four ground squirrels dressed in grey suits, splendidly tailored, but unable to hide their membership of that species of small, wide-eyed rodents of the plains. They drooled, they fidgeted, those sousliks, as they fired me with a single stroke of the hand. And not because I was crazy, but because I had stubbornly gone beyond the letter of the book. I had been warned repeatedly that history lessons had to be in full concordance with space and time, otherwise they were not lessons of history or even of meteorology. They were a waste of time, of the future, etc. I apologised. It was of no use. What are you in the end, a teacher or a mystifier? Irresponsible? I confessed that I did not know. Aha! You don't know. But who said "We will serve history only insofar as it serves life"? Nietzsche. Bravo. The second *Untimely Meditation*? Yes, I confirmed, and I could equally well invoke that quotation myself. Do not invoke anything, goodbye. I asked them then to switch on the light, so that they could at least once see the person in question, on whose account I was being expelled with such ease from the teaching profession. She was sitting in the principal's arms munching a cream cake. She had not the slightest bit of clothing on her, apart from a tiny patch of dark red velvet on her left hip. I could admire her Grecian bust, her round thighs and slender ankles, but it is possible that these appreciations were due to the fact that I was in love with her, although I knew her so well. Switch on the light, I repeated, that you too may appreciate the forms of history, look at her there, she isn't even hiding, she's tickling the principal through his trousers, yes, it's her, you absolutely have to see her naked for you to understand that clothes are of no significance, she can dress any way, in any dress, flag, sackcloth, tarpaulin, blouse or sail, putting on boots, garters or a mere velvet patch, so that you may understand that she is capable of saying anything, of inventing a society for a caress forbidden to minors, a kingdom for a kiss or sometimes for a horse, and if you went to bed with her too, and it wouldn't be hard, after all she is so beautiful, she would produce from her belly for you a whole era, a continent, an amphora, all that matters is to be able to satisfy her, only that is not important. The important thing is to be able to show her undressed, just as she is, somehow in reality, young, short-sighted and cunning, stark naked and as implacable as Venus. As truth. Handless. Get out, they howled in chorus. And I went out.

I can only remember her in her white suit, a superb suit, which she wore with grace on the most unexpected occasions. Even when I was ill and she had to nurse me. Only she could be impeccably dressed while she massaged my back or brought effervescent tablets and ointments to me in bed. She forced me to open my mouth and swallow dozens of teaspoonfuls of disgustingly bitter substances. I was so amazed at this perseverance that I would open my mouth as wide as I could and stay like that for minutes on end. Mother was the only being who never reproached me for anything. She didn't ask me why I had got sick, why I hadn't got sick, why I was alive or why I was a cretin. And yet it seems that I've managed to disappoint even her. She hasn't appeared again. All the time I've been imprisoned in this impossible place, she hasn't even come once to see me. So I am left with just the memory and the castor oil taste of childhood. In those days there were all sorts of presents, the Christmas tree, the sky, petals of cherry blossom, in Japan, easy to touch with your hand, running through the park, *Quo Vadis?* And the books of Paul Féval, crystal globes in which it was snowing even in the middle of summer, mechanical rabbits, the scooter, plastic Indians and other enchanting nothings of inexpressible significance. Only surprises, you just had to know how to hold them in your palm. For it to snow. Balms for later. But who ever thinks seriously of later? Especially when outside the snow is lying and you can hardly wait to gulp down your breakfast and go out with your sledge. I don't know why, but I have the impression that at this moment too, whenever it is, it is snowing heavily. The night solemnly depositing wreathes of little white flowers frozen solid on the ground where I am not. It is so disgusting to think what a pitiful moribund I have become. Horrible. Who said you become wiser with age? It isn't true. You become stupid. Let us pass over, perhaps I have reasons to be soft, an improvisation in B-flat minor, dear neighbours, see how I have remembered you too, it was inevitable. I put up with you, decade after decade, there are thousands of you, wondering sometimes that I didn't go mad, oh, my astonishing fellow residents, nothing separated us but a wall or a mere way of being, and yet! You thumped along the corridors, you talked ceaselessly, you flushed the toilet furiously, at all hours, and it sounded like a waterfall, please believe me, you took baths in the night, you played your astral music on the record-player or the radio, music from the countryside, as if it was everybody's, and it wasn't, at maximum volume, you didn't give a toss for the fact that you systematically flooded my soul and the ceiling of my bedroom, not to mention that you would periodically demolish the odd interior wall, to build arcades or ogives between the bathroom and the hall, or hammered nails all the time, regardless of the season, sometimes with a power drill, I don't know how you could have so many, you hammered them in a frenzy and they were all extremely long nails, maybe it turned out nicely in the end, because I could hear you shouting at each other just when I was getting to sleep, that's how I became irritable, I'm jumpy all the time and I can't stop talking about you right to the end of my life, although you never did me any real harm, although you shrieked *con tutti* and with the whole block at your collective weddings, I was jumpy again, it was rutting time, the period when even my wife became tender and told me she couldn't take any more, she was going to kill herself, I would hide the bottles of sleeping-pills, switch off the gas, block the windows and play Beethoven's Ninth, for which reason you would hammer on the pipes in righteous indignation, I was disturbing your flat seminars or your Căluşari-style couplings, and so I would switch off the record-player and listen to you quarrelling until the portraits of my provincial ancestors quaked, burst out of their frames at the slang spread over various tonal registers, and then you would start coughing, you would hack, and spit, and groan, and hiccup in your beds, and I now I would beat on the pipes, two or three times, hopelessly, melancholically, sometimes you would move heavy furniture around 11 pm, dropping metal bearings on the cement, or you would fry fish-cakes at the same hour, in the moments when I was starting to run out of air and to asphyxiate little by little, just like now. Which means that, by a slight translation of darkness, I am actually in my own home, at least for a while, maybe even beside Mariana, hidden under a pillow or in a fold of the sheet, reduced to such small dimensions that my wife wouldn't be able to spot me even if she wanted to. Otherwise I can't explain this overpowering reek of fish-cakes. It might be that I have shat on myself, but I prefer to think that only deteriorated meat smells like that. I feel sick, I am disintegrating, and my neighbours know all about it, but they have lost their curiosity because it is dinner time. Poor soul, they will comment. What a pity! And they will finish off another helping. He was a good chap. I think they could do with being fried a bit more. Because we make up one big family of neighbours. Good morning, good evening. A bit of gossip, a hundred, an exchange of calculated looks, a little help, a frying-pan, a cork, a pair of pliers, you hurt yourself. But the other one's finger can't hurt you, no matter how hard you try. So it's better not to try.

They seem to have eased, the pains. All that is left is some coloured circles floating through my hypothalamus. Like lifebelts made of smoke, mauve, red, not fully inflated, some of them yellow. Through which, when

I was little, I would pass my index finger, at least I could save it from the *Titanic*. The ship was smashed to smithereens, it seems, me likewise, and look how all I've managed to save is this nonsense that I keep talking. Mr Dick and you, Mariana would sigh every evening (not only did the comparisons inevitably start with Dickens, they also stopped with him), all you do is keep writing this stupid memorial. It's not a memorial, I would answer, it's a treatise of world history. Wonderful, everyone's really crying out for a work like that, she would scowl. Oh, but don't trouble yourself, we don't notice you're missing, carry on writing. She would tighten her lips until her beautiful mouth ended up narrower than a railway seen from above. TGVs would pass along it, coal wagons, and sometimes the odd hand car with a passenger who would wave goodbye to me. I would wave my hand too, while Mariana studied me through her eyelashes with undisguised disgust. The same as when I tried again to tell her about the CFC thing or other stuff of the same sort. And there had been a time when I thought that only she could fully understand me, that it was sufficient to sleep together to have the same dream, especially on moonless nights. When she too still clung to her hopes, lying to me beautifully, constantly, passionately. She endured everything like a martyr with a suspender belt, she smiled at me at all hours, even when I wasn't at home. But after she gave birth to Mihai and understood clearly that even on this occasion I had no intention of remaking my life, of taking up again the salary and dignity of a teacher and so finally justifying her prolonged waiting, she started to darken. One night in May she managed to become so dark that I couldn't find her in bed any more. After that true occurrence, in the rare moments when I succeeded in discovering her, she was equally sad. She would perform veritable feats of will-power to bear my touch. Shutting her eyes tight, as if facing a torment, when I tried to caress her. I even began to think I had no right to try. I tried to explain to her, to justify myself with examples from the classics, I bought her heaps of flowers, water lilies, eau-de-Cologne, ginseng, boots, dresses, I launched into confessions punctuated by rhetorical cries, I recited to her from Coşbuc, *The Queen of the Ostrogoths*, beat my forehead with my fists, gave myself bruises, asked for water. With time, the words shrivelled up, and most of the time they remained stuck in my throat, I choked, I turned blue again, I didn't ask for water this time, but I became flushed, and all I could do was to rush at her and throw her down with her skirt over her head, right there on the floor, frequently banging her head on the parquet.

The truth is that she liked it too. But she strove to give the impression that she was not participating, branding by her silence this sort of conjugal rape. The violet darkening round her eyes gave her away, so did her burning flesh, and other things. Well, no! In the end she would manage in such a way that I was left with a feeling of failure. Sometimes in a veritable panic. As if I had trespassed without a permit into a reservation protected by law. I am not sure how she transformed herself into a reservation, but certainly she succeeded.

It's still biting, the sea urchin in my stomach or in my head, for all its worth. It's pulling on my nerves with its tiny sharp teeth. But that's not the real trouble. The real trouble is that now at last I can see how weak I was. Always needing a support. First of all, Mother. She helped me get through the wonders of childhood, adolescence, maturity, old age, explaining to me that the world doesn't have to be taken just as it is. There followed a short moment of temporary revelations by the side of my friend. Then my wife came. With her hard, practical, wonderful nature, she gave me hope that in spite of the misunderstandings between us she would help me to climb the ladder, even if it was more than certain that it led nowhere. As for the children, at least I didn't have time to give myself illusions. They gave me to understand that they didn't care about me, far too many times for me ever to think seriously of getting any support from them. In fact they would have let me go rolling head over heels at the first opportunity. At the first wrong move on the steps of the 'stairway to heaven'. Of course they wouldn't have done the same with their charming mother. On the one hand because *she* is a teacher, and on the other because she brings the bigger wage packet into the house. And in any case, the money, all the money is in her delicate hands. Not in mine. Even if I do my damnedest and buy them the latest model of skates, radios, motorcycle helmets, jeans or remote-controlled elephants, out of my own savings accumulated, surreptitiously, by the sweat of my brow, it doesn't matter. It's still her they suck up to, enchant and adore, enough to make my hair stand on end. Sometimes, when I feel I can't take any more, I try to take the floor. To put things in order. I raise my tone, usually by half an octave, I try to speak in terms anyone can understand, I explain so beautifully that often I allow myself to get carried away by the unsuspected geometry of my demonstrations about life. Lay off, Dad, stop pretending, said Bogdan to me one evening, just when I had started on a detailed presentation of the modest but profound joys of my trade and of any trade, when it comes down to it, as long as you are honest. You enjoy selling slippers, like I enjoy learning history. That stung, I admit. An outspoken child, he takes after his mother. Only that to her he would never have confessed to this primitive aversion to history, for the simple reason that he could sense that she didn't like it either. We sat there, the thread broken, and I watched him chewing his sandwich unperturbed. He was looking at me too. With the same eyes as Mariana, serene, impertinent and oozing contempt for this world where, at least for a while, he was required to live. A world of which in the first and last place I was a part. Bogdan, you're old enough, I think you realise that you're not right, I suggested. Don't fool yourself into thinking you can achieve anything by irony. It's a dissolving principle. Almost anyone can laugh, but once you've destroyed what you imagined you wanted to destroy, let's see what you put in its place. And there are two unbearable things: stupidity and intolerance (there were a few more, but that's all that came into my head at that moment).

With the satisfaction of having dealt him a memorable response, I rose from the chair, went into the bedroom and came upon Mihai just as he was trying with his tongue sticking out between his teeth to fix the cable of the TV aerial to the spring of the wall clock. This prompted me to reflect that my younger son did not take after his mother. Rather he took after her mother. Intermittently overflowing with vitality, unexpectedly impetuous yet withdrawn when there was no reason to be, showing an almost enviable lack of understanding with regard to books, music or other manifestations of art, which he classified in a word as idiotic, looking at himself in the mirror more often than necessary, eating an enormous amount, which would have been an occasion for joy to any normal parent, and so was not to me, sleeping 12 hours a day, breaking, in his waking hours, all that could be broken, and on top of that, all with a deceptive air of listlessness. Asked about the business with the clock and the TV, he replied that he wanted to do what I had done in the days when I was a repairman, although I don't recall ever having tried such a combination, even in my moments of inspiration. It may be that he has, unfortunately, inherited my talent for messing things up. Perhaps also a little of my imagination. For example, one time he wanted to know the meaning of the word 'superfluous'. Mum, tell me what this is supposed to mean. Pause. Why don't you answer? I don't know, ask your dad. Yes, but I want you to tell me. Well, how can I explain... have you got to the lesson about the Etruscans? We've finished it. Again silence. Mum!

Stop going on at me! Superfluous means useless, I mean a sort of Etruscan. If you're really so desperate to know. Like Dad, said Bogdan, as he watched the TV. (I was listening at the door, I admit.) A boozer from another era, our older son went on. He doesn't know how to write poetry, like me, or to teach history, like you, or to have a good time, like our neighbours. That's why I say the Etruscan civilisation went to pot, they didn't know how to do anything except fill the skulls of their dead with wine. Then they would drink until they fell off their horses, and they lost the war. Mariana smiled slightly. Faced with such knowledge of ancient history, I can swear she smiled, I could feel it through the door. Perhaps she thought it was a witty explanation. That happened the day my canary died. Mihai had topped up its water out of a liqueur bottle in which there was still a few fingers' breadth of drink, to which he had added some detergent. And it died, the poor bird. I was found guilty, obviously, because it was my bottle. From that moment I swore to become a real drunkard. My new resolution was also supported by the incontestable fact that in most of the books I had read I had noted that alcoholics were intelligent, kind-hearted, usually artists, who had fallen prey to this rather regrettable vice solely due to the cruel workings of fate, and in the closing pages you were given to understand that they would straighten themselves out, irreversibly. At the end of the day they are the real heroes, suggests the author, who takes a bit of a tipple himself, as much as he can, from his own bar, because he too is sensitive, kind-hearted, a victim of fate, and a genius. As a result I got it into my head to be a hero. But not even that way could I regain the public of our little market town, who preferred another genre of literature. Still, I used the occasion to write an essay about the discovery of an extraordinary *perpetuum mobile, perpetuum* at least as long as I am alive. I mean the continuity of failure.

I screwed up with the university, with the boys likewise, I don't even take Mariana into account, with her absolutely nothing succeeded, apart from believing, at one time, that she might reduce herself for me to the size and shape of a drop of rain that I could keep comfortably under my eyelid. And she turned herself into a continuous fall of rain. Into a peppercorn. Why do you pretend you drink to forget? she would ask me in a strident tone, in triplets. But I don't pretend, I would mutter, ready to upset the glass. You can't forget your past, she would continue. (At this point I would become thoughtful. The delight I took in such discussions was total. I knew what was going to follow.) And I would question her in my turn about why she insisted on discrediting me every time she went to the hairdresser. And she went daily. Because I've wasted my best years for you. The saying is 'I have sacrificed', I would correct her innocently. I've sacrificed myself, yes, for an unbearable egotist who gives himself airs and writes world histories with a pencil, you've always made a mockery of me, sunk among your books and your shoes. They're not mine. Quiet! Or better tell me, have you really completely given up any kind of ambition? I would keep silent, as I had been ordered. In that case I suppose it's better that the rest of the world should find out from me what sort of person you are. Don't you think so? I didn't think so. And, as a supreme mark of disrespect, I would start reading. Radu, you're a monster! And an idiot. But you should know that I have never wished you ill. I've only tried to make you happy... Perhaps I really haven't understood you, she would sigh, blowing her little nose into a handkerchief so perfumed that it made me sneeze. I knew she hadn't wished me ill and hadn't understood me, but I also knew that my family and my house were of stone, exactly as they wish you at your wedding. A rare phenomenon. And one that you must not imagine I am not proud of. I am proud to the maximum, but if this burning in my ears goes on any longer I think I'll go out of my mind. It's probably due to the circle of red-hot iron that is tightening around my head. Gheorghe Doja, 1514. Hell, is there no doctor in this place? It can't be that no one is going to help me, because however much I would like to stay strong, not to make a fool of myself, there is no way I can prevent my eyes from watering.

My wife never believed that story about the lachrymal gland, she has no glands, and one must be strong, struggle, fight. That's what she used to say. And yet she had a moment of weakness too, at a time when we didn't yet know each other very well. I had just been thrown out of the university, the two of us were sitting in my room, in the dark, taking a gulp of cheap vermouth at intervals, when, unexpectedly, someone, perhaps Mihai, stuck his head through the half open door and whispered coolly in my direction, nobody wants you, nobody, then the door closed gently and we were left in the pitch darkness, among those words. She wept for an hour, my beautiful love, with her arms wound around my neck, telling me between sighs that I love you so much, perhaps that's really how it was, weeping in the sagging bed until there was nothing left of her but her eyes, large, defeated, forgive me, I feel horribly guilty. And I forgave her. I forgave her until, worn out, I realised that things can't be resolved in bed, no matter what you do. Only sickness and death are resolved there. Meanwhile it was now morning or afternoon, the dawn had come, swallowing the patches of darkness one by one. Mariana had metamorphosed into a flesh-coloured tear. At least that was how it seemed to me, because, as I said, we didn't know each other very well then. Perhaps it was someone else. But the dawn had indeed come, there was no way you could stop it.

Staying so long underwater. On the driver's seat. Teeth chattering. It's got terribly cold, perhaps because of my metabolism too. An interruption. I'm sleepy. But what I can't bear, even more than this endless fear, is the thought that somehow, through who knows what mechanism, I might wake up tomorrow morning as right as rain, as if nothing had happened, and have to start all over again with instalments for furniture, my children who don't love me, my wife who doesn't love me, the whole world that doesn't love me, paranoia, journeys, brandy, with detergent, meditation and such long nights. I don't think I could take it. It is a demanding and poor-quality show, I would tell the author. He would sigh, would put a friendly hand on my shoulder, would keep masterly control of the tremor in his voice and explain to me that there is no need to roar out my lines like a donkey, no way can such an anti-talent be accepted, even if you are a nobody, go and take a drink of water. You go down the stage steps hanging your head like any rejected extra. You've done all you could, your conscience is clear, but it isn't enough, you've lost the role. You can't be theatrical even down to your most intimate thoughts, not to mention the stage, the character.

So the time has come for me to take off my wig. To formulate my last requests at the wardrobe. I would like, if possible, to withdraw to the cemetery on the hill. A second-class hotel, for the dead with no future. Small, quiet, with fruit trees, just two kilometres from home. It seems welcoming, with its red walls where caterpillars climb, the mothers of butterflies, and the sign that I joked about so many times with my boys, a cardboard rectangle about 50 by 80 centimetres, painted in merry colours. On it is written: 'Sale and display outlet: padded caskets, funeral wreaths, crosses, floral arrangements, cut-price condolences, mourning lingerie and accessories, wickerwork items, oil-lamps, postcards from Switzerland'. You can buy cheaply all your heart desires for your cadaver. A real bargain. Of course my wife will speculate on this last aspect to the full. Saving a pile of money, she will show, for a few months, or hours, how splendidly dressed a widow can be. With close-fitting black stockings, a little veil coquettishly drawn over her sad cheeks and her breasts lifted by the latest model of Triumph bra, padding out her funeral dress just the right amount. She'll drive the whole town crazy. I'm sorry I won't be able to be present at this memorable success. A collection of curves of the highest class, for graduate undertakers and less or not at all grieving relatives. She will shed a tear. With great effort and no more than one, thinking to herself that it's a pity to spoil her powder, but never mind, it has to be done. While the lumps of soil falling on the lid deafen me for a long time, she will cast well-aimed glances through her silk visor, coldly sizing up the possible matches. No more errors. She will judge clearly, precisely, the future is at stake, and she is no longer as young as she was. Let's see, the son of the party secretary, the secretary himself, the mayor is too old, the doctor is married, the engineer has no money, then perhaps the dentist? The responsibility is enormous, she has to think of the children too. As she makes her way towards the gates of the cemetery supported on the arm of some young man or other, but one with great possibilities, she responds to condolences to left and right, with a divine half smile, slightly strained by suffering, she sighs, lifts her handkerchief to her eyes, several times looks as if she is about to faint. In her mind she adds to the list, puts a tick against two or three names, crosses one out, weighs up the pros and cons, sketches plans for a villa. Beside the caretaker's box she is ready to answer the priest or the high-school head that no, the loss is not so irreparable, but she manages to stop herself just in time. It's not the done thing, not right now. The bait will be flung on the occasion of the first memorial service, after 40 days. Until then, a deep sadness will shine in her eyes. She is sure of herself and has no doubts about her ability to net the frostbitten peacocks strutting after her. Yes, it's enough for you to take a few steps, my love, and your hips will deliver the propaganda perfectly without your having to construct all those painstaking terrorist plans with the taking of hostages. Practically, without your having to think any more. Anyway, you never troubled yourself much with thinking, not even then, in my rented room, the room of a man destined for a grand future as a tenant, where you came to undo your hair, you let it rest on the pillow, which was rather faded, but nevertheless the pillow of an intellectual, I would pin you down there with fine sentences taken out of history books, I would offer you a coffee, we would smoke an unfiltered cigarette together, we would listen to a record of Debussy, Coltrane or Prokofiev, *Romeo and Juliet*, the piano version, we would laugh at the landlady's paintings, then I would build up my courage, I would stroke you on the knees and so on, montage cut, you didn't use to speak much in those days, and only to number the onomatopoeia and miracles that we were convinced would come rushing over us.

I get the feeling that a light has come on somewhere. It isn't a visual perception, but a sensation. As when you spend the night in a room completely immersed in darkness and, despite being unable to see anything, you *sense* that a light has come on. In the bathroom, in the corridor, in the closet, on the street or in another town. That's exactly what is happening to me now. In a few seconds the presentiment has changed into a cast-iron certainty: I am flooded by a light that is growing in intensity, blinding me. I twist, I writhe in the midst of this brilliant white, without limit. It is as if my forehead and the back of my neck were caught between two immense rows of teeth. I turn my chin, bringing it even further down onto my chest. Next comes an appalling agony. Jellyfish with broken tentacles crawl over the sand in my eyes. (What can they be?... A gigantic hand runs me through its fingers and I drip, pain by pain, uniting with the water around me, sliding into the depths.) I revolve around my own axis, I advance among slow disintegrations that sometimes take the form of towers clothed in lace, mermaids with blown up breasts and submarine eddies of air bubbles, living proof that there, down below, a huge creature is sleeping and I am inexorably descending towards it, passing through the ever denser waters of its dream, as in a diver's faint. I allow myself to be drawn by the feet, looking from time to time at the uncertain lens above me, of ever-changing transparency. Things can be seen as if through a fog, it is very beautiful, for the moment I can no longer feel anything, fish with orange stripes pass through my body, I shrink, I end up as small as a golden syllable, it's all right, I believe I no longer want to see that wretched scene up there, with the shoe shop, tips and bending double with an audible grinding of the vertebrae, boredom, money, trains I drop things from, my accident as a pretext, the towns I have passed through, the bedroom, the white indifference of Mariana's thighs, the china elephant on the bedside table, from Italy, the carpet stained by Bacchanalian excesses, my former students now interred in teaching, in the same little town, the bare knees of history, her seraphic ankles to which I have kept trying to fit at least a single pair of boots, imported, of deer or teacher's skin, with laces, and not one ever fitted, you have a divine foot, madam, but unfortunately much too big, it has grown rather a lot over the last few centuries, it won't go into a riding boot any more, the bridge deserted, the toy snowstorm, a friend who keeps leaving, the iron balustrade, the woman in a white suit, the stained chairs, the cracked wardrobe, the children crawling through my soul, the mug of hot coffee I have scalded myself with for 30 years, the bathroom mirror, the tiles covered with photographs barely out of the fixer, the wedding kiss, the four of us on the mountain, in the living-room, in sleep, the alarm clock, and again the papered walls I had to press my back against every morning, with an appropriate grimace, so that the whole long-drawn-out scene can resemble an execution wall. The director raises his rifle to his eye.

When I recover, my head is spinning like the hand of a neurotic clock. I would like to know what time it is. The neighbours have probably gone to bed, I can hear them snoring. They smell of sweat, at full strength, as in a competition. The wave even reaches me here, in my soap bubble. I concentrate on the dense mist, I try to indentify it. The sweat of an old woman, of a teenager, of a bachelor, of a couple who have been together so long they have come to share the same armpits, of a child, of a blind pensioner. It is that air from which are engendered the twopenny dreams of a morning. I am sure that I too am exhaling, adding a sickly sweet draught to the respiration of the block or of the hotel where I am. A warm liquid trickles over my face, bringing a whiff of withered flowers. I would never have imagined that in your last moments you have to solve puzzles of an olfactory nature, experiencing the existential uncertainty associated with some smell that puts your nose out of joint while you are squeezing through this sort of tunnel slipping in and out of consciousness as at the earthquake, a narrow tunnel, full of damp, I thought death was something you sorted out more easily, with no more than a flap of the wings. None of Dr Moody's survivors ever described the tunnel like this, they all talk about a gentle light, angelic, that envelops you, it takes you from above, you feel like a glider, no way! We drag ourselves along up to the very last moment, what a wretched species of mole. I try at least to console my nostrils, thinking to myself that all the rooms where people die have the same smell. And they die in so many rooms, voices and all! I feel like throwing up. It doesn't matter any more. I throw up. All the same I try to retch pianissimo, out of modesty and in the belief that I have created enough of a rumpus already. I've been yelling, at the top of my voice, with conviction, especially in my thoughts, sufficient for a lifetime. At the present moment, even if someone could hear me, I wouldn't open my mouth any more. Not a word, not a syllable. Mum's the word. I don't know if there is life after death. I'll give the ferryman his silver coin and that's that.

Look at her standing there, with the gas lamp in her hand, calm down, my dear, nothing's happened, just a power cut, you'll see, they're fixing it. Sleep, Mother's little pet. She moves slowly away, where are you going?, I ask her, she doesn't reply, it seems to her that I know the answer, she dissolves softly into the darkness of the room, she is no more. The things around me pulsate. A power cut, that's all. My head. The imperfect sphere. That has to make one final effort. It seems to me that I can see it already, the great calm, at the end of the universe, beyond the universe, for the time being the odd little crack can be seen, a tiny contorted mauve star. I must get out of here once and for all! I try to move. An appalling pain, it takes my breath away, but that is no longer of any importance. (What a mess, you are forced to struggle, to pray even for your own end, to give a tip for that too.) One, two, three! One more time! My body has become small, with so much suffering. It has become a delirious anthill out of which the ants of time run maddened. Spreading out in all directions and leaving behind them this nothing that hurts.

Bogdan and Mihai have finished eating and now, with bated breath, they are watching the end of the film. Mariana has not been attentive for a long time, she is rolling little balls of bread with her long slender fingers and looking into space. She is wondering what has happened. Or perhaps she is thinking of our first night together, when she told me that she had been waiting just for me, always, well, there's nothing I can do, she will have to go on waiting a bit, at least until the packages with the presents are dredged from the bottom of the lake. I am among them too, even if they don't find me. The veins of my forehead strike soundlessly against the bones of darkness, I advance like a fragile train on this railway that is nearing its end. Sparkling more and more faintly under the water. Enough. Again I feel like yelling, but I have made a decision to keep my mouth shut, at least from this point on. It is a unique moment, I mustn't miss it, I am dying! I grit my teeth and wriggle towards the extremity of the contractile tube that presses on my temples and crushes my eyes. Now! How curious, there is light, the light at the end of the tunnel, they were right after all, who said it was dark? And I can hear voices too…

The doctor washed his hands slowly. "A really difficult birth. A good thing it worked out all right." The nurse laid the newborn baby on the table and started to massage it energetically. "I can't understand why he doesn't cry. After all, everything went perfectly, didn't it?... Take a look, it's as if he's keeping his lips shut deliberately." The doctor turned his head and looked over his shoulder. He smiled absently. "He'll yell all right, don't you worry."

Translator's notes

The *Pobeda* was a Soviet car of the late 1940s and '50s.

Grasa de Cotnari is a famous sweet wine, produced in the north-east of Romania.

Telecinemateca was a weekly high point in the Romanian television schedule of the communist period, in which a classic of world cinema was shown following a short introduction by a film critic.

Ion *Creangă's* (1837–1839) *Childhood Memories* and stories, often inspired by folklore, are among the classics of nineteenth-century Romanian literature.

The European *ground squirrel* or *souslik* found in the Romanian plains is a similar animal, apart from its habitat, to the tree squirrels familiar to readers in the British Isles.

Călușari are participants in a traditional ritual dance performed by teams of men in white costumes, something akin to English morris dancing.

George *Coșbuc* (1886–1918) is best known for his poems evoking rural life, though the poem referred to here, 'The Queen of the Ostrogoths' is a tragic ballad about the death of the Ostrogothic queen Amasuntha.

Gheorghe Doja, better known in English by the Hungarian form of his name, György Dózsa, was the leader of a peasant revolt in Transylvania and Hungary in 1514. In the course of his subsequent execution in Temesvár (today the Romanian city of Timișoara), he was sat on a hot iron throne with a hot iron crown round his head.

Chance

The muffled sound of the pickaxes was lost in the pattering of the rain. The three men worked listlessly, in silence, squelching through the mud. The trench got deeper and they gradually disappeared into its bowels. From the street all that could be seen of them was the the ear-flaps of their caps, sodden with rainwater. Shovelfuls of black earth kept coming up through the air, raising the edges of the pit. Smaller lumps rolled on the tarmac. Finally the pipe appeared. From a distance it looked like the belly of an enormous fish, buried there who knows how long ago. The burst could be clearly seen, running for almost half a metre. Some hole, that ... Go and see if we've got what we need in the van. Don't forget the bolts. Laur jumped onto the edge of the trench and made for the van. The windscreen was shining, covered with round drops of rain. He opened the door and started rummaging through the pile of tools. After a few seconds he looked at his watch. Time to grab a bite, guys. It's ten past three. The other two lifted their heads. What time did you say, three? Looks like we got carried away with our work, and didn't notice the time passing ... Leave that stuff, then, and get the lunch packs. You'll find them under the back seat. Laur bent down, fumbled for them, smelled them, felt his mouth watering. He came back with the lunch packs under his arm and sat down on the edge of the trench. But didn't you get the bottle? Come on, what do you think...? Here it is. Nostrils sniffing. A sigh. This bloody drizzle. Ah, it'll blow over. Begonie rubbed his numbed palms together.

After a few minutes the rain stopped. Their waterlogged anoraks stuck to their backs. With impatient gestures they pulled open the newspapers in which their food was wrapped. A sound of wet paper tearing. Cracked, dirty fingers eagerly grabbing. Where's the onion? ... Aha! Talk about hot, man! Shut up and take it with the cheese. Warms your heart, doesn't it? The food quickly disappears, leaving greasy traces in the hollows of their chins. Little lenticular spots shining faintly. Come on then, let it flow. Trandafir took out the stopper with his teeth, slugged a draught, and held the bottle out to the others. The veined throats moved up and down like pistons. Now it's raining inside too, but with fire, laughed Begonie. Cheers, mate! From time to time the odd car quickly passed by the three figures perched on the heap of earth, looking into space and chewing. Lined faces, yellowed, stained round the mouth. The sky was purple. It had gradually turned purple, like the cheek of a huge cadaver. Its a mother's funeral of a life, swore Trandafir, looking upwards. Always our turn when there's a job to do in weather like this. It was a team of nicely matched names, men with the names of flowers. Lucky bouquet, smelling of ... Listen, lay off the poetry and tell me where you put the jackhammer. I can't see it. Don't worry. It's down in the trench. No one's going to steal it. You'd do better to get some of this down your throat. That's the way. A fine steam rises from their clothes, from their lips, from the earth. What do you think, are we going to finish the bloody thing in two hours? Begonie looked down for a few moments at his mud-caked boots, sighed, and broke wind loudly. Hey, will we or won't we finish it today? I don't know, Laur, my boy. Even my mother-in-law doesn't have a crack like that. But we might give it what for by the evening. The wind had started to blow. The greasy sheets of paper fluttered gently among the remains of bread, cheese, bacon fat and onion peel. Is that the medicine bottle empty? Hang on, there's a drop left! Trandafir threw his head back and slurped the last finger's breadth of țuică. He smacked his lips contentedly. That was good, mate! All I need now is one of those whores, for a ... In this damp, that's just what I miss. A rained-on whore. Hold an umbrella over her head while you're having it off with her ... A belch and a chuckle could be heard. Wait a minute and I'll tell you something ... I don't know about you guys, but see me, once I've drunk that liquid and had a bite to eat, that's it, I'm on my lunch break. Relaxed. So listen, Laur, and I'll tell you all about it. Last week ... See me, if my stomach's full, I don't want anything else. What else should I want? Well, apparently her man wasn't up to it any more, you know, and I thought, a pity about the poor woman, so young and neglected ... Yes, chief, yes. Go and hit him over the head with something, Laur. Right, what I wanted to say is that she had a pair of buttocks like you've never seen in all your miserable life. Why miserable? That's why. Because you haven't seen them. Arse all over the place, mate, just had to move it and your trousers would drop of their own accord. Warm you up like a heater. I don't even remember how I got my clothes off ... Listen, did she not make a dash for it when she smelled your stink? What, you think she didn't smell too? Laur grinned, showing his metal crowns. What can I say, Trandafir? You're right too. Since you came into the world the air hasn't been the same again. So you smell of hyacinths, do you? You smell of corpse, mate, if you must know. And anyway, I'm wasting my breath. You understand women like I do foreign languages. The argument went on for a few minutes, then dried up, and finally they fell silent.

They looked at the tree outlined like a solitary figure at the corner of the street. Its slender form rose to make a complicated silhouette across the violet sky of the afternoon. A heavy lorry passed close to them and splashed them with mud. Hey, fuck you ... Give me a fag, will you? Laur took out a crumpled and half-soaked packet. He lit a cigarette between cupped palms, then held out the packet to the others. They smoked in silence, coughing from time to time and spitting out gobbets of saliva. Still bloody cold, mate ... I'm frozen stiff. All right, I'm getting back to work. Begonie got up, threw away the cigarette end, and jumped into the pit. He grabbed the shovel and drove it deep beneath the pipe. There was a thud, then the noise of something breaking. Then nothing. What are you doing down there, chief? Silence. He's probably gone and broken a fucking bone. Hey, answer, will you! Begonie showed his head above the mouth of the trench. He was grinning from ear to ear and laughing. Trandafir and Laur looked at him questioningly. What's got into you? Why the laughter? We heard something cracking down there. What was it? Begonie winked at them. Come on down here and let me show you something ... The two jumped without seeking further explanations. At the bottom of the trench the water welled up from under their boots. Begonie looked at them with his eyes half shut, shifting the weight of his body from one leg to the other. In his right hand he held a little skull, broken and full of mud. What do you say to that, then? Isn't it a wonder? He held it up, turning it in his fingers. Laur and Trandafir stared at the blackened cranium, and burst out laughing. But how did that get here? Could be your granny, mate. Escaped from the cemetery ... Let's take it to the museum ... Dead for a sewer! They might give us the price of a ţuică ... Another burst of laughter rose up from the trench. They laughed themselves to tears, clutching their bellies with their hands. The mud squelched quietly. When they had finished, they wiped their faces with their sleeves and suddenly fell silent, exhausted. Begonie pushed his cap onto the back of his neck, scratched himself through his trousers, and muttered through his teeth, guys, I have to tell you, I need to piss. So if no one has any objections ... He grinned and put the skull on the ground, upside down. He urinated at length, until the liquid started to pour out through the eye sockets. The other two watched without saying anything, smirking. Begonie did up his flies. All right, back to work now, he said hoarsely. Or else it will be night before we're finished.

They resumed their digging. Noises rose up, spreading rhythmically over the street. It was quiet in the district. People had gathered in living-rooms, among dishes. Boots and shoes, coats and umbrellas drying on coat stands, few words. Here's the soup. Slowly the sun emerged from behind the blocks, golden, moist. Give us that fucking hammer … Can't you hear? Begonie stretched his back, irritated. Where are you, mate? The hammer, he cried as loudly as he could. Trandafir stopped work too, blew his nose between his fingers and looked around him. The raindrops were drying on the tarmac, trembling on the branches, sparkling from time to time. Slowly Laur lifted the skull and wiped it carefully. It was so light … *Alas!* In the hollow of his palm unknown words grew, and rushed ever faster to his temples. *Alas! Poor Yorick! I knew him … He hath borne me on his back a thousand times...* What the fuck are you on about over there? Have you cracked? *Those lips that I have kissed I know not how oft...* Trandafir and Begonie stared. Hey, mate, talk to us. What's wrong with you? Heavens above! You can't be pissed out of your mind on a mouthful of slivovitz. *WHERE BE YOUR GIBES NOW? YOUR GAMBOLS? YOUR SONGS?* Hey, Laur, stop this fucking nonsense and lay off the joking. What's got into you? Suddenly the sounds became muffled and he fell silent. Clumsily he placed the skull on the ground and closed his eyes. Hell! It must have been the weather. He stood up and passed his hand over his face with a tired gesture. He could feel the sweat drying on his temples. He spat to one side, then turned his head and looked at his workmates. Trandafir and Begonie stood motionless, words stuck in their throats. The light wandered gently over their faces, then passed on.

Translator's note

Ţuică: is a traditional Romanian spirit, distilled from plums or other fruit, similar to slivovitz or schnapps.

At the Bar

The bus arrived in the middle of the village and stopped. It was a scorching, dry day, without a breath of wind. The driver stopped the engine and the old Skoda seemed to deflate, yielding up its soul through the cracks in the windows. The people got out one by one, in no hurry. Headscarves, caps, hats, worn clothes, patches, stains and hands, black skirts, plastic bags, full sacks, bloodshot eyes, voices sleepy from the hot hours spent on the rural bus. Cercel stretched his arms, sighed and picked his nose. Then he got out too and locked the front door of the vehicle. Two or three people who had been sitting on benches in front of the houses stood up and joined the travellers heading for the bar. Hey! What's the latest talk in town?... Nothing much. What, nothing? Vasile, you tell me. The individual to whom this was addressed, a young man with red hair who worked at the cement factory, gave his colleague, who was silent as usual, a bored look, then spat quickly in the dust of the street. It's really grim, old man, if you want to know. That's why I'm asking. Tell me. I'll tell you, if you get me a beer. I'll do that. Right then, in that case I can tell you that those people are going epileptic. How come? Because they're scared. Really? Yes, with all those stories about the air, the water... He's right, I think they're scared too, broke in another worker. They're exposed from all directions, nowhere to hide if it ... It's different for us here. With the forest, know what I mean? He gazed for a few moments at the hills dusted with green that surrounded the village on three sides, like ramparts. Protecting that minuscule end of the world where people still went to be cut for jaundice with the razor-blade that the old healing woman also used for her own atrocious depilation, where the phone had a handle and the moon was called God's lantern, but even then it wasn't lit all the time, for example last winter, when the wolves tore to pieces an old woman who was on her way home through the middle of the village, and nothing was left of her, not one sign that the neighbours could recognise her by, so that they said it was her for the simple reason that they never saw her in her yard again, where two years ago the mayor's brother hanged himself on a walnut tree with a lamp wick because he had been left by the most beautiful woman in the village, the midwife, who disappeared under cover of darkness, where the polecat has no bones, it's made out of nothing but gristle and well water, the ghost of the night, slips through any crack, sucks the blood of the hens and gives us bad dreams, snow, weddings, new borns, mothers-in-law with no faces, with axes in their hands, lottery tickets and hunchbacks with bouquets of flowers, we wake up with wide eyes, reach out our hands and knock over the vase, where the roads are bad during the day and non-existent at night and the buses lose their suspension, screws and petrol at every bend, as the village is a fair height above sea level, 725 metres to the lightning conductor on the school, the road climbs up between potholes, ducks, children, carts that don't get out of the way, people who come out of the bar in the most surprising directions, for they are all drinkers around here because of the altitude, and almost nobody listens to the valve radio set, what they say through the loudspeaker is trivial compared with the much more interesting local issues, who did what to whom, how many times, how and when, or compared with the feeding of animals, pigs, cows, goats, poultry and rabbits, less so dogs and cats not at all, more important is work, the scythe, caring for fruit-trees, spraying, watering, picking, making *ţuică* according to a secret method and selling it in the town, to fools, putting up a new privy, because the old one has collapsed as usual on top of someone who was relieving himself inside, deep in thought, and anyway it's well known that round here things fall down, dry out, peel off or go soft faster than in other places, and practically the whole community, some 5,000 souls, believe firmly in werewolves, visions, dead fairies and glands that are cured by getting down on all fours and crawling round the churchyard 13 times, the same churchyard where the graveyard is, which probably accounts for the superstitions, peace to those who come, joy to those who stay, blessing on those who leave or the other way round, it's not very clear, but that's what's written on the gate, for which reason there is an unshakable belief that at the end of the day *ţuică* is the best cure for rashes, burns, liver, roundworm, lungs, radiation, chickenpox and in general more or less all worldly mysteries and illnesses. So it's another kettle of fish here, agreed Vasile, taking a last look at the hills. Over there their water has been cut off. The hell it has! The whole town? Yes. And what about us? Apparently we're to cover the wells. What are we to cover them with? Cellophane? Or we can sit Traian down on them, 'cause he's just the right size to fit the rim. We'll pass him round by turns. Why are you getting at me, mate? Because you're fat. We'll wrap them in tarpaulins and hold them down with planks or branches so that the radiation doesn't fall in the water. That's what to do. I see you're taking the mickey? Who, me? There's Cercel. Ask him too, if you don't believe me. Hey, Cercel, tell us what's all this about the wells. What wells? Fountains? Aha. There's not a single fountain in the bar. Let's tell Nae he should build one in the corner. A spittoon would be more use. Because ever since you came in you've been building up phlegm. No, he's done that since he was born. He's a cultivated man. Leave that lot, Traian, and let's make it up. How about putting something away? We'll have a beer, no more than one, on my honour. Its on me. You and your honour. But if you say it's on you, that's fine with me! One beer won't burn you and what's a lot spoils because it's too little. Or however the proverb goes. Bravo, that's what I like, always ready with a traditional riddle. Nae! Give us two hundreds of the hard stuff, 'cause maybe you haven't any beer. But it had better be in glasses washed with water from a covered well… What covered well? Forget it. Those'll do. The man's come from the town and his lips are contaminated anyway. See how he spits, like an engineer. Hearty laughter. Don't you laugh, mate. And the rest of you don't wet yourselves, 'cause we'll come out of it somehow. Cheers! The glasses clink together loudly. In the bar it is almost dark. In the corners one can make out broken bottles, vaguely shiny puddles, cigarette ends, pages of newspapers. There is a strong smell of dust, sweat and țuică. Words lose their sonority almost instantaneously between the flaking, mould-eaten walls. Outside, the light sparkles on the tin roofs. The people who came off the bus make their leisurely way home. The centre of the village is triangular in shape, with the clinic and the village hall on one side and the bar and the grocery shop on the other. The base of the triangle consists of the council building, with its green fence. Here the bus route terminates. The ragged tarmac gives way to potholed tracks where silence reigns. Out of the door of the clinic comes the doctor. Tall, blond, with thin lips and round-rimmed glasses. A few seconds after him, the notary and the caretaker come down the steps of the council building. The notary is as thin as the doctor. He is wearing a suit the colour of duck eggs. He has a tie, brass cuff-links, a squat nose and trousers with elegantly creased turn-ups. Hello, doctor! Care for a quick one? Bănea, the richest man in the village, wanders up. He is fat, red in the face, and his eyes are so close together that it's easy to mistake one for the other. He makes friendly gestures with his hand. Hăpău the postman pulls up beside him. He gets off his bicycle and puts his arms round Bănea. How are you doing, Gheorghiță? Very well, and you? Hăpău pushes back his red, feathered hat. He is dressed in a green suit, which he has matched with a yellow shirt. He smiles uneasily, saying that he is not doing so badly. They both greet the people who have stopped in front of the bar to wait for them. From the house opposite, painted pink, emerges Prună, the veterinary technician. He has thin hair, sunken cheeks, and a mouth twisted into a sort of upside down smile. He comes with small steps, marked by the clinking of the vaccine phials that he keeps in his pockets. Long life to the notary, sir! Good luck, doctor! Hi, pal, says the doctor, without malice. Long life, Gheorghiță. You too, although I don't think you'll make it until morning. (General laughter again, not very loud.) Shall we go in? asks Prună. Let's go in, there's no danger. Who knows! Tell us now, postman, have you washed the strontium off your hands? Hăpău smiled, revealing his black gums. You're laughing at me, Prună. Far from it. Then what was all that about? What? What you said just now. Oh, strontium, well it's a sort of airborne death. Death to your prick. Shut up. Now that the foolish thing's come down on top of us, we can address her by name, strontium, like talking to children. Or like Dincă's wife. Well yes, obviously. Bravo, you said it like on TV. *Obviously*! What a deep word, gives you a kind of peaceful feeling, like in the army, when you hear it, and the way you say it is top class. All right, then, let's get a bit plastered. After you. There were another five or six people in the bar. Traian, Vasile and his companion had already settled down to business, in an initiatory silence. The sergeant in charge of the local police station stood with his left elbow supported on the counter, having pushed the right one forward and up, so as to be able to get the glass of mint syrup to his mouth. What's that you're drinking, sergeant? So early in the morning and all alone? Syrup. Dear me! The effects of the catastrophe are showing already here in our bar. No, mate, but I've got a splitting headache. I had to spend all night at Aurică Capră's. The notary sighs, Bănea puts his hand in his pocket to take out some money, the doctor blows his nose in his handkerchief. Come on, Nae, do your duty as host. The publican gloomily washes the glasses one by one and fills them under the attentive eyes of everyone. What a mess, man, with this explosion. Seems the radiation's got as far as Poland. Even further, I'd say… How do you know? I know, 'cause they said it on the radio. Listen, no matter how far it's got, I shit on their pills. That's not a nice way to talk, mate, and here in church too. But do these buttons really do any good? 'Cause they're giving them out to all of us. And it's too much of a free gift, you can't help wondering. What buttons, old man? The pills. Prună lifts his eyes upwards, adopting a dramatic air. They are mi-ra-cu-lous! With real iodine, so we can see in the dark. What will we see in the dark? Seems you turn phosphorescent. What if you turn stupid? It will be like it says in the book. So that we won't think any more, that's why they're giving us iodine. 'Cause even if we do have thoughts, it's all the same, even worse. We still put our hands on our chests, today, tomorrow. Put them yourself. No, Prună, this is a long illness. About 20 years later you wake up with a cancer in your backside, and you don't know how it got there. Now you know. From the rays, muttered the notary. Then God give us good health! They emptied the glasses down their throats. Either I'm out of practice or this is stronger than what I drank this morning. It's maybe contaminated? Can't be, it's in a bottle. Hăpău unbuttoned his jacket. The thing that gets me is that you can't protect yourself. I imagine in the war, for example, you would see the other lot coming and you could run away or shoot, depending on how many there were. But now what can you do? You can drink, said Bănea. Nae, run us off another round, this is radioactive thirst, from the bloody iodine. And have a drink yourself, by your mother's candle! Be a man, while there's still time. But where's the priest? asked the doctor unexpectedly. This would normally be the time when he hears Nae's confession. He's gone, said the notary. Where? There's nowhere you can go now, so it seems more decent to stay at home, quietly. With your friends. I hear in Sweden I don't know how many people are going to die next year because of the… Well, if they die in Sweden, what more can I say… We'd do better to make an early order for pine wood coffins. Oh Christmas tree … Stop it, you're singing out of key. Our land has forests green of fir, recited Cercel aggressively, looking at the shelves of bottles. Or do you mean to say that it doesn't? Could be, what do I know? But the driver's right, I mean what he's trying to say… to say! … is that the forest still protects us. It protects your mother in her grave. Don't you understand that the trouble comes from above? That's how it is, for example about two o'clock today I'd gone for water into one of those blocks of flats full of Gypsies, I went up the stairs and when I got to the sixth floor I saw a horse. What did you see? A horse, well, actually just the rear end. Are you sure you hadn't drunk anything at the factory? It was standing just as happy as could be on the landing, one end was stuck into the entrance of a flat, eating, to go by the munching sound, and the other end was outside next to the stair, shaking its tail. You've knocked us over with that one! And how had they got a horse up to the sixth floor? In the lift. I said it was stupid. Bloody Gypsies! I don't know, mate, I'm just telling you what I saw. You mean the old nag climbed up the steps, like any resident? Meaning that the Gypsies don't give a shit for Chernobyl. That's Indians for you. What have Indians got to do with it? Gypsies, mate, 'cause they landed on us from India a hundred years ago and now they're feeding their old gee-gees in sixth-floor flats. And what was the horse like? Oh, long life to the mayor! The mayor shook a few hands at random. What are you lot doing in here? Talking rubbish again? A soda water, Nae. I want to form my own opinion. Too late, the sergeant is already doing that. Silently. Ah, look at the doctor, caught in the act. What are you doing, doctor? Drinking with the peasants? The mayor turned the glass of soda water between his fingers, drank it in one draught, then went up to the sergeant. Tell me, sergeant, how was it in the end with poor Aurică? Just what you know from last night. No more than that little heap of ash. That's all that was left of the man. And that's probably how we'll all end up, observed Cercel meditatively. We couldn't even gather him all together, he was scattered all over the place. The wind was blowing… Nae! Thanks. You were saying?… A shame about him, I thought he was a nice guy. Maybe, but he drank himself blind. Yesterday evening, he could still see to put the light out, then he managed to batter his wife's face in the dark until she didn't even look like herself grown old. Poor woman, left with no home, no child, no man. He wasn't a man… I don't like drunkards. Me neither, said the doctor, ending his intervention with a small belch. Well out of it. What do you mean well out of it, doctor? You're drunk. I don't mean him, I mean her. Let's hear what else the sergeant has to say. 'Cause they've reconstructed the whole case, like a game of backgammon. The policeman asked for a beer. Now, if I've started it anyway… he apologised, looking towards the doctor. My blood pressure is all right today. I can have a beer, can't I? To drown my sorrows. The doctor made no comment. So, as I was saying, when the firemen came, everything was burning, house, barn, orchard. A terrific blaze. He had made a good job of it, Aurică had. I've got the witness declarations on me. He got himself drunk immediately after his morning cup of tea, which he drank with *ţuică*, like they do in England. Then he laid into Lenuţa, left her unconscious, and I reckon he started to get bored. So it came into his head to tie his child to a beam in the barn with his head hanging down, and tie him he did, the evidence being that we found the wire that he used to hang his little one up by the foot, with the remains of his heel still in the noose. Old Petrică, who was watching from across the road, said that to go by the screaming he must have thrashed the boy too until he could thrash no more, because it seems he was bawling that he wasn't his child, he was Bucă's, because they were neighbours, weren't they, so it's impossible to tell whether he killed him before the inferno or left him senseless and he was burned alive, poor lad, no one can say now, not even the forensic pathologist, who came just in time to be able to say nothing definite. The sergeant shook his head, took a sip from his glass of beer, and grimaced. Nae, what's this? You've put brandy in my Azuga beer, don't you play jokes on me again! Right! Anyway, it doesn't matter any more, and they all said the can we found at the crime scene, Capră filled it with diesel and splashed it over everything, himself included, then he struck the wretched match. After that it was easy. It all flared up at once, so we didn't find anything left apart from what I've told you we found, plus a dental crown of Aurică's, and that was blackened too.

(*The people had gathered in a crowd, standing there like a great fox on the prowl, moving its eyes and its muzzle, getting ready to cross the threshold between curiosity and action, so that the barn burned down as well, all jostling to get a better view, putting their hands to their mouths and crossing themselves, and meanwhile no one was left of Capră's household but his wife, who recovered from hypnosis and shrieked like the mother of fire, for that is what it was, fire, and the crowd settled down only once everything was reduced to cinders, over which they poured buckets of water in abundance.*)

Lord, how my head aches, said the sergeant in conclusion. Well, sergeant, he's burned and that's it, an evil hour! That's your explanation for everything, an evil hour. Poor man, he wasn't even 40… Leave off the keening, mate, you sound like an old woman. The guy was a jerk. So he was, and he had the good fortune not to live to see this business that's giving us all food for thought. Why so much lamenting for him? grinned Cercel. You're talking to keep yourself awake, mate! No talking to the driver when the vehicle is in motion. Do you think up there, where he may be right now, it's any better? Up in the heavens it's worse than on earth. Really bad. The mayor himself said, that the air… You mean in your opinion, Aurică the pyromaniac is at this moment in heaven? Great is the Lord! I wonder if they have a bar up there. He'll set fire to all their bloody green pastures. No, but that's where the radiation is, up there in the clouds. Don't be an idiot… Maybe the sky is full of angels flying in all directions with gas masks over their eyes. You're not right in the head, mate. Suddenly voices were raised. The mayor looked at him thoughtfully, in silence. Prună intervened sharply. Don't be so wet!

Quite so, added the notary. I can't believe we're all going to pay our debt to nature either. I mean, who would work the land then? Eh? Who would sow, who would prune the fruit-trees?... Who would kill the caterpillars? whispered Traian. You stupid ox! If we haven't been intimidated by progress, we're not going to take fright at this either. There won't be anyone to make *ţuică* either, murmured the caretaker. Really! Nae, undo another capsule. And shove your tongue back in your mouth, for God's sake, you're spoiling the party! The mayor cleared his throat, did up his jacket buttons, and said: it will be all right in the end, we'll sort it out somehow. Let's have the doctor tell us how things stand, scientifically speaking. The doctor started, trying to get out of his torpor. Well, it's impos...sible to state with any precision... Just tell us, without precision!... it's also a question of each individual's re... sistance... That's how it is with the fuse-box, agreed Cercel. Hăpău, who had just come back from the toilet, caught the doctor's last words and butted into the discussion, that's right, doctor, it's quite low in my case, my resistance. My bones are letting me down, I don't have enough calcium any more, God knows. 'Cause for 30 years I've been wandering all over on foot and on my bicycle with my satchel on my back, so it's understandable, in a way. But I can't understand what's causing this dizziness that's been coming over me recently. I can't really believe it's blood pressure, because I just see green stars, falling, they fall in front of me and there's a thumping sound in my ears, it's been going on for about five days, exactly since this business with the reactor started... What can I say? I don't have any appetite any more, said another. What about me?... I have bad dreams, nothing but rats, those water rats... And is it black? Prună chanted to himself nasally: 'And the cows die of a strange death, getting covered with boils, the young women keep hiccupping, the priest has gone, black cocks fly through the living-room, with hens following them, and the polecat comes to eat from your hand...' Eats your hand, more like. Enough of this nonsense, the mayor frowned. What the hell! It's my eyes that hurt, and on the left, sighed the notary. My head, added the sergeant. Could it not be from that stuff? asked Bănea, lowering his voice to a whisper. From the end of the room came the high-pitched voice of Dincă, the primary teacher. I've been saying since last year that this would happen. I've got witnesses too. So what if you've been saying? interrupted the mayor. I could have been saying since last year that Iuliana doesn't cheat on you. With witnesses too. Does that mean it's true? And you lot, if you stay any longer here blathering, you'll go off your heads. So then, continued the mayor, turning to the doctor. Get your snout out of that glass and tell us once and for all how things stand. But in terms we can understand. 'Cause you've been getting lots of phone calls and envelopes from the ministry? And you haven't? asked the notary. I haven't had anything. Hello, doctor... Well, as I was saying, in the first place, the organism... What's the organism got to do with it? On the radio they said that the radiation stays on the ground. I mean down it comes, and then goes into the soil. So unless we're going to bloody well roll around in the mud, nothing can happen to the organism. Or can it? The mayor gave the notary a dirty look and the latter fell silent, suddenly pretending to be interested in what he could see at the bottom of his glass. You're a right cretin, you really are. Haven't you read in the papers that we're not to give milk to children, that we're to wash vegetables I don't know how many times, like underwear, that we're not to eat lettuce, radishes, carrots or cucumbers, because these are the most affected? Vegetables? Yes, have you read? Uh-huh, but I don't eat carrots. Then tell me, don't we feed ourselves from the soil, when it comes down to it, what do we feed ourselves from? Dincă got up from his table with his glass in his hand and approached the group who were discussing heatedly at the bar. The others stopped talking, and looked at him suspiciously. They did not like the way the teacher talked, usually about the end of the world, and they liked even less the fact that when he did so he sprayed them apocalyptically with saliva. An accident like this has never been recorded in history before. It's the big sign. The sign that all the beasts, the elements and the forces of evil are going on the attack. I foresaw it a year ago. And these measures you're talking about, with water, with cucumbers, they're laughable. Dincă made a sweeping gesture with the hand in which he held his glass, pouring almost all its contents over some of the listeners who were nearest to him. It may be as you say, but I don't think there's any point in all this either. I mean, washing your clothes, or only drinking mineral water, sighed Hăpău. Well they're right about the clothes, muttered Prună, wiping the țuică-stained lapels of his jacket with his palm. And as for mineral water, at least it doesn't stink for a week. Dincă brought his glass down onto the bar. From this, no one will escape, we've had it! What are you saying? That we're going to snuff it? I mean why, old man, what's it got against me? For fuck's sake, lay off, take a sip from your glass and don't get worked up. Nae, where's Nae? He's gone out for a minute. Hăpău became melancholic. He put his arms round the teacher. Mr Dincă, maybe you're right, about this, about the New Testament and the beasts, but please don't drive everyone mad when we've taken a knocking already, I respect you, really, I'm almost fond of you, so give us a word of encouragement instead, something for the soul, like that there's still some bloody hope, something… 'And I heard behind me a great voice, as of a trumpet…' Bravo! 'And I turned to see the voice that spake with me.' And who was it? Iuliana. Laugh as much as you like… for there will be no one left to laugh when all this is over. Is that so, did you hear that women get a way out? asked the notary. 'And being turned, I saw seven golden candlesticks. And in the midst of the candlesticks one clothed with a garment down to the foot…' Oh Dincă, what did I beg you? 'And he had in his right hand seven stars; and out of his mouth went a sharp two-edged sword…' Yes, shut your gob, mate, you're sending shivers through my brain. They'll close this dive of ours down with so much religion. And it's not even a cheerful sermon, it's no use trying to change Dincă's channel, he's drunk as a newt, he only knows one message. Teacher, take a gulp from my tumbler and maybe you won't see candlesticks any more. Hey, who am I talking to, is it true that abortion is going to be legalised? 'Cause it would be a sin before God. So much effort down the drain. If you ask me, I don't think for a moment there are going to be monsters born, murmured Vasile. And what if they are born? What do you do with them afterwards, a world full of monsters wandering all over the place, and you have to feed them too? Some like Bucurică, poor guy, look how ugly he is. Which Bucurică? Prună's uncle. When I think of my Mirela, she's only 18… 'And his countenance was as the sun shineth in his strength…' I love her like the eyes in my head, she's at the sanitary high school now, but unfortunately she finishes next year, so is all this going to be for nothing? This is a matter of politics, gentlemen. The notary cleared his throat. I mean what… Tell us so that we can… understand…? Quiet, man, it's break time. Someone turned on the radio. 'The agenda of the press conference was…' Agenda, repeated the sergeant, fingering the buttons of his uniform. Nae, open… but where the hell is that man off to? 'Radiation levels have fallen in all regions to the maximum permitted dose. We continue with the meteorological bulletin.' That's just what we need now. The year 2000 is approaching. It was on the radio. 'His eyes were as a flame of fire…' Oh, Mother. 'Precipitation will persist in…' Turn it off, Cercel, as if I didn't know it will persist. But why don't they explain why it's so hot? Could be from the heat of the cloud. It floats over and rains burning ashes on our heads. And it's from the head that the fish rots, murmured the caretaker. That man's pissed, what fish, mate? Run away quickly and do the cleaning. Fish, do you hear, that's lying on his mind. Who's lying? The sergeant became agitated. When there's a national emergency? Look, you've squashed your cap. We're getting a bit plastered, shouted Prună, sipping noisily from his glass. Now's the time for another round… Doctor, what are you doing? Sitting with an empty glass… in this heat… Nae! Hell, I think he's gone to hide in the fallout shelter. In the privy, clarified Cercel. Here he comes now! 'And when I saw him, I fell at his feet as dead.' Nae entered slowly, carrying a crate full of bottles. The notary wiped his nose with the sleeve of his hitherto duck egg-coloured jacket. He leaned slightly towards the mayor. You know, for me, soft drinks, I mean wine, upset my stomach. I'd love to know why. On the other hand, when I drink a brandy, I feel better straight away. Come on, Nae, where have you been all this time? Leave the crate 'cause I can see it's wine, and bring some of that hard stuff to dry out the atoms! The publican placed the crate in a corner and took from his pocket a bunch of lettuce. He turned it in his fingers thoughtfully. Look at this… The hum of conversation stopped. They all stared at the shrivelled leaves, dirty green in colour. Yesterday it looked pretty good, firm as a rod, and now look what's happened to it. 'And thus I saw in a vision…' The Apocalypse! roared Dincă, scattering a cloud of saliva. Shut your face! cried Cercel. Don't let me hear any more, the room is spinning around me with so many swords and visions! I wonder at his wife putting up with such a crazy old bore. Everyone wonders, 'cause just seeing Iuliana passing in the lane, in profile, is enough to knock you speechless. Some started to laugh. I WON'T HAVE IT! Yes you will, 'cause you've driven us out of our heads with your prayers. He's been on a binge since Saturday, non-stop. He's like a suction-pump, man. Lay off, mate, take it easy with the bevvy, for God's sake. You of all people. The Apocalypse comes and finds you legless. Nae, what does the bill come to? Quite a lot, mayor, but if you want to pay it… well… Brandy, ţuică, bitters, that would be about… All right, charge it to Bănea. And crack us open another Swedish bitters, requested the notary. It does the organism good. Swedish? That's what the man said, Nae. And so, what was I saying?… About lettuce, someone prompted. And Iuliana, sighed Hăpău. Wouldn't mind kissing her lettuces, laughed the notary. Pigs, spluttered the teacher, choking with fury. Prună thumped his back. Take it easy, Dincă… He sat him down on a chair. Stay here and don't get so upset, it won't burn you. The thing burned five days ago. Iuliana's has been burning for 15 years. I was talking about the reactor. I see we're talking at cross purposes. Nae filled another round of glasses and looked again at the withered leaves. But it's really drooping badly. Everything seems to have gone crazy. My granddaughter has been vomiting without a break since yesterday morning, it's green, I'll bring her to see you tomorrow, doctor, but I don't believe that will help her, the cock has stopped crowing, the dog has died, my wife is in a raging temper, and I'm thinking. I keep thinking and I could almost weep. Hey, Nae, why come and sadden the atmosphere? Shut up and pour. Look at him standing there peering at that thing in his hand, laughed Bănea. The notary lit a cigarette. He threw the match on the floor and crushed it with the heel of his shoe. Now, not that he isn't right... It's not quite so bad, the doctor spoke up painstakingly, the pills... Because the radioactive iodine is eliminated by, er, competition, with the iodine in the... tablets... Prună turned towards the doctor. Forgive me, but since we're here anyway, I'd like to consult you on something. Go ahead... Well, the thing is that for some time I've had a bit of a pain in the... What could it be? You're paralytic, what else could it be? laughed Vasile. Seems there have been human sacrifices too. Where? Over where it happened. In Sweden... That's from the Swedish bitters. I mean the cloud must be quite a size if it's here above us and it reaches as far as Sweden. What's the truth, doctor, about the cloud? Well how can I put it, for you to understand, in the first place, the organism... Leave the doctor alone, he's pissed. Ask me. All right, I'm asking you. Well, the catch is that it's too high up, and we're too low down. The laws of nature, have you got it? No. Gravity, mate. You're not explaining very well, old man. Prună waved his hand in boredom. One thing is clear, he said, even if we snuff it, if we take these tablets now, no one, not even the dead that we'll be, will ever have goitre again. Iodine's the stuff! You're telling me. Pour another shot of iodine. Suddenly Prună burst into tears. He sat holding his glass in his hand, so that half the contents spilled onto his trousers, and looked sadly at the ceiling. All sorts of thoughts were dancing through his head. The diploma he had obtained with such difficulty, his wife's toes, 10 little piggies, he would say, counting them in the evening, the ornament on the shelf in the bedroom about which he could not say what it represented, but he liked it, the blue cooking pots lined up in the kitchen, the bed, the TV, the starched curtains of the windows, the smile of Claudia, his youngest daughter, the illnesses of goats and cows, the phials of streptomycin, sweetbreads, his little perks, which he ate with great zest, the plums that had to be gathered, the smell of fresh soil at four in the morning. Was all that really going to disappear?... He shuddered, ready to fall. Bucurică banged into him, in an heroic attempt to reach the bar. Prună, how old is this hideous fellow? asked the mayor. Eh? You should know, he's your uncle, isn't he? Prună looked at his uncle through the fog, slowly recovering from those unaccustomed thoughts. I don't know... must be about 80, 84. Get out of here! Bucurică finally made it to the bar. Aaah... eeeh. Baah... deeh. Nae poured him a large glass of brandy. How old did you say he is? Eighty. For a few moments they all stopped drinking and looked at the creature. About one metre forty, humpbacked, wrinkled, deaf mute. He looked at them too, stammering something in his own language and giving off a strong smell of goats and urine. He tapped his enormous red goitre, held out a crushed fistful of ten-lei notes, from which Nae took exactly what was needed, positioned his incredible felt hat, white with hen droppings, more tightly on his head, and returned to his place, beside some crates of empty bottles. There he huddled, with his glass to his mouth. Eighty-four! Unbelievable! exclaimed the notary. Just look how lively he is. With his nose stuck into his glass. That's a new habit, brandy, until now he's never drunk anything but *ţuică*. He clears half my orchard with my son every year, said Prună, trying to clear his gaze. The doctor smiled for a time, loosening the knot of his tie. He turned his head towards the far end of the room and concentrated for a while on Bucurică, from whose direction a gentle gurgling sound now emanated. That one will see us all to the grave, muttered Bănea. Marinated in spirit, eats rubbish, walks barefoot, 80 years old, and look at him in the heat of summer supping up more brandy than a, what do you call it?... A camel. Yes. Will you tell your son again not to give him money. Why not? Because he doesn't want anything else, food, clothes, even to stay with us in our house, don't think we didn't suggest it, once, all he wants is to drink and to drag himself through the mud. And does he really have no roof or anything over his head? He sleeps from time to time on the hillside, in an abandoned hen-house. And you can't say it does him any harm. He's been through both wars, and now this thing, whatever it is, and if we all go to hell, I'll bet any amount he won't be in the least bothered. He'll drink up all the bottles in the village, in the district, in the county, in the whole world! He'll be left alone on earth. And no harm done, 'cause our village, if it disappears with this illness, no one will know. Just like no one knew it was here in the first place. Hăpău worked his tongue between his upper teeth and dislodged a piece of meat left from the previous day's lunch. He spat it out on the counter. Come on now, leave him in peace, and let's risk another dose against the dust. But mayor, who's paying? asked Nae. Why do you ask me? I'm off. Where are you off to? everyone jumped. Stay with us until the cloud passes over! No, no, I'm not staying, 'cause you're all drunk. What a thing to say, mayor, us?... I'm off, goodbye. Won't you even have another little drop?... The mayor made a sign with his hand and left the bar. They saw him quickly cross the road. He came, he drank, he went away, muttered the doctor. Here, Nae, pour! called the notary merrily. In that case, notary, I must ask you, who's paying?... Paying what, Nae, how can you think of money at a time like this, when there's not even going to be anyone left to bury us? What use do you imagine money's going to be to you then? But if we make it?... If! Maybe in your trousers. Didn't you hear what Dincă said? And he's a knowledgable man, all right, listen to the way he snores. We'll all waken to find ourselves lined up nicely on the floorboards like those mice when you put down poison, stretched out one beside the other with their bellies up and their eyes wide open. Oh, shut your face, man, it won't be as bad as that, said the sergeant. Aren't measures being taken? They are. Aren't there specialists, specialists I say, not oafs like us who haven't the foggiest what an atom is, if we tell the truth? And let's do just that, sergeant! Yes, and didn't they say just now on the radio that there's no danger any more? So what the hell are you still going on about mice, dust, corpses and all the rest of it for?... Don't talk like that, said the notary, becoming sad, these are things that you never know how they are going to turn out. Nonsense! Listen here, we'll wait a bit more, and if we don't croak next week either, that means we have escaped. That's what I believe. Believe, Cercel old man, it's good for the intellect. Jesus has mercy on the multitude, cried Dincă suddenly from his chair. Then he was silent. Through the dirty windows, the roofs could be seen, still sparkling in the dazzling sunlight. This heat is really killing me... I've been sweating like a pig. What can be the matter with this sun? Bănea looked at his pocket watch. Well, it's coming up to four. I'm going home now, or my wife will eat me alive. Prună and the notary looked suspiciously at each other. The sergeant set his glass lightly down on the counter. What wife, mate?... Didn't you bury her last winter? With cancer, are you fooling about or what? He's not drunk, whispered the caretaker. Perhaps you mean that Floarea will eat you, not your wife. Or is a wedding on the horizon? grinned the notary. The others laughed quietly. No… I wasn't thinking of her… I mean… Bănea looked around him, with a bewildered air. That's how it is, he said after a few moments, in a muffled voice. She died, last winter… The shards of broken glass on the floor diffused a golden light, as if they were pieces of amber. It's the children I'm thinking of, the poor lambs, they have no guilt, it hasn't even entered their heads. As for us, we've had our youth, and now it's their turn… And then, they're the ones who are most exposed. How do you mean? Are we not exposed? asked Dincă with a hazy look in his eyes. Do we no longer count, are we the village idiots, a waste of space, or what? What village, man, when the whole world is perishing! A round on me for everyone, cried Nae, flushed in the face. Let's fucking drink, while we still can. Bravo, Nae, you've said it like in the papers, come here and let me kiss you. You deserve to stay alive! The caretaker tried to say something too, in the muted but general enthusiasm. He failed to find the right words, and fell silent. Perhaps I should go and mop the floor one more time, he thought. Seems that's the order. To get rid of the ash. That's it, I'm off to get a bucket of water. Stay, mate, where are you off to now? the notary asked him. Stay and take a drink from this bottle, 'cause you won't see another like it, Nae doesn't put his hand in his pocket twice. It takes a catastrophe for that. Let's take advantage! Doctor, a question. Go ahead, Gheorghiţă. One more makes no difference. What I want to ask is, couldn't the light, I mean the light of the sun, be infected too? That's right, because the rays go through the cloud too, don't they? added the notary. Fucking cloud, Prună cursed and, losing his balance, he fell flat on the floor. That's him dirtied his dancing suit, someone laughed. The notary bent over to help him up. It's all right, I can manage on my own. After a great effort, the veterinary technician fell again. God, it's still hot, said Cercel, observing Prună and pouring a large bitters for himself. Hăpău blew his nose with his fingers, and looked at them. And it'll get hotter… Won't it, Dincă? Go on, tell us how we're going to roast like horseflies in boiling pitch. Dincă had dozed off with his head hanging onto his chest. As he looked at him, Bănea felt overcome by an irresistible sadness. The huge house, the orchards, his whole life suddenly seemed pointless, and Floarea, the woman with whom he now lived, far short of what his wife had been for him. A delicate, beautiful woman, always smiling. He felt dizzy, and gripped the edge of the counter with both hands. Through spinning red circles, he saw the children who had left to seek their own way in life. They only came on holiday, to get *ţuică*, apples and meat, which they loaded into their car boots and then left, leaving behind a cloud of child dust. When they had gone he was left all alone in the big house, with curious thoughts buzzing for a while through his head… He sighed quietly. Cercel was thinking of the Skoda now, spare parts, petrol, catching a wink of sleep, cold food. Nae took a last look at the bunch of lettuce that had now turned almost black. Closing time was approaching. The Doctor coughed and passed his hand over the two days' growth on his unshaved face. Suddenly and to his surprise he remembered drinking bouts with an air of pathetic rebellion, the immense despair of the 18-year-old, the passionate idiocies poured out in the company of his now so far away friends, he hadn't seen them for years, the neon sign of a restaurant lost in the fog, as if it was a UFO, the blonde girl of that time had murmured, a gust of wind hiding her face in the fluttering of her hair, night duties and sick people, tens, hundreds, thousands of sick people on the march, a few of them dying, not before feebly taking his hand and looking into his eyes, I'll get better, won't I, doctor? of course, others simply disappearing, into the world of sick people, only to return after a longer or shorter time, but I'll get better, won't I? of course, we all get better in the end, in our room, or in someone else's, in his room where there hung a permanent and unbearable odour of medical books, of lecture room benches, the legs of female classmates, the smell of the sea, of a little local cinema full of old folk with moths flying among them in the beam of the projector, pages turned in peace, in the library, a twilight on a sofa, two nights, nothing more beautiful than those two nights, and all this silence and terrible heat. Because the half-life of iodine is 14 days. While the half-life of strontium is 90 years… The symphony of destiny, bam, bam, bam, bam… Don't get me wrong, doctor, but we can't understand anything you're saying… it's as if you're singing. Prună leaned well forward trying to hear better, and was in danger of falling again. I say the worst of it is that the radiation accumulates. You get a dose today, you have no idea, another dose tomorrow, and so on. 'And there appeared another wonder in heaven; and behold a great red dragon, having seven heads and 10 horns, and seven crowns upon his heads,' cried the teacher suddenly, waking from his sleep. See what he teaches them at school, is it any wonder the kids go off their heads? 'And the fifth angel sounded.' Belt up, old man, you've made us right dizzy, the whole room is spinning around us. 'And they had hair as the hair of women, and their teeth were as the teeth of lions.' Bloody well do something to keep him quiet.

SHUT IT! yelled the sergeant. Right, it's time to go to our homes. One by one they banged their empty glasses down on the counter. They pushed their way jokingly towards the exit. Over in his corner, Bucurică burst out in a high-pitched shriek, jerked convulsively, and rolled his eyes. With the notary at their head, they emerged from the bar. The heat outside hit them full in the face. Cercel, you're the driver, take us home. You take the wheel. Hăpău, indicate left. We shouldn't have drunk so much, mumbled the notary reprovingly. Well, it's a holiday… What holiday can it be today?… They stopped on the steps of the bar, shielding their eyes with their hands. In the dust of the road, a scraggy old dog passed them. Hăpău bent down, took a stone, and threw the projectile straight at the animal's head. The dog let out a squeal, turned around on the spot, then lay on one side. It breathed with difficulty three or four times, then stopped breathing. Got it, what do you say to that? Right in the head. The doctor looked strangely at him, took a few steps and bent down over the dog. What did you have against it? It would have died in a few days anyway, said the notary in disgust. In that case I've spared it a worse end, laughed the postman. Look at the God of dogs, you miserable bastard. They all stood in the road and looked. The doctor felt the crushed skull. Prună stepped forward too, trying to look interested. Maybe a phenobarbitone… You know, said the vet after a pause, I'd like to call in on you this evening, I wanted to ask you something… if you could stamp my medical card. The doctor did not answer. See you this evening, then. Around seven, all right?… I'll bring you some sweetbreads… and some cheese. Seeing that no notice was taken of him, Prună stood up, blew the dust off his trousers and said lazily, over his shoulder, listen to me, give it a phenobarbitone. Between the eyes, he added in a whisper. The customers were leaving the bar, trying to protect their eyes from the sunlight. Vasile took a few steps, stumbled and fell in a heap. His companion, who had taken no part in the discussion in the bar, preferring to concentrate quietly on drinking, tried to pick him up. Beh, said Vasile. Quiet, up you get. Beh! Bănea watched the scene for a while, then with difficulty started off homewards. What a bedlam, he thought. So it is, agreed the notary, heading towards his car. Hăpău nodded his head energetically, to signify that, yes indeed, it was a bedlam. Well, good luck! They all muttered hurried goodbyes and each set off on his way. The dog had died. The doctor stroked its fur absent-mindedly and looked around him. The last drinkers were coming out, hurried on their way by Nae. Purple in the face, with misty eyes. Give me a whistle to waken me. Laughter out of tune. Whistle yourself, on your you-know-what. Bring the chain-saw round to me about eight. Dincă stumbled out, and collapsed on his back beside the fence. The people were gradually dispersing, leaving in their wake little clouds of dust. A fine, light dust, which rose in hermetic bluish-white calligraphy as soon as you touched it with your foot. The sergeant unlocked the door and fell into the chair behind his desk. He remembered Aurică Capră, brandy, fire, radiation. With a tired gesture he took off his cap, then looked at the phone. He lit a cigarette and picked up the receiver. Hello! Hello! He pressed the cradle several times. The light was shining straight in his eyes and he decided to draw the blinds on the windows. Above the hill on the left a strange broad stripe had appeared, like a sort of bruise. The notary climbed into his old car. His head was buzzing terribly. After a number of attempts, he managed to get the key in the ignition. He turned it. Nothing happened. I bet the starter motor's failed on me. He pulled out the choke and twisted the key one more time. In the bar there was now no one left. Nae counted the money, locked it in the drawer, looked around him and went out. He closed the massive door of the bar, fastened the padlock and looked for the key. First in his trouser pockets. Then in his jacket. Where the devil did I put it? He turned his pockets inside out. A few coins scattered on the cement in front of the entrance. He bent down to pick them up, then stopped, bent double, and studied them. They seemed very old, with a coat of arms he had never seen before. Hăpău parted from Bănea over the bridge. Now he walked briskly, holding his bicycle by the handlebars. His thoughts, however, were going much faster, straight ahead, already arriving in his room at home, in the bookcase, the upper right-hand shelf, where he kept his *ţuică*. He was so absorbed by this image that he did not notice the pale, very thin man who hurriedly crossed the churchyard. A healthy tumbler of *ţuică* will sort me out. What I suffer with those little glasses of Nae's, finger-sized, no good at all, by the time it gets to your stomach it's evaporated in your throat. God forgive me, I've had one too many. I don't know where I am. I don't recognise these houses. Bănea carefully closed the gate behind him, fixed the chain, and called Floarea. Nobody answered, so he guessed that the woman was not back yet from the haymaking. He went into the house and sat down on the first chair he saw. His wife approached slowly, coming up on him from behind. She softly put her hands over his eyes. Hey, let go of me, what's got into you? Shhh. Don't turn round. Guess who! I'm tired, he complained. The curtains were drawn and in the house it was almost dark. A fly buzzed on the window-pane. Bănea gently took hold of the fragile fingers that held his eyes captive, and turned round. He passed his hand quickly over his face, as if to push the half-shadow aside. Then he remained riveted to the spot, wide-eyed and voiceless. The notary hesitantly got out of his car, checked the starter motor, the battery, the oil. He swore furiously and sat down again at the wheel. He turned the key in the ignition and heard the same short click. On either side of the road the hills scattered a golden light. The doctor undid his shirt collar. This afternoon it seemed to him that all the houses were different, as if they were smaller than usual. He kicked at a deflated blue ball that lay in the middle of the road. Contrary to all expectations, the ball bounced elastically and hit a window. He saw someone's face quickly withdrawing behind the curtains. The road was deserted and the air was now starting to take on a violet colour. For a whole hour, Cercel had been trying to find his bus. What the devil! I left it here, in the square, didn't I? Or maybe not, and I'm too drunk to remember. I must have stopped in front of old Petrică's yard. There he is standing at his gate, gawping at that terrific blaze. Where can it be, anyway? Petrică, you haven't seen my bus, have you? Quiet, can't you hear how that man's beating his child? Poor little lamb… Cercel hurried away, so as not to hear the screams any more. He passed the churchyard at about the same time as Hăpău, but on the other side, and caught sight of the individual who was going into the building. That's not the priest, said Cercel to himself. He noticed that something fell from the stranger's coat, a yellow object. He waited for a few minutes, then entered the churchyard and bent down to see what it was. How beautiful they are, thought the doctor, stretching out his palms and trying to catch one of the golden globes that were slowing falling through the air. The caretaker went into the council building, took a bucket of water and a cloth from a corner of the hall, and started to wash the floors. It doesn't come off, what can these bubbles be, like phlegm? You'd almost think a consumptive horse had come in here and spat on the ground. That horse on the sixth floor. It won't come off at all, they seem to be stuck to the wood. It won't come o-o-off, he began to sing under his breath, as he scrubbed with all his might. They've all gone into their houses just at the moment when the prince ought to come. Or the witch. In fact it doesn't make any difference, muttered the doctor. Cercel picked up the object that shone in the grass. It was like a miniature version of his bus. A yellow plastic toy. In reality, the witch might not be old, sinister, humpbacked and hook-nosed, far from it. She might even be blonde, green-eyed, wearing a bikini, with long thighs and a cigarette in her fingers. That's the way I imagine death, a writer said, Vilallonga I think. A happy girl jumping from a springboard, splash into the water, you're not even sure she'll come up again, she jumped from too high up, but here she is, enticing, with drops of water scattering on her breasts, smiling encouragingly at you, she makes a sign for you to follow her up the steps, high up, to the thousand metre springboard, did you see how easy it was? she'll say to you when she sees you hesitating, don't be frightened, we'll jump together, one, two, three, and you'll jump at the same time as her into the pool that from such a distance looks no bigger than the open mouth of a blue worm. Hello. Hello!... The exchange is out of order, damn it... Prună fell close to the bridge. He got up on all fours, adjusted his cap on his head. 'Precipitation will persist...', the voice of an announcer could be heard coming from a radio set. He felt a few warm drops on the back of his neck. In God's name, is it raining out of the blue in this heat? Yes, it's raining, and there's the bar. I left an hour and a half ago and there's the bar in front of me. He stayed in the same position and looked up. Not a cloud. Just a violet line, like the trace of a blow, crossed the sky. The light pulsated between the stones, on the walls. HEY! IS THERE NO ONE HERE? cried Hăpău. He turned around on the spot, with his arms stretched out. Large beads of sweat appeared on his forehead. The notary dropped the ignition key from his hand and looked through the windscreen. The doctor closed his eyes. Hello! Hello!... Bucurică climbed with difficulty out of the ditch beside the bar. He put a hand to his ear. His eyes almost popped out of his head, he blinked rapidly, several times. No, he was not mistaken, he could make out as clear as could be the creak of wood, the rustle of grass, the clink of coins rolling on the cement, a distant voice asking if there was anyone there, the squealing of pigs, the ticking of a clock. He took out the rotten apple that he carried in his jacket pocket and bit into it with all his might. He could *hear*. For the first time in his life, he could hear the sound of his own teeth, the drops of saliva flowing down his throat. On the horizon, the purple stripe disappeared. Bucurică stretched out his hands. He gasped. Then he burst into laughter. A harsh, resounding laughter that immediately enveloped the village, the whole district, the forest, and the hills.

Translator's note

Țuică: is a traditional Romanian spirit, distilled from plums or other fruit, similar to slivovitz or schnapps.

The Door

He swung his foot a little, looking at the polished surface of his shoe. In front of him, the two women wearing white overalls on top of their coats went on talking. He sat on the edge of the metal table strewn with observation charts, swinging his foot and trying to pay attention. The delicately bitter smell emanating from the cup of coffee tickled his nostrils.

"Tell us precisely, please, how long? How much longer could he hang on?"

"Maybe until this afternoon, maybe until tomorrow, or another two or three days at the most. More precisely than that, I can't tell you."

"But he can't hear us, can he?" asked the wife, looking in the direction of the ward. "I mean …"

"No, the door is closed. There is no way he can hear us. And apart from that, he is almost unconscious."

"Oh Lord! We were thinking, you know, it might be better if he stayed … At least it's a hospital here, and …"

"I think you need to make up your minds. After all it was you who asked me to let you take him home."

"That's true, but …"

The doctor looked at them patiently.

"I've already told you, there isn't any way we can help him now." He reached out his hand for the cup of coffee. "He could go into a coma any moment."

"All right, doctor, but how do we transport him? It's more than 40 kilometres," said the daughter.

"Hire a taxi or something. Unfortunately we can't offer you the ambulance. We'll get him positioned nicely, and one of you will hold the drip until you get there. That's all you have to do. It's no big deal."

"And what if he dies in the car?"

The encouraging smile faded on his lips. He looked at his watch. In 10 minutes he had to be in the operating theatre.

"That's very unlikely …"

"Yes, but with all those potholes and bumps in the road, you can't imagine. It'll shake him like hell. I'm afraid we won't get him home alive …"

"No, nothing will happen," he added quickly. "He'll make it home. And in any case, one way or another, you're going to have to take him some time."

"Yes, but what about the money? Forty kilometres in a taxi will cost a lot of money," whispered the daughter. "A lot of money."

He got down from the table.

"Believe me, you've chosen the best solution. It's much better that he should die in his own bed. That's what you told me. I quite agree. On top of that, you're against having an autopsy. And it's extremely hard to get permission to remove the body from the hospital without an autopsy being carried out. In fact it's impossible. I don't understand why you are hesitating so much …"

A nurse passed him, carrying the tray of syringes. For a moment his eyes followed her shapely legs, whose outline showed through her white skirt. From the dressing ward came a sudden scream.

The two women continued their discussion in lowered voices. He looked at their black shoes and swollen ankles.

"So, what are you going to do? Are you taking him or not?"

"Oh, doctor, he's brought us nothing but problems! All the time! Nothing but trouble. Even now … Even dead," the wife burst out, clutching her black handbag to her chest.

That's right, that's right, my time is at your disposal. Even dead, meditated the doctor. He made a short gesture with his hand, as if to cut short any discussion.

"Ladies, I have an operation to attend to."

"Yes, but where do we get the money for a taxi? He hasn't left us anything …"

"And we certainly haven't got money for the funeral. Who would have expected it? So fast! And without leaving a penny! Mother's pension will go on the coffin, if we have one, and then we'll be squeezed dry …"

Oh my God, thought the doctor.

"You say you're sure, doctor? There's nothing more you can do? …"

"And the priest? The food? The wreaths? … What will the family say, and the neighbours? We'll be the talk of the whole village. Nothing is ready. Oh yes, his nibs was always one for a party. He laughed when we used to tell him to put something aside, because your never know. And look at us now! We've got to manage on our own, to pay out money … A waster, that's what he was. He drank away the house and the vineyard, the lot! Where can we get hold of so much money?"

The April light slipped gently through the tall windows, bringing with it a scent of acacias. Which immediately mixed with the smell of formalin and medicines.

"We even had to borrow for my girl's wedding. He made our whole lives a misery … What does he care!"

The doctor looked again at his watch. Another four minutes. He spoke calmly, with a tone that allowed no reply:

"Please make up your minds. I think I have given you enough explanations."

The wife and the daughter exchanged a look. Then they spoke rapidly to each other in a whisper.

"All right, doctor. But could we make a phone call? In two hours, two hours and a bit, we'll find a car. After that, it's up to the mercy of God!"

"Of course. The phone is on the first floor. This way please!"

The doctor hurried out, followed by the two women. From the dressing ward came the same long scream.

The nurse pushed the door handle and entered the ward. She noticed that the door had not been properly shut. She approached the bed, checked the drip, and glanced at the skeletal man who lay in the bed, covered by a sheet up to his chin. He was breathing heavily, with his mouth wide open. A few drops of water remained on his grey cheek. He's going, she thought, as she took his pulse. She adjusted the needle in his vein, fixed the sticking-plaster, looked in the mirror and went out, closing the door carefully this time. Caught in a ray of sunlight, the drops of water on the cheek of the sick man lit up for a moment. Then they slowly went out, one by one.

The Joke

"Mr Prosecutor, I'm innocent."

"That's what they all say…"

The magistrate sat back in his armchair, chewed his nails and looked into space. The clerk's quill was racing over the paper. I rushed up to him and grabbed him by the arm.

"What are you doing? I haven't even started speaking…"

"I know very well what you are going to say! They all tell the same story," growled the clerk, pulling his arm from my grasp. "Scumbag!"

The judge hammered a few times on the sheet of glass that covered his desk, calling for silence. At the third blow, he managed to crack it. Now he had a star on his desk.

"You see, in the beginning things went pretty well. I mean as long as it was just us three. Mother, Father and me. We had no choice. We lived on the edge…"

The prosecutor rested his chin on his fist and gave me a bored look. Through the windows of the chamber the branches of the trees could be made out on the other side of the street. The sky was breathing heavily, barely audibly, and its ribs could be seen dilating. In the end it succeeded in spitting out the blood-red globe of the sun. This fell right in the palm of the city, and it was morning.

"It's morning," said the judge yawning. "And where did you say you lived? Show me on the map, if you please."

I pointed with my hand, vaguely, towards the centre of a world map that hung on one of the walls:

"There…"

"There is Africa," said the clerk, writing all the time.

I continued:

"It was a special feeling, hard to describe… Alone, in that endless field…" I stopped, realising that no one was listening to me. The clerk's quill went on scratching. "I guess I should reproduce as closely as I can all that he's writing there, shouldn't I?"

"Do as you wish."

"Yes, but I see that that gentleman is taking notes faster than I can speak! I believe he's already at least two or three sentences ahead of me. If you forgive me saying so, from a judicial point of view, such a method is rather peculiar."

"I don't see it that way."

"Very well, if you say so... So, up until the birth of my brother we lived in a fair degree of harmony. The mistake was that from the very beginning no one took him seriously."

"What did your parents do?"

For an investigating judge he was not at all disagreeable. Moreover, he had a face that seemed to me vaguely familiar. Perhaps I had met him in the street, I don't know. Anyway, I had been warned that he didn't take bribes. Everyone had a laugh at his expense. He was an honest man. In the morning, when he went to his work, people made faces behind his back. They fell down laughing.

"I asked you what your parents did."

"Well, Father was a mild man, sometimes sad, very rarely grand, but always devout. He used to kneel everywhere and pray, with tears in his eyes, recalling sin, forgiveness, repentance, lights, that sort of stuff. Apart from that, he didn't do anything. Oh, actually he did, from time to time he made coloured balloons and ran with them in the field, holding them tied to a string. He could hop around for hours on end, until Mother called him for dinner. He would come quickly, in a sweat, and let the balloons slip from his hand. As for me and my brother, he didn't treat us badly, he just gave me the feeling that he hardly knew we were there. Mother, on the other hand, kept us on a tight rein, always had her eye on us, and was on at us every day to do our lessons, that is, to keep in mind how rich and happy we were. She made us learn, and even sing it. 'You must *never* forget,' she would say, 'that all this is ours!' And we had to repeat in a chorus: 'The ea–earth, the for–rests, the moun–tains, the ca–ttle, the shee–eep, the goa–oats, the wolves, the waters, the fish, the bees, every blade of grass, every stone.' '*All* is ours,' she would conclude emotionally, stretching out her arms on both sides. She would stay like that for several minutes, like a cross stuck in the middle of the kitchen. A blessed moment of silence fell and we breathed with relief. Then Father would draw the conclusion of the day. It was the same every time, namely that this *all* that Mother spoke of with such passion was worth no more than a shit in water."

"Very picturesque. Try, however, to pass over details of that sort. We are interested in facts, psychological evolution. Do you understand?"

"Yes. Well, the way things evolved, my little brother took to weaving all sorts of intrigues, losing no occasion to set us against each other. For his own amusement, I presume. That was the reason why gradually I became my parents' favourite. My brother stirred up hostility and…"

"You have already said that."

"He was a tell-tale. Lazy. Lame. And for all that, so good-looking that he would have made even a saint sick. That blond hair… his perfect features… his nose."

"What was the conflict, in fact?"

"In a way, I could understand him. The poor boy would try by any possible means to attract attention. By making himself *ugly*, for example! Psychoanalysis is full of such examples. He would behave unpleasantly, he would put paint on his face, he would pluck out his eyelashes… So that someone would be fond of him too. A tragic figure, if you stop to think. But that's not what's important."

"Indeed," whispered the prosecutor.

"The years passed, I was growing up, my brother was becoming more and more good-looking and more and more imbecilic…"

"Look, we are in court, not at home in your mother's kitchen!" the judge burst out.

The clerk lifted his eyes, questioningly.

"Should I write that too, Mr Prosecutor?"

"No, delete it. And you, measure your words! And don't take any account of what he writes or doesn't write in the record!"

They were beginning to get their teeth into me.

"In the evenings," I continued uncertainly, "we stayed in the house… There, in the middle of the wilderness, we looked at each other and listened to the dripping of the falling stars, and it was fine. Then we went to bed. It was always Mother who gave the signal. She got up, tall, blonde, her hair flowing over her shoulders, her eyes sparkling, and looked at Father in a certain way. Poor Father! She was so beautiful that I got sleepy straight away, by the time I got into bed I was already asleep. But my brother would wake me, usually around midnight, 'I've seen them,' he would say, 'they're like two goats! Mehhh!' He was determined to tell me in graphic detail everything that he had seen through the hole he had made in the wall. He chattered away, chuckling with his high-pitched, abnormal laugh. I was dying for sleep and he wouldn't stop wittering on, talking rubbish. I could have murdered him…"

"Consequently, you are violent. Clerk, take that down!"

"I've taken it down, Mr President," replied the clerk proudly. He was sitting in his corner, he had stopped writing and was chewing a cheese sandwich. I could smell it from the bar.

"And I've underlined it, in black," he added.

"One day, Mother said to us, 'This is how it is, boys, the time has come for you to get to work. It can't go on like this, everything's going up the spout, with that man doing nothing. It's not my fault, I had no choice. In the end… But I wouldn't have expected him to be so easygoing. Your father doesn't respect his obligations, he hasn't the slightest sense of responsibility. He's irresponsible. So, you have to work!' My brother immediately started screaming that he was too little, that he was infirm, and that when it came down to it, why should we have to work since we were so rich? With so many mountains and birds. It would be the height of absurdity! He had no success, however. And the next day we had to set about it. Being the elder, it was my job to establish what each of us would do. I decided that my little brother would look after the sheep, which was lighter work anyway…"

"Why do you say it was lighter?"

"… while I would set about working the land. It seemed to me a fair division. Well, from that day on I didn't have a moment's peace. I don't know if you have any idea what working the soil involves…"

"No."

"Ploughing, digging, sowing, reaping, gathering… And apart from that, of course everything that had to be done about the house fell on my shoulders too. Because my younger brother wasn't even capable of hitting a nail without something collapsing or the nail falling out.

"Time passed, as I have already said. Father with his prayers, Mother with her mirror, little sibling roaming around, and me with difficulty…"

The judge turned his chair round and started drawing a sheep with chalk on the blackboard.

"Sometimes when I caught sight of him stretched out in the grass, among the sheep, looking up at the sky and humming a sort of melancholy tune through his nose, it really made me livid. But the anger didn't last long. He was my brother, after all."

"Very nicely done, Mr President," said the clerk, looking at the drawing on the blackboard. "Just like the real thing!"

"He had nothing to do but to idle the time away. And he wasn't even happy. That capped it all, you might say."

"I wouldn't say that at all."

"Even more than that, the youth used to get bored! He couldn't live without playing all sorts of daft practical jokes on us. He made our lives a misery with his tricks. What beatings he took, the poor boy... And still he wouldn't give up."

The judge turned in his chair, and gave me a disgusted look. Then he looked at the clock, muttered something incomprehensible, looked at me again and, probably thinking that he would miss his lunch anyway, took a package out of a drawer in his desk, unwrapped it and started eating.

"Would you like a tomato, Mr President?" asked the clerk.

"If you've got..."

The clerk leaned across the desk and gave him the tomato. The magistrate took a bite out of it with zest and a few drops of juice trickled down his chin. I felt sick.

"Look the other way," he advised me, munching.

I turned my gaze towards the wall, approached it with slow steps, and turned round the world map that hung by the window. On the reverse side could be seen the enlarged photograph of a girl, blonde and naked, reclining on a sofa in a shockingly suggestive posture.

"She looks like Mother."

"Put that back at once, just as it was," thundered the judge.

I turned the map round with care and went back to my place. Perhaps all this is part of the procedure, I thought.

"I told you to speak louder, I can't hear you. Or better, come closer."

"One very beautiful spring, Father finally gave signs that he acknowledged our presence. He had an inspired air about him. He looked at us as if we were beings that he had never seen before, took us into the living-room, invited us to sit down, sat down himself and began to make an extremely long speech, which I confess I didn't pay too much attention to. When he had finished what he had to say, he stood up to his full height, he was over one metre ninety, and commanded us starting from the following day to take gifts to the eastern edge of the field, where the abandoned garden lay. And the same again every Saturday or else we would get a thrashing. I have never been able to understand why he asked us to do this. The fact is that he upheld his decision with truly astounding firmness, considering the row that she kicked up daily about this latest bee in his bonnet, as she called it. So expressive."

"It wasn't a bee in his bonnet, it was bribery."

"Oh, no!"

"Bribery, bribery, bribery!" yelled the judge, striking out through the air to right and left with his gavel.

"Very well, it's all right, let it be as you say. Anyway, from the day we started to carry out his wish, Father calmed down. He started to wander naked through the house."

"What a family!" exclaimed the clerk, bringing his hands together.

He was severely admonished and asked to refrain from comment in future.

"He would try to convince us that it was absolutely normal to go about like that…"

"Nudism. Exhibitionism. Have you made a note?" asked one of the panel.

"From the time he gave up wearing clothes, the old man missed no occasion to tell us that he wanted to emigrate. He seemed to have an obsession. 'For such a journey you have to be prepared at any moment,' he would whisper mysteriously, raising his index finger towards the ceiling. And, as if training with a view to this departure, he hurried about this way and that, turned purple in the face with no warning, and had more and more frequent and more acute crises of authority. He would pull the barn door off its hinges. How I struggled to put it back in place! He would put out the fire in the oven, throw dishes out of the window, and swear at Mother with curses on her rib. The finale was always apocalyptic. He would overturn his chair, sometimes break it in pieces, and go to the bedroom with the air of one misunderstood, especially as he draped himself with the tablecloth. At these moments, Mother would let loose such a flood of words through the house that you could see the walls getting damp. In the end, the voice of Father, timid, like a paper boat, floated over that whole flood, 'But don't you understand that we've lost it, maybe, forever?' 'And so what?' replied Mother. 'Now we are free. So come back to the table at once!' Then there was silence and Father would reappear in the living-room clothed from head to foot in a sort of white resignation."

"Listen, if you're going to continue to pour out idiotic metaphors like this, the record will end up a mockery. Are we at the writer's club or in court, where the hell are we?" roared the prosecutor, striking the desk with his fist. "Where are we?" he yelled again, with a flushed face, looking fearfully around him.

"Take it easy, Mr Prosecutor, we're here, in our own chamber," whispered the clerk.

"I apologise," I interrupted humbly. "However, I believe I have to recount such matters."

"Yes, yes…" said the prosecutor, absent-mindedly.

"You see, Mr President, life is made up of details. Not of essence. In reality, essence is far, far away!"

"Enough of that! Tell us about your dad."

"What can I say, I loved him, oddball as he was. He wouldn't have been capable of hurting so much as a bee. He also had a marvellous talent for storytelling. We used to listen to him with our mouths wide open, even though he only knew one story. He told it so beautifully, however, that we never got bored."

"And what, to be more precise, was this story that he told you?"

"The tale of the garden. Now, let it be said in passing, Mother screwed up her nose, she didn't like other people's stories. She had her own, and plenty of them, the ones about our boundless riches and power."

"You swore to tell the truth. Why don't you tell the truth?"

"Father described the garden as the most beautiful place on earth, the playground of rainbows, sugar rabbits, unknown flowers, rare birds, trees coated in lustre, fairies, high-speed angels, fireflies and toy clouds. When he got to the bit about the clouds, Father would sigh."

"The accused is requested to get back to the subject."

"Moreover, the garden was traversed from one end to the other by a great silver-plated river, in whose waters miracles floated. Seemingly they floated so slowly that you could gather them by hand."

The judge looked out of the window, dreamily. Full of zeal, the clerk hastened to do the same. The twilight caught their faces in the glass, faces ground down by so many years spent in dark courtrooms, among the condemnations of unhappy individuals, faces petrified among papers, tons of papers, the smell of mildew and words. So many, many words. Mutilated, blind, ash-grey.

"Someone's died again, it's the Funeral March. Nice piece of music."

"Why have you stopped? Speak, I'm listening!" muttered the prosecutor to me.

"Well, that garden was in fact no more than a heap of rubbish, in the middle of which you could see the bed of a river that had been dry for a million years."

"Were there snakes?"

"I don't know. I can't remember…"

The clerk slipped out soundlessly, he probably had felt slippers, and returned shortly with a stuffed snake, which he placed on the desk. It was horrible.

"What's that?" I asked.

"An example of cobra de capello, the common name of a venomous snake of the genus *Naja*. I stuffed it myself… Beautiful, isn't it."

He thrust the reptile under my eyes and continued in a thundering voice: "Confess!"

Eyeball to eyeball with the snake, I stammered, I got intimidated.

"Yes, Mr Prosecutor, I admit it! I knew what was going to happen…"

"Aha! Well, now we can go for dinner with a weight off our minds." The judge leaned across the desk and addressed me in a benevolent tone:

"You know, that trick never fails. With the snake, I mean."

I wiped my damp palms on my trousers.

"But it's completely absurd! After all, so many years have passed since then, the limitation period has expired, it's over…"

"You are playing with words, and you go so far as to accuse your brother by claiming that he was to blame for all that happened, just because he used to invent games. *You* invented them. You, the respectable man, good at everything, completely guiltless, and all that. You pitiful wretch! Put an exclamation mark to that, clerk."

The clerk began to laugh, while at the same time continuing to write and eat his cheese sandwich. With great difficulty, I refrained from stuffing his goose quill down his throat. Complete with his cheese, ruler and record.

"Keep calm! You have nothing more to do, you've confessed. It is officially recorded."

"You made use of hypnosis… I retract!"

"What do you retract? You can't retract anything. Where would that get us?"

"To the truth."

"The way to the truth is not by retracting," said the judge coldly.

I blew my nose. The judge rested his cheek in his palm. The desk lamp drew a sort of white star on his cheek. There was a similar star on the glass top of the desk.

"More than seven hours ago you declared that *you* decided what sort of work each of you would do. Do you admit that?"

I kept silent.

"So, you cleverly prepared everything, long before. Let's get everything wound up, please." The man of law suddenly seemed tired. He rubbed his eyes significantly. "The motive. Tell us what the motive was, and you're free!"

I breathed in deeply.

"It all started the day it was noticed that the offerings we took into the garden disappeared. At first we didn't give this any importance, it could have been wild animals, beggars, however that was not very likely because, you see, there was a *selectiveness* in the theft. All that was swiped was those wretched scabby lambs, brought by my little brother. Curious, wasn't it? My gifts, loaves of my own home-made bread, which would make your mouth water just to smell them, and which broke in your hand like cakes, were left untouched. No, they – or he – only took lambs. And the devil knows where they took them, because I searched all over and didn't find any trace. Perhaps they ate everything. Fleece, horns, hooves. In the end, this was the pretext used by my good brother to maintain that only I could be the thief. On top of that, I don't know how it happened, but at that time I had rather put on weight. So, I was the one who was eating the lambs. In a way, I admit it was logical. But it seemed to me way over-the-top! After I had worked on my own from morning to evening, after I had taken the burden of the whole house on my shoulders and…"

"Limit yourself to the facts and stop beating about the bush!" yelled the judge, bringing the gavel down on the glass top of his desk. This time he managed to smash it.

"His control of the gavel leaves something to be desired, that's for sure," I remarked to the clerk.

"It's not his gavel," he replied, making a vague gesture with his hand.

"Smashed to smithereens!" said the judge, coming back to himself. "A little bell would have been better."

"Don't get me wrong. I just wanted you to understand that our life had become a hell. I was the number one suspect, but the truth is that everyone suspected everyone else. The only one who seemed relaxed and happy at the way things were developing was my brother. He had found a new source of entertainment. I would like to be understood clearly, he didn't care two hoots for the truth…"

"How, in fact, do you explain this phenomenon? I'm referring to the disappearance of the animals."

Seeing that I was silent, the judge leaned on the back of the chair and started to pick his teeth with a matchstick.

"I don't know. All I know is that I wasn't to blame…"

"Obviously. That's all that interests you, you poor idiot!"

"Mr President, please, control your language…"

"Very well. Clerk, cross out the word *idiot*. Replace it with something else, you decide…"

The clerk looked back, leafing rapidly through the voluminous pile of paper filled with his tiny handwriting, found the word, crossed it out and got back to his work.

"I could stand it no longer. So one fine day I took my brother to one side, to try and clear things up. 'Come on, let's go to the field,' I said to him, 'let's go into the garden and stay there as long as you like, a day, a month, a thousand years if we have to, until I can convince you that I have nothing to do with what's going on.' He burst out laughing, he dragged his feet a bit, but in the end he agreed. We set off right then. It was a splendid day. We walked quickly, impatient to get there and to put an end to the whole story for good. My brother came behind me, almost running. He was wiping the sweat from his forehead and hopping along in a funny way with his one leg shorter than the other. We arrived around lunch-time. It had got very hot. We saw that everything was in its place, his two lambs, and my loaves. We sat down and undid our bundle of food. Bees were buzzing through the air, the day was so clear, so…"

"Bees were buzzing!"

"… perfumed, that you almost couldn't smell the odour of fermented waste that rose from the garden. We made our resting-place beside an old apple tree, which was rotten but still gave us a bit of shelter from the sun. I fell asleep immediately. I don't remember what I dreamed about. In any case, towards evening I awoke, with my brother shaking me. 'Well, what do you have to say now?' he yelled. I looked around me in a daze, indeed the lambs had disappeared. On the other hand, the loaves were untouched, a few ants were clambering over their golden crust. I looked at the sky. Threatening, purple clouds were gathering over our heads and the heat had become unbearable. My brain felt like a sponge. 'You took advantage of the time I was asleep and now you're playing the innocent! Come on, tell me, where have you hidden them, you bastard?' my brother cried. Shortly after his question, large, warm drops of rain started to fall. I got up and set off for home without a word. I couldn't understand… Even now I don't understand."

The clerk put his quill in the ink pot, smacked his lips with delight, and held the paper out to the judge. I stood on tiptoe, trying to make out something of the record, and I observed that the greater part of my account had been crossed out with red pencil. All that was left was seven sentences. When the judge had signed, the clerk withdrew to the door, walking backwards. Before he disappeared from the room he blew me a kiss. I swore at him through my teeth.

"Why do you swear at him? There's no point, he's just a poor functionary," said the judge.

I was silent. Suddenly a great weariness had come over me. I asked permission to sit down.

"Of course, take a seat, please… Look, you've kept me here for a whole day to give us, wait a moment, exactly 90 words."

It was now evening. Something was creeping over the windows of the chamber, a sort of snail of the night, leaving behind it long trails of darkness. The judge brought the small lamp with a yellow shade that stood on the desk closer to the file. I couldn't contain my fury.

"All right, but what was that man writing for all those hours? He was writing all the time, wasn't he?…"

"What a child you are! Of course he was writing, but he crossed out with red everything that wasn't important. So that, as you see, all that is left is seven sentences. Come on, son, why don't you just tell the simple truth without digressions? You've made my head buzz so much with all those details that I no longer know who I am…"

"You are Mr President."

"You see, you don't know either, do you? I'm the prosecutor!"

After a few seconds, however, he asked anxiously:

"Or am I the judge?"

We looked at one another for a long time. Without seeing each other very well.

"In the end, it doesn't matter too much who you are. What matters is to be objective."

"My dear fellow, it's obvious that you haven't the slightest notion of the judicial process. In the first place, in order to be objective, one must be indifferent. That's elementary! So, indifferent to good or evil. Reward or punishment, guilty or not guilty…"

"You mean the distinction is of no importance for you?"

"I am of the old school. I believe that between the beginning and the end there is nothing. So it is of no importance."

"And then?"

"Then it means that you are guilty. Anyway, it's clear, you're even marked, you've got a sign, there…"

"All right, but it's not true! I'm not at all guilty. I've got a wife, a child… Look, here's a photograph of the three of us! That's my wife."

"Listen, have you got witnesses? No. Have you got counsel? No. Why don't you have counsel?"

"Because no one wanted to…"

"There, you see? What's the point of discussing further?… You would do better to accept it with dignity!"

I felt a hollow in my stomach. If I had wanted to be sick again I don't know how I would have managed. I would have died of shame.

"Please, Judge, Mr President, Mr Prosecutor… I swear with my hand on the Bible that I am innocent!"

"There's no need. We have no Bible here," said the judge grimly.

"Then I swear by my father's head! My child's, the clerk's, anyone you like. I'm a serious man, it's a shame you don't want to look at this photograph… You have to hear me out…"

"It's extremely boring, you know. Still, on you go, if you absolutely insist. However, I warn you it's useless. And hurry. We don't have much time left."

I looked around instinctively. Perhaps at least I had time to run away.

"Try! I'm not your guard," said the judge. His left cheek, the one illuminated by the lamp, seemed wrinkled, as if the man had been laughing silently. It had turned very cold in the room.

I went up to the blackboard, I wiped off the judge's sheep, and I started to draw, to illustrate the story I had to tell.

"The rain had drenched us to the skin. We walked homewards, making slow progress through the mud. The full force of the storm was now unleashed, and a sort of soot was whirling through the air. Lightning flashed without a pause. (I make a zigzag on the blackboard.) With water running down his face, with his clothes flapping, my brother roared like one possessed. He seemed to have gone completely out of his mind... (With a few lines, I sketch the schematic outline of a man with wings.) However, I was too worn out to pay him any more attention. After a while I spotted my plough, which I had left in the field two days before. I headed towards it. 'Where are you going?' yelled my brother, with his eyes bulging out of their sockets. (I draw a cross.) I shoved him hard and he fell in the mud. 'It's all your fault!' he cried, his whole body trembling. He stopped almost at once, interrupted by a fit of coughing, but after a few seconds he started to scream again: 'We're condemned for ever, and you're to blame... You stole... Father's curse! You stole it, you stole it!' my brother kept howling, beating his hands in the mire. I bent down over my plough. It had rusted. Beside it lay the tools with which I had been trying to repair it. (On the blackboard I write a string of figures and letters in an ancient script, a question mark and a hammer.) There I was bareheaded in the rain, worn out, on my knees in a muddy pool. I don't know how long I remained like that."

Just then the cleaning woman came in. Although very old, thin and dressed in a dirty overall, she nevertheless bore an extraordinary resemblance to the girl whose photograph was on the back of the world map. She swept up the papers scattered on the floor, gathered those on my lectern, with a few careless movements, dusted the crucifix that I only now observed, and went out again.

"At a certain moment it seemed to me that I could hear footsteps, padding lightly behind my back. And suddenly that wild, strident laugh of my brother's burst forth. I turned round at the last moment and hit him with the hammer right in the forehead. (I drew a figure lying on the ground, and I pointed towards it with the chalk.) He fell like a sack, without even a groan. It was only then that I saw that in his right hand he held a tin star, a toy."

I sat with my eyes turned towards the window, finding again in the outside darkness the scene that had taken place such a terribly long time ago.

"Accused, stand up!"

I rose with difficulty, my hands and my feet numb with the cold.

"You have been found guilty of murder… premeditated… The sentence will be carried out…"

The rest of his words were lost in an unintelligible murmur. The judge had withdrawn from the cone of light spread by the desk lamp and I could no longer see him at all.

"*Hic et nunc!*" came a voice, barely perceptibly.

"Mr President," where are you?

I groped in the darkness, with my hands stretched out in front of me, making for the extremely faint light of the lamp. From the direction of the window came a quick muffled snigger. At a certain moment I thought I heard it again, somewhere to my right. I tripped and caught hold of the corner of the desk just in time. My fingers involuntarily grasped the judge's gavel. Suddenly, his face appeared right in front of me.

"Now do you recognise me?" he asked.

"You!" I yelled, taking a step back. Then I felt a movement behind me, as though someone were ready to pounce on me. I turned and hit out blindly with the gavel. There was a dull sound, then another, louder, like a chair falling over. Then nothing.

The lamp had fallen too, breaking on the floor, which seemed to me to be covered with drops of rain. I bent down over Abel. He lay stretched out on his back, with blood all over his forehead. Hell, I thought, I'll never be finished with this until the end of time.

Translator's note

Hic et nunc, here and now (Latin).

Black Encephalitis

Black encephalitis, formerly known as Elsinore sickness, is a chronic contagious disease, caused by the AD virus (*Alterations of the Dendritic prolongations*). The illness is characterised by a polymorphous clinical presentation, in which neuropsychological symptoms predominate.

Aetiology. Seen under the electron microscope, the AD virus has the form of a revolver bullet.[1] Several subtypes have also been found to resemble the well-known moth *Acherontia atropos* (death's head hawkmoth). It is of large dimensions (180 nanometres) and belongs to the rhabdovirus family, together with the rabies virus. It is very mobile, moving with the aid of its tentacular prolongations, of glycoprotein nature. It is cultivated on ostrich embryos or on human nerve cells. Attempts to induce the disease in laboratory animals have so far proved unsuccessful (the illness is specific to humans).

Epidemiology. Black encephalitis or encephalitis B has been recorded since the earliest times, in the form of sporadic cases, in Canaan, Mesopotamia and India. By the nineteenth century, a number of instances had also been described in Copenhagen, Bonn, Rome, Madrid and Prague. For almost two millennia, contagiousness remained very reduced, with some documents attesting that the disease was considered the appanage of exceptional personalities. Both appanage and necessity, according to Paracelsus. At present, however, we may speak of a veritable epidemic, with black encephalitis now spread throughout the world, with the exception of the Gobi Desert and, to a certain extent, Japan. The latest statistics released by the International Organisation for Medical Enquiry and Research (ORAM) demonstrate that the scourge today affects at least a third of the population of the globe, and is of particular concern to developing countries. These observations have been taken as strengthening the hypothesis according to which socio-economic factors have an important role in outbreak of the disease. In cities, the encephalitis comes in waves, every one to five years; in rural areas it appears at greater intervals (due to the beneficial role of water, animals and wild flowers).

---

[1] Baltiev, Ariadna. *Rabia. Boli infecţioase* (Rabies: Infectious diseases). Bucureşti: Editura Medicală, 1980

The only source of infection is a personal contact with an already infected individual. Contagiousness is very high, and in some cases lasts for many years.

Transmission takes place directly, by way of drops of a nasal-pharyngeal secretion that the infected person scatters on the occasion of speaking, coughing or sneezing. Cases have also been described of infection via contaminated objects (books, underwear, paintbrushes, medals, drinking glasses, toothbrushes, statuettes, etc.) and also, more rarely, through sexual contact.

The portal of entry is normally the nose. Sometimes the mouth.

Receptivity towards the disease is universal. No inherited immunity has been noted. On the other hand, there are numerous cases on record of hereditary transmission of encephalitis B.

Pathogenesis. The AD virus persists at the entry portal for months. It is not destroyed by heat, ultraviolet rays or antiseptics. At a certain point, due to causes as yet unknown, it emerges from its inertia and begins to propagate itself by way of the nerve pathways (by neuroprobasis, or climbing) towards the brain, at a rate of approximately two millimetres per month. In the next stage, it invades the neurons, multiplying rapidly in their nuclei. This is the moment when psychological symptoms appear. Finally, the virus spreads throughout the organism, reaching the eyes, blood, saliva, sperm, lymph gland and skin, sometimes giving rise to an extremely serious form of the disease, the Moorhouse-Ibsen syndrome (characterised by total deafness, muteness and blindness).[2]

Fortunately this syndrome occurs very rarely and generally affects individuals already suffering from dangerous conditions. In the history of medicine a single case is recorded, by the illustrious phrenologist Franz Joseph Gall, in his work *Aesthetics of the Internal Organs*. The patient studied had been dead for several decades, and was one F. Goya, a Spanish national. On the opening of the neurocranium (the skull had been removed from the coffin by a group of students), it could be observed that the entire cerebral crust was covered with black spots.

Pathological anatomy. As is well known, the cerebral crust is made up of six layers of cells, between which there are complex connections, provided

[2] Not to be confused with the Waterhouse-Friederichsen syndrome, a form of super-acute evolution of meningococcal meningitis.

by the prolongations of each layer (dendrites and axons).

Recent research has shown that the AD virus produces the complete degeneration of the dendrites. As a result, the six layers become separated from each other in certain zones, which in the end come to resemble the appearance of bricks in a wall. It is of course well known that bricks do not have prolongations (a notion reaffirmed by American researchers). Thus it is suggested that in the case of encephalitis B, the cerebral crust may be compared to a wall. Nervous information no longer circulates. The connecting pathways are interrupted and, as in a flood, whole areas of the cortex are stricken, threatened with submersion. The nervous centres of decision, integration and interpretation are transformed into cerebral 'islands'. In the cytoplasm, the neurons display Black corpuscles (agglomerations of rudimentary control apparatus – generally inhibited and colourless – which go on to take over control of the cell to the point of its total digestion: autophagy). The affected regions determine the mottled appearance of the brain at autopsy[3], nacreous zones alternating with dark patches, visible to the naked eye. More than 30 names for these lesions, some very pictorial, may be encountered in the literature: acherontia atropos, zona interdicta, lili, the great spots, la douleur, the caprices, the transient, stress fractures, lace and garters, etc.

Clinical presentation. The average incubation period is three years. Shorter periods have been recorded, in individuals predisposed to the disease (artists, philosophers, politicians, prisoners, Eskimos, etc.)

In *the prodromal stage* the disease establishes itself slowly, with early symptoms passing unnoticed or, at best, being mistaken for a simple head cold. The patient is apathetic. In time, he becomes demanding. For the time being, he displays a constant nostalgia for the far off.

The *full-blown stage* comprises two stages: the phase of unease, followed by the phase of detachment. The first is characterised by minor psychological disturbances (absence, verbal incoherence, agitation). As it develops, the patients become interiorised. They become irascible; sometimes they feel suffocated. Gradually they give up their friends, comfort, family life. They smash their phones. Thus, already in this stage there appears a tendency towards isolation, which will become accentuated in the course of time. On

---

[3] Seddon, H. Le Cerveau saucisson. *Étude anatomopathologique du bigarrure*. Paris, 1976

clinical examination there may be noted a diminution of secretions, inability to maintain a vertical posture, and a fall in temperature. The mucous membranes are dry and shiny. The patient shines for a while, then acquires a more and more impersonal facial physiognomy. The cheeks swell, wrinkles disappear, and after a few months of suffering, patients come to be confused with each other (the twin or regiment sign). There follow gazing at the ceiling, rigidity, and encephalitic screaming, which marks the transition to the second phase of the illness.

The detachment phase. This is irreversible and is defined by the classic triad: disturbances of hearing, speech, and sight.

Disturbances of hearing are due to the fact that area 22 (the psychoauditory centre), the place where acoustic sensations are analysed, is affected. At first the patient no longer understands the significance of sounds. Words, for example, are perceived in the most diverse ways: as a clanging, a ticking, a hammering, or, most frequently, as the noise made by a coffee grinder (the grinder sign).

Disturbances of speech, produced by injuries to area 44 (the motor centre of speech), lead to difficulties of articulation. The result is a pseudo-aphasia. Due to the fact that on the one hand they cannot hear correctly, and on the other they can no longer discuss, individuals affected by the virus initially speak very loudly (the megaphone sign). There follows a period of stammering which becomes increasingly accentuated, finally resulting in the patient no longer being understood even by family members. Already in the 1970s, several authors observed that this type of aphasia led to the emergence of a specific, individual language, characterised by a considerable number of new words.[4] However, it was noted that these were isolated cases. Most patients speak more and more unintelligibly, and become vulnerable and absent when faced with problems of a social nature. Thus is accentuated their isolation or 'curling up inside their own peel', to use the famous expression of Chinese scholars.

Disturbances of sight, due to the fact that area 18 (the site where visual sensations are organised) is affected, follow the symptoms described above. Incapable of understanding words, powerless to express himself, the patient also loses the capacity to interpret images. In his eyes, the world around him takes on strange forms, and then is gradually reduced to smaller and smaller

---

[4] Maljin F. and Pearson R. *Linguistics and Its Consequences*. Chicago: Year Book Medical Publishers Inc., 1956

patches of light. The patient can see a star very well, for example, but is unable to determine whether it is a star or a boil.[5]

Clinical examination. The patient is generally pallid, with cold, damp skin. A guarded or distrustful look may be observed. Neuropsychological examination shows evidence of disorientation in time and space, confusion, and reduced libido. In ordinary cases, a dominant feeling of frustration is observed, which appears at irregular intervals against a linear background of absence (theta waves predominate on the electroencephalogram). In the final stages of the illness, a state of profound inhibition is noted, with patients becoming melancholy and inoffensive.

We consider erroneous the view that black encephalitis leads to loss of affection and optimism, to the point of resignation and abandonment. It has been noted that, subconsciously, the patient continues to hope for a cure. For this reason, immediately after the Second World War, encephalitis B came also to be called *tunnel disease* (E. Sábato).

To sum up, from a clinical point of view, the first manifestation of the disease is superficiality. Gradually this gives way to indifference, then to the most serious symptom: isolation. Death comes much later, after prolonged suffering. By studying an impressive number of cases, Professor Stall has shown that in addition to the disturbances of hearing, sight and speech, patients also present a marked lack of interest in phenomena that do not directly affect them or have no connection with their own illness. Their sole desire is to live in solitude. When they were obliged for experimental purposes to live in groups (the so-called *recreation parks*), patients presented visible signs of alienation. These noted included: meanness, bodily uncleanliness, gastronomic perversions, envy, egotism, lack of illusions, flight from ideas and from responsibility, somnolence, etc.

Recently, an ORAM report has reaffirmed some of the classic signs of the disease. The report concerns the *AB* test. The patient is asked: if you had to chose between *A* your own extermination or *B* that of your family and the extermination of the whole world, which would you choose? Without exception, patients opted for the *B* response. Consequently, this test provides a rapid means of diagnosis, even if not a totally specific one.

As for the *Advertisement* tests, we would emphasise that, although outdated, they continue to constitute a frequently used method in practise.

---

5 D'Annunzio G. *L'Innocente* (the second treatise in the trilogy *Black Encephalitis: Casuistics*). Ed. Santa Maria Maggiore, 1892

By means of these tests, the reaction of the patient to reality is examined, together with his degree of trust in society. Normally use is made of coloured leaflets, brochures, marches, authentic cases of healing, films, vibrations, sweets, injections, Mother regarded as society and vice versa, cancer overcome, TV programmes with advice on how be a success in life in 10 sessions, immortality by refrigeration, decorations, samples with the sun of the future, etc.

Patients have unanimously shown an extreme reticence towards *Advertisement* tests, as indeed towards tests in general. Thus, the doctor can rely only on the art of questioning to give the patient the possibility of confessing his suffering, knowledge being in fact a recognition, 'anamnesis', according to Plato. This important principle is illustrated in the medical dictionary under the letter B, where the most significant dates in the evolution and knowledge of black encephalitis are set out. We present them below, with the observation that they are in general of no practical interest (extract from *Medical Dictionary*, 4th ed. New York, Bantam Books).

Principal stages in the history of encephalitis B (M.D., 1983)

> 421 BC – the first cases, recorded by Hippocrates of Kos. Over the next 14 centuries a total of 666 cases were reported.
> 1783 AD – Francesco Goya's hearing disturbances become accentuated.
> 1808 – first performance of Symphony no. 5 in C minor: Vienna becomes a hotbed of the disease.
> 1853 – the case of Sören K. *The Sickness unto Death* is brought to the attention of the Danish Academy of Medicine.
> 1896 – noting the havoc created by the disease, the inventor of dynamite provides in his will that his income will be used to establish an annual prize, awarded to an exceptionally serious patient, starting in 1901.
> 1912, 18 January – Scott reaches the North Pole; the same day he discovers the tracks of Amundsen.
> 1915 – publication in issue number 3 of the journal *Weissen Blätter* of the study entitled '*The Metamorphosis*', by Franz K.
> 1941–1945 – the first successful experimental transmission of the disease to human subjects (volunteers); Adolf H., Allan Dulles.
> 1948 – introduction of the term *tunnel disease* (E. Sábato).

1953 – first attempts to use psychotherapy as a *method of investigation* and *constraint* in the treatment of encephalitis B (Stall and his collaborators). The Red Cross declares 22 November a perfect day for bananafish (the Salinger proposal).

1956 – several experimental attempts at transmitting the disease to animals (Hope, Blumberg). Inoculation of rats and chimpanzees with the disease led to their rapid death.

1960 – Professor Trust's famous monograph: *Egocentrism or the Absence of Love*.

1961 – death of L. F. Céline.

1970 – visualisation of the AD virus in saliva and faecal matter.

1978 – the anti-encephalitis vaccine is declared obligatory, but does not produce the expected results.

1979 – *Il nome della rosa*. Gruppo Editoriale Fabri-Bonpiani.

It may be observed that encephalitis B is a disease that has been known for a long time, even if its detection still comes up against great difficulties. In one of his last treatises, Professor Trust tried to offer a number of criteria for immediate diagnosis. Using a cohort of almost 1,000 patients, selected in such a way that each of them constituted a representative example, the famous scientist succeeded in characterising the most important symptoms of the disease in an original vision. We now present one of the cases he studied.

OBSERVATION CHART No. 890. Name: A.X., sex: male, age: 33, profession: doctor.

Reasons for admission: insomnia, agitation, alternating with periods of somnolence and apathy.

General clinical examination: faeces pale, tongue coated. Skin cold and damp. There are slight disturbances of sight; the patient confuses the notions of up, down, right, left, forward, backward.

Previous history: According to the information gathered by the special medical investigation team, A.X. had an ordinary childhood, lacking in joys. After finishing high school he went on to the Faculty of Medicine, enjoying as a student the admiration and envy of his colleagues, and the appreciation mingled with suspicion of the staff. At the end of his university studies he came second at national level, and his graduation dissertation,

Lack of Interest in the Struggle against Disease, generated a veritable revolution of principles in the field. As result of this success, he won the right to choose between resignation and assignment to a posting that did not even feature on the maps of the M.D.H. (Ministry for the Defence of Health). After two years of placement crowned by astounding professional achievements, A.X. was transferred to the capital, by a special order of the College of Discipline, in order to be kept under permanent observation. Associated illnesses: confabulatory neurasthenia, myopia, intestinal worms. Aspirations: to be always at the service of people, even when there is no particular need. Favourite sports: chess and high jumping, practised for a time with the motto 'winning is everything'. Distinguishing marks: none. Two photographs have been taken, full face and profile.

Diagnosis on admission. Approximately 10 months ago, the patient put in a request for transfer to another country, for professional reasons. The request was sent to our clinic and filed under 'Nostalgia for the far off'. Thus, when he presented himself for admission, we were prepared for a special examination of the patient.

Case history

"At first it was rather difficult," the patient reports. "Nobody believed me. It bothered them, I imagine, that I wasn't the same as the others. And so, I pretended. As a rule you've got to seem good, honest, cultivated, generous, professionally well prepared, etc. I found myself in a diametrically opposite situation. In order to succeed, however, you have to overcome suspicion and perform a few plausible miracles."

"What were your relations with the other doctors?"

"I tried to understand them, to get close to them, but without any result. I hid my disappointment in resignation and modesty. I had moments of weakness too, I admit, when I felt I was far above them all… But nobody has the right to judge people, precisely because they are so vulnerable. Fragile."

"What do you understand by fragility?"

"The fact that they complained about me. My colleagues, my neighbours. Nothing happened to me, for the simple reason that I was alone. Thus inoffensive."

"Explain to me."

"What can I tell you? It's nothing special, a story like any other. If you are in love with the world, you have to distance yourself from it, like it or not. It's not solitude that counts. The important thing is to be of use. I worked my heart out. I went out to see my patients. Most of the time I went to no purpose, I mean from a medical point of view, because it wasn't the injections that counted, but the simple fact of my presence. They would give me a begging look, with big round eyes, have you noticed that sick people have very round eyes? And they would invite me to have a cup of tea, a piece of cake. What unsettled them completely was my lack of material interest."

"Do you consider this to be a professional success?"

"To a certain extent. *Siddhartha*... Have you read *Siddhartha*?"

"No."

"It is a book that talks about love. It made a great impression on me."

"When did you start to practise this type of medicine?"

"From the moment I understood that nothing can match the feeling you get when somebody you don't know smiles at you. Just like that, out of the blue. So many faces pass by us! People who want to be noticed, listened to. To be able to tell you about work, relatives, trolleybuses, moving to a new house, children, money, tiredness, their husband's or wife's indifference, damp walls, the bed that creaks, the leg that hurts, flowers that can't be found, cans of food past their expiry date, the heater that doesn't work and the cake that's gone off. That always goes off. You see, the light has to come from here..."

The patient puts his hand to his heart.

"Very good!" (Theta ideas of an infantile type. Androgyne symbolism?) "Sit down on this chair and look at the board in front of you. Read aloud the letters inscribed on the third row."

"M, E, M, E, N, T, O, M, O, R... I... O? I can't see any more. Forgive me, I can't see any more. Some sparks..."[6]

"Endogenous depression of a sentimental character."

"This has been happening to me for about two years. At night, when the lights are out, I have the impression that I can see dozens of figures flickering across the windows of the blocks. Like ghosts, with candles in their hands. They keep appearing and disappearing, confused by this resurrection into an age in which no one needs them any longer, because no one hopes any more for another life, in the age of the conquest of the cosmos. The soul..."

"The cosmos of the soul?"

---

[6] Aesopic language (author's note).

"Please, you weren't paying attention. I believe I am the patient, and you are the doctor. Of course it could be the other way around, we are colleagues after all. However it seems to me that I am not mistaken if I state that, in contrast to yourself, I have always been of the opinion that the body heals the mind. You know, on sunny days branches of rosemary grow at my temples. On other days…"

At the *AB* test the patient hesitated for a long time, finally opting for a compromise solution: response *A*, towards *B*.

The second section. Date of admission: 15.07.198… (Continuation of observation chart no. 890.) The patient has returned to the clinic much changed. On an initial examination, the admitting doctor noted a pronounced state of physical and psychological debility. Unshaven beard, stained clothes, stooping walk, incoherence in speech, smell of perspiration. From the report of the Institute of Hygiene and Social Control, it emerges that the patient has been repeatedly fined for these reasons. However, informative notes received at the *Notifications–Patients* office create a somewhat contradictory image. Thus it is made clear that, on a professional level, A.X. has recently succeeded in gaining the trust of those admitted to the hospital where he works. Note 11, dated 4 February, brings to our attention the fact that initially the patients manifested their aversion in the form of overt hostility. Whenever the doctor entered the wards, he was met with vociferations and projectiles of the most diverse origins: eggs, pieces of bread, medicine bottles, bandages, slippers, dressings. This regrettable behaviour was followed by an unremitting silence, then a state of indifference, only for A.X. to end up the most loved doctor in the hospital. At least in appearance.

"I have to tell you how one day, a female patient tried to give me an ordinary bronze statuette," he relates. "Of course I refused. Then the patient in the next bed took me by the hand. 'Be good and accept it! It's the last statuette she has left. She is giving it to you with all her heart, anyone would do the same. You know, when you come into the ward it's as if morning has come. Everything becomes brighter, we forget about our pains, about …' The other patients were quick to give their assent, nodding enthusiastically. I mumbled something about not having any special merit, but my eyes had moistened. I had no alternative, I had to accept it. From that day on, my room started slowly to fill up with bronze."

"How do you explain this success?"

"I don't think I really had a method. I had just managed, after repeated efforts, to make those people happier, more reconciled to their own end. They were now giving each other presents, laughing, sleeping well. Even the smell of medicine seemed to have disappeared. I had just been a catalyst. The world had become a better place, at least as far as was possible. In that building."

"When did the first signs of the illness appear?"

"One day I went into the doctors' room to look for a virology book. Several colleagues were there, caught up in a heated discussion. From the way they fell silent when I appeared, I realised that they were talking about me. I rummaged through the bookcase, and then I sat down on a chair, with the treatise I had sought in my hand. They remained silent. I lowered my eyes, pretending to be absorbed in what I was reading. At a certain point, I heard one of them whispering, 'Look at him, he's come to spy again. What did I tell you. He's from the CIBA for sure.'"

"So, mistaken analysis and interpretation of auditory information. Area 22. Try to remember as precisely as you can how you perceived this statement: as a clanging, as a ticking, or as a noise made by a coffee grinder?"

"No, nothing of that sort. It was more of a visual sensation, a hammer striking the head of a sparrow. I immediately left the room. The door handle was dangling from my hand, when I set out with big strides along the corridor. I threw it away. Almost without realising, I arrived at the staircase that in the old days used to lead down, to the morgue. Now, since no patient was allowed to die in hospital any more, the stairs had been abandoned. I sat down on a step and looked out of the window. It was snowing. I stayed like that, motionless, for more than an hour, then I turned my head. The stairs had an iron rail, painted green. Here and there the paint had flaked off. Far away, down below, like a grey eye, the concrete glimmered. All of a sudden I felt sick. The silence had begun to get to me, swallowing little pieces of my tongue."

"Disturbances of speech."

"Possibly. But I would rather say sadness. I looked down once more. You know what I was thinking about. So many dead people had gone down those stairs… Their coldness was now coming up into me. Behold, I thought, the true face. Suspicion. My naïvety. How things crumbled, like so much old bread. What an overpowering need to harm, to spit on everything! The cigarette I had lit was burning my fingers. I got up, and a sharp pain in my eyeballs made me wince. I could no longer see clearly. The staircase had become an endless tunnel."

"The start of the visual deformations. The disease is advancing very fast. Go on!"

"How should I go on? All my life I have sought to make friends.[7] I have achieved only the opposite. At the end of the day, perhaps enemies are some use too. In the weeks that followed, I could think only of one thing, what to do to regain their trust. To demonstrate that they were mistaken. One day I took the bull by the horns and grabbed the hospital manager by the arm. He turned towards me, bored. It was only in that moment that I realised that it was all nothing but a vicious circle. If I had tried to exculpate myself, I would have hardened their suspicions. And if I had continued to act as if nothing had happened, they would have thought I was putting on an act. I observed this last thought, I saw how it walked like an ant across the manager's iris. It was heading towards the white of his eye."

"So, an ant. To be entered on the observation chart: manner of expression indicative of grave psychological disturbance. Zoopsy."

"The world is not used to innocence. Don't let anyone come and make us fools. Lying is our only way of bearing the truth. Take a look at this! He works hard, is generous, well intentioned, naïve. What can be the reason? He is sincere. Why is he sincere? He seems a highly trustworthy man. Unless he's leading us up the garden path."

"Confusion is setting in. The cause seems to be an accentuation of the Freudian complex."[8]

"If we imagine the gaze as a bridge thrown between us, from one solitude to another, we have to accept also the risk that the supports, in time, will crack. A single crack, and no one will use the same bridge again. We will build another, further down the bank. *Con tutti*! After a few generations of disillusionment. In the meantime, we will each remain on our own side. And cock a snook at each other."

"A comic image. The patient has a sense of humour."

"From more or less camouflaged accusations, my colleagues proceeded to deeds. They started sprinkling drawing-pins in the beds in my wards. The most ferocious of them mixed up my observation charts, poured water

---

[7] Pascal, B. and Noica, C. *Maladiile spiritului* (*The Maladies of the Spirit*). Republished. Editura Medicală, 2008

[8] Heine, H. and Wagner, R. *Tannhauser*

into my fountain-pen or sneaked into the kitchen and laced the food with chilli peppers, rat poison, walnut shells, purgatives with rapid and sometimes total action, used matches, crushed bat, or round-headed pins. The food of my patients, of course. One day they got it wrong, and poured caustic soda into the soup of an ulcerous director, the patient of our hospital manager. A monstrous row followed and, as was to be expected, I was held responsible. Forty percent cut from my salary for three months, a written admonishment with a warning, and suspension of my right to use the doctors' toilets. It was proposed that I should be forbidden to converse with patients, but a few, more conciliatory, opposed this. They opted instead to install a recording device in my stethoscope."

"Persecution mania."

"The days began to tick by. Yes, just like a clock. 'Let's unite in the face of danger,' I could see them saying. I was the danger. 'Watch out, don't let him listen to us, talk to us, because he'll be keeping tabs on us all. He'll be dishing the dirt on us in who knows what reports.'"

"Paranoia?..."

"I understood that there was no longer any point... They were avoiding me all the time. I think they hated me. Every morning, when I entered the surgery, I could see some of my colleagues slowly pushing the landscape away from my window. That was when the weather was nice. They would replace it with a big piece of cardboard, with 'RAIN' written on it. There were a few clouds drawn in the top left corner. All in grey."

"What else troubled you?"

"A permanent sensation of cold. I put on thicker and thicker clothes, I took more than an hour just to get dressed. Because I was shivering I dropped all sorts of objects from my hands, syringes, statuettes, plates..."

"Did you condemn society for the appearance of these phenomena?"

"At first, yes. Then I realised that condemning it all by myself was rather idiotic. I was ostracised. The light..."

"You mentioned the light before."

"And I may mention it again. The first cause of things..."

"Psycho-rigidity.[9] What did you do next?"

"Nothing. I became inattentive. I stopped brushing my teeth. The

---

[9] An unflinching tendency to persevere with one's own ideas and convictions, accompanied by a lack of adaptive dynamism (Wax, W. 'Against Narcys.' *Triangle*, 1920).

patients noticed, they always notice, and they gave up offering me statuettes. My colleagues stalked me, grinning with satisfaction. Every day it rained and rained. It said so on the cardboard. I was sad."

"You wanted to be original."

"Perhaps. I don't know. It seemed important to me to be able to disperse yourself in others.[10] That's what I believed for a long time. Robinson didn't."

"No, Robinson didn't. You've read a lot."

"Yes, but it seems it hasn't been of any use to me. Shavings, words like moles, spirals of uncertainty. Books cannot help you to become a personality, to be appreciated, loved... On the other hand, they make you transparent."

"Did this happen to you all at once?"

"The process was slow. Little by little my features lost their form and were deleted. My face no longer had a mouth, no longer had eyes, no longer had anything. I bought a mask so that I could be recognised by the hospital doorman. I trampled the phone under my feet. I made paper aeroplanes out of all the newspapers that I kept receiving, although I had cancelled my subscription. I threw them around the room... I became mean and incompetent, and I began to dream every night that I was erecting an enormous building in the desert.[11] Nightmares. I was afraid... an undefined peril. I painted the walls of my flat black, to accustom myself to the state of non-being. I lay for hours on my bed, with my hands on my chest, scarcely breathing, until sometimes I almost died. Time, the outlines of things dissolved. I could never tell what time it was or where I was."

"Temporal-spatial disorientation. At the *AB* test, the patient chose response *B*."

The last conversation. Disturbances of hearing and speech now very advanced. The dialogue took place through a translator of bioelectric impulses.

"What things have you found especially interesting lately?"

"Fireflies. Food and salvation. America. Wild flowers... Not being nagged at."

"Do you now consider yourself ill?"

"I don't know... I can't remember."

After giving this reply, the patient failed to present himself for further

---

[10] Pichot, P. *Le sens de la vie*, Paris: Editura Payot, 1950

[11] Răzvan, P. 'Cîteva noţiuni de arhitectură.' (A Few Notions of Architecture) In the volume *Eclipsa*, Editura Cartea Românească, 1993

consultations. A hospitalisation warrant was issued in his name, but subsequent events made any intervention pointless. The earthquake of 31 December claimed our patient among its victims. By reconstructing the events, it has been possible to supplement the observation chart that we have been studying. The earthquake lasted one minute and 30 seconds. It was morning, the attendance register had just been picked up. After the first 12 seconds, the electricity was interrupted. A.X. was left stranded in a service lift. Seized by panic, people began to rush helter-skelter down the stairs, screaming and trampling on each other. A.X. was beating his fists on the door of the lift, calling for help. The people continued to dash about frantically, coming to blows as each tried to defend what they had hastily snatched up: cutlery, lamps, surgical instruments, blankets, water heaters, mirrors, carpets. In the rush, as she passed very close to the door of the lift that had stopped between floors, one of the nurses maintains that she heard someone weeping inside. She did not give this any importance right then, because a section of wall had collapsed a few steps below, blocking her way. At two minutes past seven, the quake ended. The hospital had remained standing, apart from a few minor cracks. The sanitary personnel and patients had managed to save themselves. However in the course of later investigations, it was observed that one of the service lifts had been seriously damaged. The mutilated body of a man of around 30 was removed from the cabin, and was presumed to be that of Doctor A.X. No autopsy was carried out. *(Buletinul Medical*, no. 184)

There is another version, according to which it was the body of an unidentified victim, probably a recently admitted patient. However, we should mention that A.X. gave no further sign of life and no sightings of him have been reported anywhere, despite all the investigations that have been carried out in the period since the accident (10 years). Consequently, such a version cannot be officially accepted.

Conclusions. The case described above seems to us significant, in the sense that it demonstrates that black encephalitis cannot be pre-empted. At the fourteenth meeting of the Organisation for the Struggle Against Viruses, the sociologist and psychiatrist A. Töffler summed up his presentation with a very suggestive quotation, taken from an old treatise on entropy[12]: 'The diagnosis of this disease constitutes a question to which the future will, perhaps, give us the answer. If it still exists.'

---

[12] Töffler, A. *Future Shock*. New York: Random House, 1970

Prognosis and treatment. The evolution of encephalitis B is deceptive, but prospects are always very reserved. Aggravating elements in the prognosis are: sex (the malady predominantly affects men), profession (sedentary occupations), concomitant psychological problems, alcoholism, haemorrhoids, decompression sickness.

It must be made clear from the start that as yet no treatment has been established that leads to a complete cure. In the course of hospitalisation attempts are made to reintegrate the patient in the life of the collectivity (audio-visual means, games, conferences). Group psychotherapy, especially by means of the Aeschylus method, permits patients to emerge from their state of inhibition and isolation, through theatre. The repertory is varied, but as a rule psychodrama is preferred. Although many theatre groups made up of encephalitics have won special medical prizes, no long-term improvement in their state of health has been recorded. Existential analysis (Daseinsanalyse)[13], by means of which it is possible to decipher the symbolic aspects of the patient's biography, has a twofold disadvantage: the excessive length of the treatment and the production of free associations of ideas. At the beginning of the present century, great hope was put in the large-scale use of armed suggestion[14] (protreptica), a treatment based on the combination of pedagogical methods with those of non-verbal communication (Faraday currents, subcutaneous injections, trepanation, etc.).

Individual dialectical psychotherapy, introduced by S. Freud in 1895, proposes that repressed experiences should be brought to consciousness, so that the disease may be regarded as a mode of existence. The merit of this therapy is that it increases patients' tolerance of frustration, leading to their integration or 'immersion in reality'[15] with, obviously, considerably lowered aspirations. Modern neurophysiology, to which the Bio-feedback method also belongs, uses as its therapeutic means the inducement for a short time of a return to early childhood, sometimes permitting the recovery of positive psychological characteristics (optimism, for example). At present the method has been abandoned, because it increased the level of subsequent inadaptability. At the end of the treatment, patients refused to

---

[13] Heidegger, M. *Being and Time*, 1927

[14] Bismark, O. *General Tactics in the Conflicts of the Spirit: Suppression and Supremacy.* Coco Chanel Publishing, 1897

[15] Cousteau, J. *L'étoile des abîmes*, Tokyo: Ming Publishing, 1945

return to their biological age.

As black encephalitis is a disease that is almost uninfluenced by medication, the basic treatment can seek only to diminish the more serious symptoms. Papers have recently been presented claiming that temporary recovery has been achieved in some cases through hypnosis, animal magnetism and directed reverie.[16] The old method of therapy through work (ergotherapy-Kheops), though patients bear it with difficulty, especially when associated with convulsive therapy, is tending to become once more an important weapon in the struggle against viruses, but it is dangerous. Sedative medication is used to control agitation. To reduce cerebral oedema, bilberry tea and aspirin may be used. Cortexobol (obtained from human brain extract) has produced good results but has been abandoned, as it is a very expensive medicine and is thus beyond the means of the great mass of patients. The disturbances of the sense organs can be dealt with be means of prostheses: artificial eyeballs, microphones implanted in the larynx, etc.

Surgical methods continue to be controversial, as in addition to a mortality rate of almost 98 percent, they have brought no amelioration in the case of those who have survived.

Measures required within the hospital. Care personnel must be trained for their own protection (masks, gloves, impermeable costumes, communication with the patient only through special peep-holes, etc.). Rigorous procedures must be enforced for the disinfection of medical staff, and of all objects that may happen to be contaminated with patients' blood, saliva or sperm.

Prophylaxis. Over the last few decades, encephalitis B has become a public health problem on a world scale. The disease has spread dramatically, and is difficult to detect due to an acute shortage of the means of investigation. In spite, or indeed perhaps because of so many signs and symptoms, black encephalitis passes unobserved in a very high percentage of cases. As has been shown, a sure diagnosis is unfortunately made post-mortem. Consequently, the gravity of the illness might be summed up in Black's well-known law: 'The patient does not perceive, but nor is he perceived.'

Prophylactic measures regarding sources of infection. The identification of all carriers of the virus is a major objective, though it is impossible to achieve. A number of organisations of the Red Cross have proposed a rapid and original selection method: healthy individuals are identified first. Once they have

---

[16] Copelius, B. *The Decline of Vigilance in Man*, Paris: Éd. Pasteur, 1990

been isolated, the remainder of the population may be considered to be infected.

Protection measures for those receptive to the disease. From the earliest times, various means of pre-empting the disease have been tried: social promotion, incantations, exorcism, alcohol, family, lobotomy, oneiroidism[17], decorations, etc. Religion had an important role in maintaining certain restricted hotbeds of the disease over many centuries. At present, things have changed. Of the hypotheses that endeavour, empirically, to explain the unprecedented spread of the disease, one of the best-known refers to the gigantic leap forward of the exact sciences, especially astronomy, which, in record time, has succeeded in discovering hundreds of galaxies, nebulas and uninhabited planets. The demographic explosion which has resulted, as a compensatory phenomenon, has caused an unstoppable rise in the number of encephalitics, who have now come to predominate in the population (taking into account especially undeclared sufferers). Never in the history of medicine has a numerical superiority of sick in relation to healthy individuals been recorded. We are witnessing a serious imbalance between the two forms of existence. The black encephalitis virus, as it finds ever more propitious conditions for development, is wreaking havoc. Human nature and society are in peril. The 'twilight states' theory has gained ground once again and, in some countries, there have been attempts to apply resocialisation on lower evolutionary levels, making use of mass spinalisation. However the results obtained have not been particularly encouraging.

Recently, a group of experts within the International Organisation for Medical Enquiry and Research took issue with the very use of the term 'disease' to describe encephalitis B. As shown in the report presented to the Congress, individuals affected by the virus cannot be considered ill since (with a few exceptions) they continue to work just as well as before, and in the majority of cases even better. After an exhaustive analysis of the symptomatology of encephalitis B, the conclusion was reached that indifference, solitariness and egotism do not constitute sufficient motives for us to speak seriously of a state of illness.[18] Certainly the cerebral lesions of affected individuals cannot simply be passed over in silence. On the other hand, the question was raised whether these lesions represent any danger

---

[17] The mixing of dream and reality (Mahler, G. *The Book of the Grotesque*, vol. 7, republished în 2011)

[18] Graciansky, P.D. *La société, l'individu et la maladie. Où est le péril? Étude.*

for society. If the patient finds nothing wrong, or hardly anything, if the family finds nothing wrong, if nobody finds anything wrong, what sense is there in continuing to talk of a 'disease' unless we are trying to invent one? In the closing paper, it is claimed that encephalitis B is simply a new state of health, and that the carriers of the virus find it easier to bear their social rights and obligations. Thus, at the request of delegates, the ORAM Congress put to the vote the proposal that encephalitis B be declared a 'Modern Factor of Progress'.[19]

Nevertheless, several members abstained.

---

[19] Nietzsche, F. *Jenseits von Gut und Böse* (*Beyond Good and Evil*); preface to the final paper of the Congress: 'The Triumph of Encephalitis?' by Gabriele D'Annunzio.

Diary of a Flat-dweller
(February–June, 1990)

I live on Mirage Street, at number 9. It's an old block, grey, well looked after. Rats rarely get inside. There are cockroaches, though – red ones that come up the pipes. I live on the eighth floor, in a flat with two rooms plus kitchen, bathroom and walk-in cupboard. The windows are big and I have a nice view. I can see the tramlines, the people waiting, the bridge, the park with its stunted trees, the lake, and the buildings on the other side, bathed every morning in the light of the rising sun. Most of my fellow occupants are pleased with this view. They are quiet, meditative people, with serious occupations. We get on well together as neighbours.

However, for some time a strange epidemic has been striking the block. It all started one overcast morning in February. I was going downstairs slowly with my mind on the paper I had to hand in, when I was surprised to hear a harmonious sound that within a few moments was resonating right up the stairwell. It was as if a monotonous and rather sad song was spiralling upwards. I hurried down the stairs, two at a time, with my hand on the banister. The melody grew steadily louder. On the ground floor I found a crowd of people, lighted candles, a tall thin priest, and a shiny, brand-new coffin with brass handles. Flat number 1. Panait had died, the writer. No point in getting too upset, I thought. The man had been well on in years, and his standing in the eyes of posterity was assured. Nevertheless the event made an impression on me. He was the first to die on our stair.

A few days later, four to be precise, I heard that song again. I put on my slippers and went out onto the landing. Driven by a curiosity that I could not repress, I tiptoed down a few floors. Yes, there could be no doubt about it now. Apostol, the bookseller, had passed away. A highly cultivated man. What wailing! I went back to my flat and turned on the TV. Then the radio. I ate an omelette.

When Lola Baltag, the violinist, died too, I felt ill. Probably indigestion. I remembered how beautifully she used to play Mozart's concerto for violin and orchestra number seven. There must be a virus going round or something of that sort. I carefully studied the press, the phone, the voices of my friends. There was nothing out of the ordinary. Everything seemed to be in order, life was going on in the usual way. Just to be on the safe side, however, I bought four packs of Talazol. And a record with Lola.

Another five days, and the architect Baciu was carried off to the sound of a brass band in the direction of the elegant district cemetery. The brass fittings sparkled, and the people walked slowly along behind the open van. That was the third floor cleared.

Although I had no relevant expertise, I spoke up on the occasion of the first block residents' meeting. I gave a brief exposition of the subject that was troubling me, and no one listened. No one except an old man in a cap with *Pyrates* written on the peak, who gave me a dirty look. Immediately after my speech, they got down to serious matters, with voting, like in the old days. Henceforth, the ground in front of the block would be converted into a little park for children. To give the children somewhere to play. I made no comment, and inwardly prayed that I was mistaken. Perhaps I was taking too dark a view. If only God had granted it so.

Just two days later, the engineer Fulga, aged 28, and Ganea, the great historian, who was 60, or would have been in June, made their exit from social life with due ceremony. They were both very yellow and smelled strongly of Bulgarian perfume. You couldn't get past on the stairs, there were so many friends, relations, colleagues and neighbours. The funeral went on late into the night. Tributes, obituaries, hiccups, toasts. Verdi, the *Requiem*, unbearable outbursts of weeping, the Beatles, shrieks, tapping of feet, bottles thrown out of the window, in memory of the deceased, the *Requiem* again, vomiting, caviar. I had to swallow a diazepam to get to sleep.

When I woke up the next day, there was another. I nearly fell flat on my face when I tripped over the wooden cross that had been carelessly leaned against the wall. Without wishing to, I read what was written on the ribbon: *We work; we do not die.* The message was lost on me, but it had a nice ring to it. Out of the flat in question, whose door was painstakingly fringed with black, came a heavy smell. So Almaş the pharmacist had departed from among us too. But not before passing on the illness, or whatever is was, to his wife, a tall lady with an elongated figure, who presently followed him along the same road. With the priest – now noticeably plumper – leading the procession, religious banners, the full show. There were not so many people, but they were all very well dressed.

From Saturday onwards, the deaths really gained momentum. Not even children were spared. The undertakers had to give up the carved ornaments, generally representing wreaths and ballet scenes, on the coffin lids. Now they delivered simple, roughly planed ones, with splinters. Fourth floor, sixth floor, back to the fifth for a widowed lady lawyer, seventh, eighth. Worse than the earthquake. What could be done? Nothing appeared in the papers. We went on looking at the sunrise every morning, as if it was from there, from the little reddening sun, that the key to the problem would come, like the solution to a puzzle. One day I wrote in my diary: 'The little red sun looks like a pupil.' Crăciun, the ophthalmologist, Manole, the editor and Axente, the chemistry teacher no longer saw this wonderful view. For the moment the most they could see was a sort of darkness. Once again I heard the funeral music.

There was nowhere else in the city where they were dying at this rate. After spending some time in reflection, I started to keep records. I sent letters to magazines, to ministries, to the passport service, to the president. Meanwhile, the gas pressure dropped, the hot water supply was interrupted, the light began to flicker. From everyone I wrote to, I got nicely drafted, typewritten replies, tactfully advising me to stick to my own job, not to worry, to find myself a girlfriend. Consequently I had to give up. And to get used to flowers, incense, the smell of death, headlights switched on, horns blaring, black armbands – I put one on too – funeral tears, and the priest's increasingly hoarse chanting. He had become obese. And very talkative. I made the mistake of asking him on one occasion if he really believed there was an afterlife. He looked at me, then looked at the stars (it was night, and the funeral of a great poet had just come to an end) and belched. After which, plainly irritated, he told me that there was. I apologised, but apparently to no avail. He turned his back on me and never spoke to me again. The days passed. I watched them every morning dripping from that reddish pupil. Or perhaps violet. It made no difference. The epidemic continued.

On Monday, at eight o'clock in the morning, three individuals dressed in white turned up. The inspection committee, I thought, feeling a reborn hope that things would get back to normal. They asked for information in a friendly tone of voice, peering this way and that. They checked. They wrote in their notebooks. The notebooks had grey covers. They rummaged, felt, banged on walls. In less than an hour they had crowned themselves with a visible halo of professionalism, and they left, telling us they would be back.

On Wednesday, at intervals of a few hours, two families of actors, the sculptor Badea and his mother, an impressionist painter, and then Ene, Jitea and Paraschiv, opera singers, all departed this life. Ionescu the illusionist, the only person in the block without a degree, tried, before going into a coma, to avoid death by turning himself into a statue. However, this phenomenon was recorded by the doctor in the ambulance as the cause of death. The koliva was delicious. Lots of cars, even more umbrellas. It was bucketing down.

The last convoy had scarcely disappeared round the corner of the block when the wailing started again. The Gutenberg family on the ninth floor. I had listened to their child prodigy once, playing the flute in the Athenaeum. They put his flute in the coffin with him. Then I saw them loading their furniture into a lorry. I got dressed and went to visit someone in the city centre. I came back in the evening and was quite surprised at the long-drawn-out echo of my footsteps on the stairs. Perhaps the empty dwellings were now acting as echo chambers, like the bodies of so many violins. But without strings. On the eighth floor I met the caretaker of the block. A well-known literary critic. He was leaning on the banister in his pyjamas, smoking a cigarette. Have the Gutenbergs moved, Mr Pană? I asked. He gave me a tired look. He was pale, unshaven, with dishevelled hair. Goodness knows how many books he had had to read for his reviews. They've moved, he smiled. In a sense… He crushed the cigarette end under his slipper and went into his flat.

Since yesterday the block has been deserted. If you strike the walls with your fist, they sound hollow, although the flats are still full of things. Apart from the relatives of the little flautist, no one has had time to take them away. A deep silence reigns, which thrills me. If I wanted to, I could wander unimpeded through the furnished rooms, I could gaze freely at the paintings, books, ornaments, mirrors, photograph albums, I could sniff the eau-de-Cologne and perfume, I could roll on the carpets and Persian rugs with fringes, I could play with the fringes, cut them, tear them, switch on ceiling lights, table lamps, bedside lamps, try on nightdresses, socks, pants, suits, put on lipstick, play musical instruments, of which there are hundreds, some of them extremely old, declaim loudly in various roles, throw pillows, weep among strange objects, open doors and drawers, listen to records, cassettes, musical boxes, eat caviar and cake, drink brandy or champagne, go to sleep in any of the beds, find out what sound the china in the cabinets makes, break crystal glasses as I pass from room to room, from flat to flat, momentarily caught in the pale glow cast by the street lights outside.

I lock the door and put the chain on. I get into bed, under the duvet, and try to think of something nice. A beach. A deserted beach where seagulls are feeding. When you approach they step back, hopping about, not very frightened. One of them has only one leg. Its cry is more piercing than the others'. Unfortunately its cry is not enough to drown that singing that keeps on sounding in my ears. An aspirin, a glass of water. The TV doesn't work. Nor does the radio. There is probably a power cut, because the lamp doesn't switch on either. I have the feeling that I am left alone among echoes that are getting further and further away, leaving the framework of the building. The block is frozen by silence, a white, spongy silence. I look up, and see that the glass in the window has frozen. How curious.

This morning, when I went out I bumped into a tall wire fence. My briefcase fell from my hand. The street, with its fruit-trees, leaves and rubbish bins, seemed to be misted over. As if it were seen through broken binoculars, with the eyepieces full of fluff. I hurried back up to my flat, gasping for breath.

A ray of light sparkles in the upperpart of the pane. A little rainbow. It disappears. I go to the window, look out, and realise that the view has changed. The sensation may be due to my position, or to the fact that the building has sunk by at least one storey. I fill a glass with water and drink it. The water has an unpleasant taste. I look at the glass, then at the window.

Everything is creaking, snapping, cracking. My head aches terribly. As if I had a lump of ice, there, under my forehead.

Translator's notes

Koliva is a ritual food made of boiled wheat, eaten after memorial services for the dead in the Orthodox Church.

The Romanian *Athenaeum* is a famous nineteenth-century concert hall in the centre of Bucharest and one of the city's iconic buildings.

'*We work, we do not die*' ('*Noi muncim, nu murim*') parodies the slogan 'We work, we do not think' ('Noi muncim, nu gândim) of the miners summoned to violently break up pro-democracy demonstrations in Bucharest's University Square in June 1990.

Rubato

Take a seat, please. Yes, there, on the couch. On the couch? Of course. It seems rather worn, says the patient. And why do I have to sit on it, don't you have a chair? Indeed I do, but I'm sitting on it. In fact you don't have to sit, I suggest you *lie down*. Like in your own bed. Then relax. There's a pillow too. Lie down, you say? And what if I fall asleep? Look, I'm in no mood for jokes, there are others waiting outside, if it doesn't suit you, you can go. The patient laughs. He is a tall man, solidly built, he has a thick neck, small close-set eyes, and he is dressed in a blue serge suit, a bit too big for him. I am short, anaemic, I have one eye clouded over by leucoma, and the other wide open on the world. I wear a white coat. In front of me, on the desk, are spread the papers on which I daily note down phone numbers, draw or scatter ink from my fountain-pen, prescriptions, observation charts. In a small glass vase I keep my pens, pencil and hammer for reflexes. A little further away, the packet of cigarettes for patients, my lighter and a mug of water. Beside my left hand is the bag of sweets that, at a certain point in the course of the day, when it becomes absolutely necessary for a certain type of patient, I pop, to give them a fright. Something tells me that today I'm going to use it more often than usual.

The patient has stretched himself out, at last, after testing the softness of the couch with his hand, and remarking that it is sagging. He looks at me with misty eyes. Take your shoes off, I whisper (I can't say precisely why it is advisable to speak to them in a whisper, but I suspect it calms them). Take my shoes off? Yes, that's the usual thing to do. All right, I'll do it too, but they might smell, I'm rather embarrassed… It doesn't matter, I encourage him, I'm a doctor. The patient takes his shoes off. The room is immediately filled by a grey smell. It reminds me of photographs. Have you brought photographs? I ask. After a few moments' thought, the patient gets off the couch, pads across the carpet – he has taken off his socks too – and presents me with two photographs, full face and profile. They've come out very well, I comment appreciatively. They're done in our institution, he says proudly, then turns back to the couch, lies down and closes his eyes. Twenty or 30 seconds go by. I look at him and get the impression he is ready to fall asleep. Now tell me what is troubling you, I invite him politely, in a moderate tone.

Well, I don't really know where to begin, how should I say, maybe you won't believe me, it's like this, I mean, by the nature of the job, I do a bit of beating. It's all criminals that come and what else can you do with them, they won't learn sense, you've got to quieten them down somehow, so they'll be afraid the next time, that's the rule, although personally, all those years, if there's one thing I've learned it's that they don't settle down, on the contrary, you can lay into them like crazy, nothing gained, worse than before, it's scary, but what really scares me is what's been happening to me lately, I'm ashamed to tell you this, but I feel I'll burst if I don't do it and it hurts me too, there, I've said it, that's it, it's knocked me flat. It started around December, I'd caught this guy, said he was a pilot, passenger aircraft, pilot, eh? I asked him, the way I usually ask, while two colleagues got him down on the concrete, and we gave him a few hard whacks across the hands, by the book, with a stick, until we heard a cracking sound, then we let him go 'cause there were others waiting their turn, and he was finished with, well, as I said, that's when it all started, to be exact the next morning when I woke up with my hands swollen and a pain that nearly made my eyes jump out of my head, I went to our doctor, 'cause I couldn't even hold a truncheon in my hand, and he said to me, nothing is wrong with you, mate, don't you come to me with nonsense like this, when the whole country's on fire, can't you see you're healthy as an ox?, and I guess I calmed down a bit, but not long after that I beat another one really badly, nothing but bruises all down his back, he was howling, something hellish, and I was hitting him, it's my job, what can you do, and three hours later there's me with a cramp down my back that brought tears to my eyes, nearly stopped my heart, and when I looked at myself in the mirror, in the toilet, my back was all blue, nothing but bruises, all the way down, all that week I couldn't get out of bed, maybe that was my good luck, 'cause some of our unit had a really rough time of it in that period, and the doctor, he's like the hell you have, pal, get it into your head once and for all, you want me to make a report?, are you crazy? Then the penny dropped that maybe that was what it was, I wasn't all there up top, especially when it started to happen to me regularly, right now, for example, I've come straight over from our hospital, I had tests done on my liver, they came out good, about three weeks ago I beat a guy who was, let's say, on the fat side, I put a plank on his belly and jumped on it a few times, on the plank, so as not to leave marks, you know, and I didn't leave any, but the way my liver got to me, doctor, nearly drove me out of my mind, I was all yellow, right out of control, didn't eat for eight days, lost 15 kilos, you can see for yourself how my clothes hang on me, like on a pole, and on top of that my workmates make fun of me, they're like look what's become of the *executioner*, poor guy, 'cause that's what they call me, the *executioner*, and to crown it all, now I forget things, I keep forgetting, it's horrible, maybe I thumped one of them on the head, who knows? Let me give you an example, I set out on a certain trail, if you get my meaning, and on the way I *forget* who I'm supposed to be following, I'm walking along the edge of the lake, and all sorts of rubbish comes into my head, poems, pendulums, that sort of stuff.

Did you have a normal childhood? Yes, I'm from the country. Nothing out of the ordinary ever happened to me, ah, yes, there was something, one day I threw a cat from an upstairs floor. You had a house with upstairs floors? No, I went into town specially to try it, I wanted to see if it was true that a cat always lands on its feet. And? It landed on its feet. From the fourth floor. But I was so sorry afterwards… I cried for days on end. All right, now try to calm yourself.

The nurse opens the door abruptly, although I have asked her so many times not to do so. The patient is thrown into confusion, gets up from the couch, hides his face in his hands. I give him a prescription. On the way out he forgets his boots. The nurse takes them and puts them in the hall, under the table with the glossy magazines.

The next patient looks for a long time at the photographs for the psychoanalytic test, screws up his nose, separates with great difficulty the pleasant ones from the unpleasant ones, asking me if it wouldn't be better to distinguish the beautiful from the ugly. I understand him, he is a ship's captain, I write him a referral and a prescription.

A woman enters. She has a muffler wound round her head. The muffler is made of wool. She informs me precipitately that the bin room in the block of flats where she does the cleaning is always dirty. The stairwell too. And the lift. People block the rubbish chute with all sorts of stuff, bottles, exercise books, table lamps, pieces of cardboard, and then they leave their refuse on the floor, on the landing, because there isn't enough room for it in the bin. And the thing is she has a horror of mess. The refuse ferments, who knows what rubbish the residents eat. Yesterday she saw a rat fighting with a bird, she couldn't tell precisely what kind of bird, but she thinks it was probably a pigeon. The rat won. Indeed she saw the same rat, a little later, scuttling around among the broom bushes beside the block.

*

A short pause. I crumble a little bread and put it on the window-sill. I drink the water in the mug. The water is cloudy. Crawling, for sure, with future intestinal parasites. All the inhabitants of the town are infested. But they have no way of knowing. Or they aren't interested. I lose myself for a few moments in reflections of this kind. The door opens again. Perhaps it would be better to take it off its hinges.

A young man of around 30 sits down on the couch and sighs. I offer him the packet of cigarettes and a lighter. He lights a cigarette. He is silent. While he remains silent, I sketch his portrait in a few lines. He is chubby, with small, white hands, which keep trembling. I add to the drawing two or three parallel curving lines, to suggest the tremor. His eyes are expressive of great suffering. He sighs again. He is wearing a worn beige trench coat, which reaches down to the ground. He has tousled hair and his nose is running. He speaks very quietly.

I have no reason to go on living. Absolutely none. It's cold. My mind has set off along narrow tracks. Contemptible ones. The pay is insubstantial. To buy a kilo of tomatoes I have to write three poems. And rhyming ones at that. People have a hostile look, they talk a lot. I hide, sometimes I stay for a whole week hiding at the place of a friend who is mute. Thinking to myself that there is no way he can give me away. But he manages all the same. He ties a bottle to a string, puts a slip of paper in it, saying where I live, and drops it out of the window. He lets it hang at the level of the heads of the passers-by. It's impossible for someone not to bang their head against it, not to break it, not to read the contents of the slip of paper and not to come at top speed for me. In vain I've broken the doorbell. They all hammer the door with their fists, until I have no option but to open it for them. On the other hand, the plumber is a good man and repairs my doorbell each time. The same with the phone and the TV. He's very capable. Talks piquantly. For hours on end. I have to listen to him. He gives me subjects, inspires me, so he says. I feel best of all in the basement of the block, where even the cleaner doesn't penetrate, because she's scared of spiders. Down there I drink wine, I write. I'm afraid to go out of the house. Beyond the door of my flat a hostile world awaits me, trolleybuses, potholes, who knows, maybe even snakes. I'm nearly 30. And my name is Popescu. There are other Popescus too, they say, who write poetry. I suspect they're just pretending. I believe in God. And yet I'm poor, I have no responsibility. I swallow too many sleeping-pills. They don't help me. Not even if I take fewer. Perhaps I would end up a great poet. In fact I'm an engineer. My family adore me. On Thursdays they quarrel with me. But I think they're pretending too, my family. Too much racket around me! Even my typewriter makes a lot of noise. Yesterday I struck it with a hammer. When I was little I couldn't hit it. But now I know where I have to strike. In the centre! When I think how many women have loved me! But not one would have given her life for me. In my childhood I liked to get hornets out of their holes. I used to fill the hole with water and out they would come. They didn't know how to swim. After they learned how to swim, I invented another trick, the one with the strand of wool with a lump of modelling clay tied to the end. The hornets would get their legs stuck to the modelling clay, and that way I managed to pull them out. I used to laugh until I collapsed. I could emigrate. But, let's face it, I'm lazy. Or the native land and all that stuff. My hand trembles when I think of something. It trembles when I don't think. My wrists are so delicate! How can I write, with wrists like that? I'm bored with friends, they're all the same. And with women. They're the same too. I have bad dreams, always worms. With big heads. What does that mean? I've got protruding eyes. Some say I've also got talent. I want to kill myself! The trouble is that I can't decide on the method. It's disgusting what's left of you after you throw yourself from an upper storey, after a bulldozer runs over you, or after you hang yourself. Someone told me your tongue sticks out an arm's length and stays like that for a few days, a show-piece of a tongue, for your relatives to see. A painter injected industrial solvent into his arm. That didn't work. Cut my veins? In the bath! But in my block there's only cold water, two hours per day. I'd have to heat the water on the cooker, in pans, run with them from the kitchen to the bathroom, lots of times. And after that, you also need a good blade, the forgiveness of sins and a watertight plug, for the blood not to run away. It ought to be seen spiralling over your body, that creates a shocking effect. It's complicated and takes too long. You can change your mind, you call the ambulance, they save you. Sleeping-pills, then. And a bottle of rum. Anyway, the problem is that I don't want to commit suicide on my own. It's banal. It's sad. It would be a different matter if someone would offer to commit suicide together with me. It could be anyone. I have no pretentions. It could even be a dog catcher. Someone to take my hand, on the roof, and off we would go. Both screaming all the way down, to the tarmac. Heave ho! Or whatever one shouts on such occasions. Someone I could lay my head beside on the railway track, just when the express from Sinaia is due. Or from Berlin. Someone to shove the pills down my throat, at the same time as I shove them down theirs. I would even have the courage to hang myself alongside someone. Me at one end, them at the other. I think it is possible. I'll stick labels on all the lampposts in town, labels in which I will address a decisive and gentle appeal, in verse, to all those who want to commit suicide in a twosome. Or a threesome. In fact, maybe even more.

*

I push my bonnet to the back of my head. Then I place it over one eyebrow, raffishly. The bonnet makes an impression on the patients. But today's are banal cases. Aphasia, agnosia, apraxia, alcoholism, imbecility, autism. I've had nothing but boring cases for some time. Nothing serious. They are no longer the madmen of yesteryear. I ask the poet a few questions, I give him a nudge, he doesn't react, doesn't even laugh, I sound his unconscious, I confess to him that I read his latest poem in a literary magazine with a large print run, which almost no one reads, that I liked it. He won't commit suicide. I don't give him a prescription. We take leave of one another using the Roman salute and he's hardly out of the door when in comes a woman dressed in a dubious manner and with garish make-up. Her skirt is short, stained with oil, and when she lies down on the couch, I notice that she is wearing no pants. She waits calmly, looking up at the ceiling and noisily sucking a tooth. Then, with a sudden movement, she half lifts herself up and takes off her winter coat together with her pullover. I ask her to dress again, it's cold in the surgery. My plumber isn't a good man, he doesn't come to repair my heater, or if he does come, he repairs something else. She makes no move. I urge her again, more sharply, to get dressed and to tell me what is bothering her.

*

I'm a simple girl, from the country, never went to college. At school I used to steal pencils. I got up to other stuff too. That's why I was made to leave in the ninth grade, which was no great shakes anyway, the teachers kept throwing me out until I couldn't get in again. Then my mother and father sent me to take the cows to pasture, 'cause Mother's got a sister in Holland and we bought some cows. Later, it was them that asked me to steal calves. Although it was fun, I have to say that calves wasn't like pencils. It got harder searching for them, baiting them, at night, not to be seen by people.

I managed not badly. With a bit of gentle coaxing and a bit of driving with my rod I brought them home, and in the yard, in the pitch-dark, father banged them on the head with his mallet, then chopped them up, and the next day he would sell the meat. It was big business. Not that I'm any kind of beauty, but once we started the meat thing, 'cause you couldn't get it anywhere, the lads in the village started courting me, like the saying goes, one day four of them had it off with me one after the other, when I was 15. They liked me, that was it. 'Cause I was well developed for my age. And that's how it happened that I got pregnant, I kept feeling dizzy, couldn't catch calves any more. I didn't go back to our doctor, 'cause he made me climb on that table, I see you haven't got one here, the one with straps where you put your legs to the right and the left over a little tray, 'cause I'd never had my legs so far apart in my life, and he kept looking into my you-know-what, though I don't think he could see anything, 'cause he was drunk most of the time and he had these great big glasses that he used to leave in people's houses, around the village or at the bar, so I was embarrassed, why not, with a strange man looking into your... just like that. He even stuck his hand in too, glove and all, and tickled you, I guess he did it to help him see better. And to cap it all he had that mirror with a light bulb on his forehead. I don't know what use it was to him, 'cause it was always askew, so that it shone a different way. Now, with my belly swelling up, no one was interested in coming to court me any more. I just lay around the house and yawned. Well, after the people caught the doctor and my father, 'cause one was cheating them with the scales and the other out of sickness, I got clean away with my baby and with a label pinned onto me for life. Like I was *that girl from Sindreni with the doctor*! Although with the doctor nothing had happened, but that's how talk spreads. Maybe, I say *maybe* it was his child too. Who knows. 'Cause I loved a lad once, he was really sturdy, a railwayman from our village, but when we were almost ready for the wedding, he got run over by a train. For which reason I decided to marry whoever the hell I could get. There was one guy, Ceapă, played in a dance band, went around with a bottle of *ţuică* in the bellows of his accordion, he hung around me a bit, but after I'd left him a few times he said he didn't want to get married any more. So I said to myself I'd better look somewhere else. I went to the station at Ciocăneşti, then to Titu, but everywhere there was nothing but Gypsies, vagabonds, drunks, or the kind that just stayed there for half an hour, 'cause they were in a hurry so as not to miss the eight o'clock to Bucharest. I wasn't lucky. When I remember, everywhere baskets, ducks, pigs, depending on the season, agricultural seeds, crumpled paper, spit, I think you could make a statue just out of all the spit I've seen, they pissed all round the toilet, it's like we're free, that's what they said. What can you do with them? Some gave me wine or stockings, they were good too. I had almost started to get used to it. Anyway, I liked it better than milking the cow and father coming and swearing at me or emptying the bucket over my head. Or Mother drunk. It counted as being in town, although it wasn't that big a place, on Saturdays I would go to see a film, get myself a cake. But what made me sick, even if I took a yeast tablet or two beforehand, 'cause lots of them, in transit as they say, asked me to go with them to the toilet, to the gents, I gave the attendant a tip for a quarter of an hour, what made me sick was the smell! That stench of drink, doctor, so foul it brought tears to your eyes, not to mention the words of love, 'cause some of them came out with that kind of thing too. What white paps you've got under the black veil, a peasant said to me once. And I had to splay my legs over the Turkish hole, with my hands leaning on the wall. The wall where the bastards wiped their bottoms, with their fingers. I could hardly find a place that was a bit less smeared, my eyes hurt with straining to see, 'cause there wasn't a light bulb. The guy behind me didn't even notice, in and out, quick, not to miss the train, and I was moving my hands about this way and that so you'd have said I'd got the fidgets, with disgust, you know, no way was it with joy. 'Cause you felt like throwing up all the time. Well, now I'm unemployed, so to speak, no one comes into the toilet any more to seek their pleasures. They're all in a rush, as if there was a hand behind them with a whip. They don't even pee like they used to. And then I've got this eczema that doesn't heal, no matter what I try, I've put on ointments, powders, goosefoot, dung, the way an old granny taught me, a plague on it, I haven't got anywhere, it's stayed the same, eczema, brownish, flaky, it puts the fear of death in them all, no matter how much I tell them it's not catching, and I've got to bring up my kid, haven't I? Well, how can I bring him up, if I've got eczema? Where by the fates at its mother's birth can I have got it? Won't you have a look? 'Cause I was with this gentleman who was, you know, getting on a bit, he took me twice to the hotel and it was nice, even if there were bedbugs on the ceiling, but I don't think it was from him, from the gentleman, 'cause he could hardly do anything. I don't know, God, is there anyone in worse shit than me! I had high hopes of the capital, but I can hardly find clients, those city girls, they've got no kids, to hell with them, they catch them all so, like the saying goes, there's nobody left in the world for me, and they've got face-cream and fancy shoes, talk more proper, I haven't a chance against them? Only if I sell my kid for dollars, and I won't do anything like that, a guy tricked me once by giving me a piece of paper that said 50 dollars, but it didn't have the serial number. Anything at all, rather than go back to that toilet, I'd sooner be dead!

Until now I haven't had patients of this sort, but nothing surprises me any more. All the same, I ask her why she has come to me. She squirms on the couch. I thought I'd give it a try, 'cause it couldn't do any harm, if you're a doctor maybe you can treat me for eczema, plus for a while I've had a kind of white discharge. I liked it while I was waiting in the hall, there was a boy there reciting poetry, I said to myself that you might be some kind of writer too, 'cause they're all writing nowadays, I asked that boy what you do in here and he said it's like you pick apart our childhood, so I got the idea of telling you what was on my mind, for you to write it down, maybe you'll give me something for the story, or for the discharge. 'Cause I've got no money, I can only pay in kind, whatever it costs. Although I don't expect I'll make myself better just with that.

She goes out, after I give her two ballpoints, 50 lei and a referral. Three patients come in, one after the other. They have marital conflicts. The third also has incipient baldness. I listen to them, ask them precise questions, disinhibit them, help them to express themselves, to feel good, at least here, examine their different reactions, their conjunctivitis, their clothes. The first two speak fluently, but stick at certain letters, the last one punctuates his silence with little cries or random words. Two hours go by. I fill my fountain-pen.

*

Next come four people with problems of adaptation. Contrary to custom, I receive all four at the same time. They have phobias of the most usual kind. One of them can't stand the colour green, another porcelain, the other two parks. In general, the environment makes them ill. Through the environment they understand almost everything. Family, weather, politics, newspapers. I study their psychology, I show them a possible path to adaptation. I try to enlighten them, to convince them that they are almost healthy. I invite them to look out of the window, by turns, for half an hour. After they have gone, I get up intending to go to the toilet, but another patient comes in. A woman. I sit down. I look at her, a little tensely. She is tall, supple, with green eyes. An editor. A music critic. An essayist, a graphic artist, unmarried, a soprano in the TV choir. She immediately lies down on the couch, casually throwing off her shoes. One of them lands in the sink. You have large feet, I comment, taking a sweet. She takes no notice of me, and gets straight to the point. Some portions of her story are sung. She talks, talks and, suddenly, starts to hum. This is one of the reasons why I don't have a radio in my surgery. There are a fair number of patients who sing, whistle or groan. The soprano's voice is pleasant, with an attractive timbre. Her musical interventions consist of sections of arias, some well known, others less so or not at all, but all in C-major, as far as I can tell. I can no longer stand, I can no longer stand, the head, the polyphonic tradition, homophonic thinking, an ample fresco in which the aesthetic ideal that pleads in favour of an expressive melodic quality is replaced by a metastylistic attitude, metaphysical, melted in the absorbent orchestral paste, you drown, you cry for help, all that helps you is percussion marking the passage from the archetype to the prototype, the cymbals strike against each other, my grandmother cut in pieces, conscious, subconscious and universal unconscious, with an axe, everything that is happening now is a return across the bridge between sensation and memory, D, D, F, the eardrums and the mountains whistle, the footbridge is narrow, fragile, can only support one crossing, the metamorphosis of the concept of literature, it metamorphoses, it doesn't metamorphose, look at the beetle too, big and black, a little further away the waves, *La tempesta di mare*, profound spiritual and naval turmoil in *fugato* style, listen to the suffering, doctor, the exuberant optimism, the anxiety and trauma of natural childbirth, how everything comes together in the darkness veiled in mystery. Soon the baritone soloist comes in and calls on the crowd never to have a different perception of space or of time, to be united, there are people who stand on their heads, on nails, for nothing, they can't glimpse Olympus, transference and sublimation, abyssal states converted into serene, opaque symbols, look! the author stands at the window of an inn and sings *Il cardellino*, giving voice, through a wonderful onomatopoeic illustration, to the tireless outpouring of the goldfinch. The perfume of bucolic life, mummified, 'My dear granddaughters, I can't take all of you,' how my head aches, but not all the time, the beetle, as I was saying, the effects obtained by contrast, they are all that counts, veritable musical, literary daguerreotypes, the gallery of faces, the blood, how everything spins around me, as in the works of Veronese. The transformation of the thematic ideas that participate in the construction of the edifice of sound is real, it takes a certain degree of disorder in the mind to create masterpieces, doesn't it? said Rimbaud, alienation in a coagulated, crystallised form, G, we pass through probing, experience, I experience, I wash, I iron, I cook, metamorphosis, I write, I sing, I draw, draw, Kafka was cross-eyed, combed his hair with a centre parting, *Presto*, with the subtitle *Fantasmi*, where there is an evocation of nightmare visions, combines, cranes, broken carapaces, worms, let us raise the ephemeral and the everyday to a state of grace, but even rendered ephemeral the everyday will not allow itself to be raised.

*

G-sharp. What is the true *purpose*? To breathe. To pray. To sleep. To write about the morphology of decomposition, as if about a leg of pork in a broken refrigerator, about the poetics of violent decay, precipitation, have you heard of the precipitation of love? it is deposited on the bottom of the test-tube and that's it, that's all there is, the concentration of the artistic impression, a figure, on the embankment, in the fog, making desperate gestures, with an axe, yes, the siren of the boat sounds, the implosion of art, Picassobraque, both in one word, but only at the beginning, *allegro molto vivace*, I drink, yes, I have lovers of both sexes, I make love anywhere, the edge flashing, I just haven't tried it in public toilets yet, but when I feel the thrill of masculinisation I write and draw on the walls of the cubicles, like Mallarmé, I killed her to steal her jewels, when she was passing through the woods in a carriage, she was an actress, and why? doctor, I've been to Paris, yes, it's beautiful, the lights, the fountains, they all laugh like fools, life seems wonderful to them, shop-windows, coloured labels and cathedrals and bridges, the inner clock of a sick spirit, I know, we can float, it doesn't match the time, but I live here and now, on the couch, I can see the beetle, there, on the score, you can't tell me it doesn't exist, I can see it very well, hit it, it's sitting on the note *A*, grace has disappeared from the world, humanity is vague, shaken, the tenor wants to save it, in the middle part, and at the edge of the inferno, medicines can't be found, don't give me a prescription for nothing, in fact what do you keep writing there? they can't be found anywhere, not even onions, not even understanding, nothing, D, maybe just the mechanically animated grotesque, that can be found. We have lost the state of spontaneous communication, we ought to invent tactile, olfactory words. Gustative even, the same with sounds and colours, to touch them and eat them, does that seem nonsense to you? to make an imaginary art, unmaterialised, unexteriorised, *inexistent* consciously, that's what we need to get to, it would be a solution. Radio waves are penetrating us from all directions, lighting Christmas tree bulbs in our heads, but not the sands of Clergue, fertilised under the holy footsteps of Jesus, they only penetrate our noses and eyes, we struggle to go into churches, we stumble on the fountain-head of any kind of scripture, which is found in the rhythmic incisions of cave art, with the Magdalenians, the allegory of becoming is sand, the thin murmur that scares insects, think of this, 'The nun sits / in the convent there / with her white paps / beneath the black veil,' we are all so beautiful, there is screaming, whispering, roaring, the apocalypse unleashed, *adagio molto cantabile*, fleeting apparitions in the *scherzo* of the ninth, crêpe paper aeroplanes, phallus, the principal theme is picked up by the wind section, make an effort of will-power and take that beetle off my stomach, they've all gone mad, F, F, D, but it isn't an authentic madness, it's a sham, cardboard and glue and plastic fir-trees, now I'll do a high C, attention, doctor, C-C-C, phallus, to the highest summits, we learned, they tortured us, we became proletarian, monk, student, soldier, prisoner, scholar, woman of easy virtue, clown, executioner, at least those are the professions preferred by romanticism, history confirms it, who said that? do you know? they all chop and hang, they like it, they do it casually like the long-term executioner, who I saw coming out of your surgery, the swaying of lame happiness, I know him, he lives in my block, he throws cats from the fourth floor, 'but just then the Count falls,' in cacophonies, Spanish poetry, burning in the temples, the meticulous polishing of forms, *when maidens sing sweet barcarolles…*

I take out the sweets, blow up the paper bag and burst it. The patient falls silent. I look at her feet again. Very large, indeed. I call the nurse, for her to see them too.

I look out of the window. Over at the Ministry of Post and Telecommunications they have opened all the windows.

Without knocking, a short, fat woman wearing an overcoat comes in. She looks at me in a hostile way. I invite her to lie on the couch. She sits down groaning, then gives me another dirty look. Unperturbed, I look around me. Everything is spotlessly clean. You wouldn't believe that so many people have been through here. A small lamp, which casts a restful light, hangs on the wall. I switch it off and on several times.

I'm afraid of birds, doctor. You are a doctor, aren't you? 'Cause on the door it says psychiatrist, or psychoanalyst, I can't remember. Yes, madam, it's almost the same thing. At least in some cases. I fold my arms on the desk. Then I lay my head on them. So, you are afraid of birds. Tell me something about your childhood. I'm afraid of birds. I understand, you've already told me... And they keep coming and sitting on the balcony, because my little boy puts food there, although I've told him so many times to stop doing it, it seems like every day there are more and more of them and they crowd onto the balustrade, onto the kitchen window-sill, 'cause the kitchen looks onto the balcony, peck, chirp, flap their wings, strut about, whole flocks of them, they look at me and I hide in the cupboard. Alright. In the cupboard, I've made a note. And I lock myself in. Doctor!... The woman unexpectedly grabs the sleeve of my white coat. She has surreptitiously got up from the couch. Without looking up, I hit her on the hand with the reflex hammer, not too hard. Around my cheek the mints lie scattered. They are not of equal sizes. One of them is very close to my right eye. I ask the patient, who in the meantime has sat down again on the edge of the couch, what sort of birds they are. She doesn't answer, she takes from her pocket a small metal box, red in colour. I asked you what sort of birds they are that are besieging your balcony. Woodpigeons, crows, sparrows?... She massages her forehead intently, her fingers greased with a brownish ointment that has a somewhat pungent smell. Oh, yes, they're sparrows. Little sparrows, you know, the grey and brown ones. They don't do any harm... Suddenly she starts to cry. I offer her a little water, but I remember, too late, that I have just drunk it. She lifts the mug to her lips, however, and leans her head back as if she were taking a deep draught. She wipes her lips with her sleeve. I follow her with my good eye, half shut. The cheek resting on my arm has gone numb. The woman has a large, hairy wart on her upper lip. That's not what the trouble is, she tells me, between sobs. What is it, then? I ask, playing with my fountain-pen, rolling it this way and that on the desk. I killed them, the poor little things... I put out poisoned bread for them... All right, don't worry, madam, hey, hey, calm yourself! The woman blows her nose and looks at me in confusion. So you don't want me to lie on the couch any more? Not at all. You can remain seated. Your problem is a false problem. These are things that can happen to anyone, more often than one might think. I myself had a similar experience. A year ago. I was standing on the balcony watching the passers-by, when a sparrow landed on the balustrade. It was very sweet. At first I wanted to drive it away, because sparrows make a mess and I'm a very clean person. It seemed curious to me that it didn't fly. It stood there and looked at me. The next day it came again, hopping about on the kitchen window-sill. It had been snowing. I went out and spread some breadcrumbs for it. Little by little, we got used to each other. I even built it a nest, which it never went into. I often used to stay with my nose pressed against the glass, waiting for the sparrow. One day it settled on my palm.

The patient looks at me in disbelief. I wouldn't have had such courage… to stay and let it eat from my hand. What if it pecked you? Encouraged, I resume. You know, madam, it's a great pity you kept hiding and never touched that frail body, through which you can feel the heart beating. Or that you never looked a sparrow in the eye… The woman bends her head. No, she says, there is also that human badness, they wait in queues and hit each other over the head with shopping bags, slap each other in trams, run like crazy after money, after houses. Go on strike. Why do they go on strike? As it seems to me that the patient is prepared, I decide to stop.

What, did you kill it? She asks horrified. Her pupils have dilated. Yes, madam. I have made an experiment. And it has worked! The woman remains motionless, with her mouth open, forgetting to keep smearing her forehead with that foul-smelling ointment. She still holds the red box in her hand, however. And how did you…? she whispers. With a catapult, I answer. Of course, I could equally well have crushed it in my fist, but that can't compare with the sensation you experience when you lie in wait and take aim. I suspect you have never fired a catapult, have you? My pen races across the paper. All right, but it's… horrible! she cries out. Well, you see, madam? And yet it wasn't any big deal. I aimed with care. And when it settled, as usual, on the window-sill, I fired through the window, at less than a metre. Everything exploded, the window, the sparrow, and two flowerpots. Smashed to pieces.

I lift my eyes. The room is empty. The clock shows me that my programme is over. I am a little tired. I go to the sink and wash slowly, as I do after any normal working day. First my hands, then my face. I remove my white coat, take my overcoat off the hook and go out.

As I enter the house, I hear the phone. I cover it with a pillow. I switch off the radio, which I always leave on when I'm out at work. I go into the living-room, pick up my violin from the couch and start practising scales. A, A. *Rubato, dottore, rubato!* cries a neighbour.

Translator's note

Ţuică: see note to 'Chance'.

Where are You, Eleonora?

I was standing outside the grocery shop, I wanted to get milk and this man started yelling 'Where are you, Eleonora?' and tugging at the wire grille. You know the wire grille there, don't you? To be honest, no. On Fall of the Bastille Street, at the first crossing. Beside the clinic. Uh-huh. Well, and do you know what he did? He tugged at the gate until he pulled it off its hinges. I thought you said it was a wire grille, not a gate. It was a wire grille with hinges. And stop fussing about details. All right, and didn't anyone react? Who? I mean, so many people pass by there, and then there's the policeman at the corner, drinking Coca-Cola. He's not a policeman? No? That's a good one! Are you sure? I'd bet my life on it. Strange, it's the first time I've heard of someone drinking Coca-Cola just so people would think he was a policeman. Do you want me to tell you something? Not desperately, but I imagine I have no way of stopping you. That isn't even Coca-Cola. What is it then? I couldn't tell you exactly, you'd do better to ask him or the girl who sells it. Look at her rolling her eyes and she's got false eyelashes too. Lilac. Anyway, they don't make the soft drinks of yesteryear anymore. Indeed. That's from Villon. Do you mind if I light another cigarette? Not at all, we're in the open street, aren't we? and there's already smoke from all those cars that can't wait to run you over. Right, and you say he was shouting... He wasn't shouting, he was roaring. I looked at him, I could see how he was suffering because of the gate, because of Eleonora, and I called to him. Ah, you knew his name... No, but it wasn't hard to guess, 'cause he seemed to be a sort of writer, I mean I asked him, are you looking for Eleonora? She's moved. No response! He kept on yelling like a madman and tugging at the wire grille. Or was it on Dorobanți Way?... Madam, isn't the Turkish embassy somewhere around there? No, it's a bit further away, in among the blocks, but he had a voice like in the opera. And the policeman? What policeman? The one with the Coca-Cola. Oh, didn't I tell you a minute ago how things stood with him. He had drunk it. He had been thirsty, he had finished his drink, his lunch break, wiped his mouth with his sleeve the way they all do, and that was him, gone. Or maybe he felt sick, 'cause they stick all sorts of rubbish into the bottles, once I saw a mouse in one of those liqueur bottles, a little one, don't ask me how it got there, still alive, blind drunk though, and that was that. But in any case it wasn't the same policeman as the one that we can see now. They keep changing. They do indeed. And the guy that was shouting for Eleonora, what happened to him? What was to happen? He just went on shouting. It seemed to have an effect, 'cause at a certain moment this woman came out onto her balcony, in just a nightdress, turquoise, at 12 noon, but in the block across the road. So it wasn't Eleonora? Now, at that distance, how could I know? In conclusion, you didn't know. No, I just thought. 'Cause I was wondering, in fact who are you? You start up conversations with people just like that, without saying who you are… Never mind, it's not important. We may as well talk, 'cause we're going in the same direction anyway. Tell me more about Eleonora. Eleonora doesn't live in our block. She couldn't possibly, because we close the outside door at 10 o'clock at night. It's a very good safeguard, you know, there's no need to smile. We each have our own key, they all fit, and we keep watch in our flats with our ears glued to the door. I've noticed that recently all sorts of individuals have been coming into the block, electricians, nannies, criminals, some just come to relieve themselves in the rubbish bins, children with air pistols, Gypsies, spies, invalids, drunks, dogs, 'cause some folk on the second floor feed them, throw them meat from the balcony… You're right, their numbers have been getting out of hand. I've got one myself. *Canis familiaris*, domesticated carnivorous mammal, mine's an Alsatian. He's called Vasile. Maybe you can afford it, but what am I to do with a miserable salary, smaller than a pension, after I've worked so many years and I'm still working, throwing it away on a carnivorous mammal? It would chew up my carpet too, and just one egg costs more than what I used to earn four years ago. I would like to be able to contradict you, but I have no arguments. It would be better if you told me what happened next on Fall of the Bastille Street. Nothing much, the man was determined to roar out 'Where are you, Eleonora?' for another half hour. I don't think he was older than 20. And the people round about just stood watching him without intervening? What people round about, are you starting again? Pardon me, madam, but it seems a bit odd, it's a big street after all, with the Turkish embassy, the clinic, the kiosk with the policemen, literary critics, educated people, actresses, was there really no one who could ask him what he wanted, to stop him or give him her address? I didn't find out, all I can tell you is that a lady, a neighbour on the eighth floor, threw a packet of cotton wool down on his head. Heavy? It's clear you haven't a clue, of course it wasn't heavy and it didn't even hit him. But it fell on the stall of that man who repairs cigarette lighters and something caught fire, the gas I think. There he is, still keeping the cotton wool beside him… At the entrance to the metro? Yes. I see him. And then what else happened? Who to? What do you mean who to, what are we talking about? Oh, you're referring to Eleonora! She left long ago, if she ever lived in the district at all, 'cause I've never seen her, and the boy who was calling for her was tidily dressed, in a denim suit, you know, just with a rather big nose, the way young men are, and a greasy stain on the left or right lapel, or on the trousers, I'm not sure any more, 'cause I didn't look, and he kept shouting with all his might for Eleonora. It seemed like he'd gone off his head. After a while my daughter's mother-in-law answered him, 'cause she's got the same name, and said if it was her he wanted, she was coming. And what did he say? He didn't say anything, first he gave her a deep look, like this, 'cause he had green eyes, and then more of 'Where are you, Eleonora?' And what about your daughter's mother-in-law? How can I explain, she doesn't hear very well, so she went down. Not in the lift, 'cause it doesn't work. She went down in her slippers.

I imagine the young man got a bit of a surprise when she turned up in front of him. I've no way of knowing, but either the block started to shake, 'cause if you remember there was an earthquake that day, grade five, or the traffic lights changed, anyway something made him fill his lungs to bursting and this time he woke the children with 'Where are you, Eleonora?' Because in our block the children live on the ground floor.

You had to pity him, you really did. Not that Eleonora is an ugly name, although personally I don't like it, but around four he shouted in high C, which, let's face it, on a rainy day is enough to get on anyone's nerves. Are you a musician? No, I'm a seamstress, I don't get too many orders, but since my man left me I've been singing. Despite the fact that I've rather put on weight. Look at this dress on me, it's almost bursting, it makes me perspire… Don't worry, it doesn't show, and the lower part suits you very well. Thank you, you're very sweet. In fact you're all very sweet. Even that boy… A good thing the Turkish ambassador didn't turn up. Well, and even if he had it would have made no difference, the kid was shouting for all he was worth, people were going up and down taking no notice, like bedlam, why the hell they don't lock them up I can't understand, 'cause they make our windows rattle with their lorries and it won't be long before they fall out, and I don't have money to buy putty, but what I like now is that everything seems more normal, we find out the truth, so you can learn something about the human race, for example yesterday, I bought a paper and read that an old woman mutilated her grandson with a pestle, I turned the page and saw a chap that blew himself up because his girlfriend left him, with two bombs that he put in his pockets and he set them off from a switch, or maybe he plugged them into the mains, in any case in the picture it looked like there had been an air raid, I got another one, in colour, and what did I see on the cover? *A naked woman*! And she wasn't just naked any old way. How was she naked? She was seen from behind, if you please! Perhaps it was better… What a thing to say, it was worse! And then in the evening I watched a Romanian film on the TV, very good, something with the railway. I watch those films more often now, 'cause they don't have subtitles that come too fast and I only manage to read half way, I watch the odd serial on a German channel, or an Italian one, it's a shame I can't make out what they're saying, 'cause they chew their words, and then our lot put in music that really touches your heart. And the subject of the film at one moment was the spitting image of what happened to our young man outside the grocery shop. 'Cause about five o'clock this heavily built guy came from the snack bar at the corner, and started quizzing the lad, I mean, who is this Eleonora, pal, cause you're driving us all scatty? And he laid into him. Who? This guy, the waiter. And then something strange happened. The kid, I mean the lad in denim, hit him just once, I don't know where, although I had my binoculars on the two of them, and knocked him flat on the tarmac. After which, of course, he started up again, with WHERE ARE YOU, ELEONORA? Quiet, madam, don't shout like that, or everyone will hear us. Yes, indeed, I got carried away with telling the story… Anyway, if it had been me, after a scene like that, if I was that Eleonora woman I'd have come galloping down to him three steps at a time. But my name's Maricica. Not to mention that I can't gallop, 'cause I've got an ulcer, you know, from the drink. I'm sorry. There's no need for you to be, 'cause you smell too, so that it's a wonder those people in the tram stop don't fall over. Madam, you are mistaken, it's deodorant. Really? I thought it was brandy. I just don't understand why you splash it under your armpits. All right, if that's what you think, I splash it under my armpits. That's your business, but it's not a good idea.

My guess is that this Eleonora never showed up, did she? No, who knows where she lives? 'cause I looked for her myself, I asked this and that person, maybe she lives somewhere on the edge of town, in some shack, or in a burial vault, 'cause I saw once on the news a man in a beret, he wore it pulled down over his eyebrows, who seemingly his girlfriend had thrown out of his flat. He had bought it, he lived there with his mother who had come out of a psychiatric ward two years before and stayed there, in a corner, all day long, and Cerasela, that's what the guy's popsy was called, tricked the old dear, brought her sweets, candles, thread, until one day she got her sloshed and made her sign a receipt by which she donated the house to her, and that was it. Cerasela legalised the paper at the notary's and as soon as she had all the stamps in the right place she kicked her fiancé out of the building, with his togs and all, and put a new Yale lock on the door, so that he, poor chap, suddenly had nowhere to sleep. He found himself out in the street with nothing but the clothes he had on him and what his sweetheart had thrown out of the window, from the first floor, a blue cardigan and a backgammon set with three white pieces missing, he had replaced them with buttons, but the old dear had taken those too, to play with. And what about the old lady, did she put her out too? They didn't say, or maybe she died of rage when she came to and realised how her future daughter-in-law who had been so kind to her had tricked her. Or they stayed on together. Anyway it doesn't matter, it was about his situation, not his mother's. He went everywhere, to the caretaker of the block, to the town hall, at the counter they gave him a cigarette, to the government, the church, the papers, until they wouldn't receive him anymore, because there was nothing that could be done. He couldn't find a house. When the man realised that he wasn't going to find anywhere to stay, he decided to move to his workplace, 'cause he was a gravedigger. He chose one of the more comfortable vaults for himself, rigged up electricity, borrowed a pillow from the administration, and started sleeping next to the wall, but he wasn't content. He felt cold. Behind him he could see the photographs of the owners, a young woman, a brunette, and a man with one of those oval faces. I guess that what with staying there with them, he must have started looking more attentively than he had ever done in his life as a gravedigger at the faces of the dead, and at what was written beneath them, b. 1960 d. 1996 for her, and for him the d. had been rubbed out, or maybe it had never been there, imagining, when he came home, between two burials, or especially in the evening, how the two had met, in the park, probably, over a beer, or, even better, in the cemetery, as they were accompanying some mutual and distant relative on his last journey, she fainting with grief, he catching her just in time to stop her hitting her head on the cross, and then they went to the memorial service together, told each other their life stories, ate well, the relative had been rich and had left the refrigerator full, drank, she played a romance on the piano, she had been to the Conservatoire, had come out top of her year, he listened to her with his eyes shut, he was a doctor, tall, strong, with slightly greying hair, and after another four or five glasses of Aviator champagne the pupils of the two of them suddenly sparkled and the love scene began, with the lights out. It was a scene from a dream.

What a lot of people have crowded into the station! It doesn't matter! Where was I?... Yes. Two months later they got married, the gravedigger – let's call him Codruţ, although they didn't reveal his name – could already see them somewhere in front of his eyes just by looking at the photographs and hammering on the wall where they were laid to rest, he even came to call them by name, Crina and Nucu, and after an unforgettable honeymoon, which they spent in his block in Militari where he had two rooms that they didn't come out of once in 30 days, Nucu got involved with the senior nurse, he didn't love her, it was just a slip, a careless lapse, one night on duty, he was worn out after eight hours of heart surgery and Crina wasn't there to congratulate him as she was away on a tour of Europe, so Manuela congratulated him, the senior nurse. That scene always brought tears to Codruţ's eyes, but in the end Crina came back from Paris and everything was explained, first of all with screams, then with vases, and finally with caresses, because that was the beauty of the story, this is the secret, their love couldn't be overcome by any senior nurse. So Manuela went off to the country, to her parents, to a wretched little dispensary, and then the first child came, Cerasela – now Codruţ was calling Crina Cerasela – had got into the ASE too, they had finally managed to buy a three-room flat in Pantelimon, by putting all their money together, and she was behaving like an angel with Brăduţ (that was what they had called the boy) and with Codruţ, who no longer worked in the cemetery and had got his doctorate in surgery, the same Nucu he had imagined sighing in the vault in those long nights of happiness, and in the morning the alarm clock rang, a Slava, and the doctor and the singer went out to walk their child, who was growing up now, and astonishing his teachers and winning all the competitions. Then Cerasela was expecting their second child, the pregnancy went wonderfully, she had become a bit fuller in the face, and she had taken Codruţ's mother into the house too and looked after her like a daughter, bought her chocolates, cupping glasses, lamp oil, however a few years later, when the children were away in America with scholarships, she didn't feel so well, she was pining, had insomnia, was haunted by images of burial vaults and a gravedigger looking at her, got pregnant a third time and caught a cold at a benefit concert, it developed into septicaemia, but at this point the man with the beret returned to the honeymoon and shut the door of the vault, 'cause it was February.

And Eleonora? I can see you won't let go of her, you could almost be that boy, although you're wearing glasses. Tell me, do they actually help you at all? 'Cause my poor mother wore glasses all her life and she couldn't see a thing, not even when the lorry ran over her... Excuse me, madam, please keep quiet a moment, it sounds as if someone's screaming... Sounds like what? It's just the noise of the train. No, I think someone's calling 'Where are you, Eleonora?' Really? I don't get that impression. Maybe it seemed that way to you because of the story. That's it, it just seemed that way to me. Only I don't understand why the metro is running late, how long have we been waiting in the station? And I see no one out of all this crowd is getting fidgety, what's going on? We've been waiting for at least 20 minutes. There's no way of knowing exactly, 'cause the sign just says 00. Is it a strike? I don't think so. But equally I wouldn't have thought, even if someone had told me so, that there could be birds flying in a metro station, and yet there are. I've spotted three so far. What did you say? The birds, madam, don't you see them? Where? Oh yes, it's got its nest there, under the neon lights in the ceiling. It's watching us standing here. Right, if it's watching us standing here anyway, I'd like to tell you, if you don't mind, that it seems to me that this whole story and especially the question about Eleonora, sounds like the title of a stupid film. Why stupid? And don't let me catch you calling me auntie again. But I never... Though in that white dress, with frills... I made it myself, from cotton, and I can't imagine where the hell you see frills! You seemed to like it, when we were above ground. It's all right, I know your type! Auntie here, auntie there, and then, when you're not careful, bang! Enough to make your eyes pop out. And don't you think you look a fool using that language that all the cretins use? 'Use' twice? I'll use as many times as I like, 'cause you've turned yourselves into a bunch of smart-alec spivs, graduated who knows what twopenny-ha'penny faculty just so that you can pick up women and that's the end of it, so ta-ta, laddie! Honestly I haven't the faintest idea what you're referring to, if it's about the dress, I apologise, I don't know what gets into me sometimes, I see frills and they drive me crazy. Please calm down, madam, look, here's the metro. Yes, you're right, I get carried away too sometimes, I can't understand why. Anyway, it would be better if I told you about a film. Don't take this badly, but I really don't wish you to tell me about any more films. But I haven't even… Oh yes you have. The one about the gravedigger. About Codruţ. Listen, aren't you a writer or something? 'Cause that's what I thought from the start. I had the impression I had seen you before somewhere, and now I come to think about it, I really have seen you, in a photograph. Where? In a photograph I found in the street, I stepped on it, but I still recognised you. It doesn't matter. So you must be something of that sort, a writer, a journalist, a singer… Maybe yes, maybe no, in any case it is of no significance and in fact I don't believe anyone has managed to find out what I really am, not even my father. Even though he's a radiologist. Or rather he *was*, until a few days ago. Or months. My condolences… Or years! Well, you shouldn't suffer so much, if he's a radiologist it means he stays in the dark. He does. However, what interests me is Eleonora. Who she is, where she sleeps, whether she is tall and so on. What world she lives in, with her fiction and all. But what have you lot all got against Eleonora? Maybe she ran away, 'cause those pigs did very well for themselves before too, and now they're senators, businessmen, presidents, steal everything they can get their hands on, bankers, traders and wear beards, say they're patriots to save the country, what country?, 'cause it makes your skin crawl when you think of all the thousands of years they've kept this people in a stupor with its golden hen and her chicks, crooks that they are, and they still lead them by the nose, in a wisp of hair greased with sunflower oil that leaves you speechless on the pedestrian crossing, they lead others by the nose, philosophers that don't know what world they live in and it never ends, it's a country full of philosophers with a vocabulary in which you don't understand anything or of 10 pompous words three of which are about Mother, not their mother, another one, in the general sense, nothing but crooks, with three-storey villas in the mountains, in the meadows, and wives in town, with phones in their hands that they pretend they're talking on from Fords, lift their elbows as high as they can with the receiver, to be seen through the windscreen hairdos and all, pressed against the roofs of their cars with springs with which they run over old ladies coming back from the market and cyclists that don't get out of the way in time, and leave them crushed on the stony road, all twisted handlebars and bells, only to spin a load of lies afterwards, about how it wasn't their fault, no way, the cyclist had his cap over his eyes and didn't see the white car coming up behind him, which came and made mincemeat of him, it happens, first the front wheels and then the rear ones, so no one can recognise him now, maybe he wasn't even a cyclist, and the police captain knows us, we're relatives, and as for the old dear, she lost her balance as a result of rheumatism and jumped out in front of us without any warning. Or she had cancer. To be practical about it, we saved them a lot of suffering and on top of that they didn't even know they were dying. Who wouldn't wish to die like that? Don't get so worked up. How can I not get worked up, can't you see them? Oh yes, but I've got another problem on my mind, I'd like to find out why that young man was so troubled… All right, let me tell you the story of the film, to give you an idea.

Was she sick, Eleonora I mean? Well, I don't know exactly who she was or what was wrong with her, but she looked worn out, with staring eyes, four white tubes in her elbows and shadows this big under her eyes! And him? Which him? I mean the doctor. But there was no doctor involved here, she was locked up for experiments in a dark room, however the boy that loved her finally managed to climb up the wall to where she was and he cut the bars of the window with a file. And what do you think he did next? He kissed her! He pulled her out of bed and held her tight in his arms so that he knocked the pole over. All the little bottles of morphine, sterilising cases, phials of Saprosan came crashing down… *Attention, doors closing!* And he kissed her again on the mouth, 'cause she had purple lips from the perfusions, but long, you know, with smacking lips… Do you mean to say he stuck his tongue into her mouth when she was a patient? That's nothing to what followed. And they showed it? Yes. He took off his hospital coat, the girl still had a needle in a vein, but that didn't matter in the end, 'cause they supported themselves on the oxygen apparatus in such a frenzy of joy at seeing each other again, because they never thought they would. *The next station is Dristor, with the platform on the left.* And then the murderer appeared. I don't understand a thing. Well, he had been lurking in wait from the beginning, hiding in the bathroom, in the bath, and he came into the room with a pistol weighing about three kilos, like I've never seen in my life before. But what did he have against the poor kids? *Or with the platform on the right.* Those two weren't kids, they were over a 100 years old. They were vampires. And they were kissing each other's lips in the hospital? Yes, 'cause they loved each other. They had done for 80 years. Which means that even vampires suffer. But so what, why shouldn't they? Right, and the murderer? Oh, when he saw those fangs of theirs, how they stuck out of their gums, he was overcome by tears. After that I think I fell asleep, but when I woke up, the guy wasn't wailing any more, he had remembered something in his childhood that had marked him for life, an image with a woman and a whip, I think it was his mum, he got angry, the pistol trembled in his hand and he shot his sister who had just come from the station in the head, she had just appeared in the doorway with her mind set on saving him, luckily he didn't kill her, but I started crying too. Why? How do you mean, why? Because it impressed me. How could it not impress you when he pointed his great big shooter right at her hairdo and blew away her hairpins and half her face, and then the ambulance came and they operated on her face so you wouldn't even recognise her? 'Cause now she looked like the first one, that old vampire. *Attention, doors closing! The next station is Dristor.* But what's up with him, didn't he say before that the next station was Dristor? I hope we're not going round in circles. No, madam, it's a tape. They record it in the morning, at the depot. Maybe, if you say so. But it doesn't sound like it. *With the platform on the… with the platform on which side?…* I see their tape recorder's broken. Or whatever it is. Most likely, but what I wanted to tell you is that you shouldn't take all this to heart, about the film, there's no point in crying, because no one loads the pistols with real bullets. That would be something. All right, I know, but if they had put a meat cleaver in his hand? Eh? Oh yes, then things would have been a bit more complicated, the truth is that I myself have a neighbour, on the fifth floor, who's got a meat cleaver and sometimes three sometimes two cats. You can't mix them up, they're never the same. So she's got more? In a way, yes. She makes wigs from their fur. *Attention, doors open. The next station is Dristor.*

You mean she makes wigs from the hair of the cats that she kills with the meat cleaver? I don't know, madam, if you have ever listened to *Et la lune descend sur le temple qui fut.* I beg your pardon? Please excuse me, that's how it's written and how it's heard sometimes in French, the language of Debussy, interpreted by Horowitz 30 years ago. Despite the fact that he, I admit, never plays *qui fut.* Quite right too, it sounds ugly, and these children only learn rubbish. But still, why doesn't he? It's not normal. Perhaps he doesn't have that note, perhaps he doesn't press the pedal, his legs aren't long enough to reach it, or someone's peeled the felt off the piano hammer. Oh, does a piano have felt? Yes. Anyway, listen to what happened next.

Finally a doctor came, the guy fired twice, she was tied up, then he slapped her, the girl ran into the cupboard and he cut her throat with a violin string, hanged her, then banged her head against the wall. But what was the point of all that? Didn't you hear they were vampires? You never know with that sort, they can come straight back to life, so, thump, he battered her until the plaster fell off the wall. And she died. My dear lady, she didn't die at all, you know, I watch TV too, and I saw her the day before yesterday in another film, she was chewing gum and attacking a bank. You don't say! The woman with the smashed head? What, do you take me for a fool? Yes, it was really her, only now she was wearing a military beret, so you couldn't see the condition of her cranium. And if I remember correctly, it wasn't gum she was chewing, but candyfloss, blue. The stick was extremely thin, so you could hardly see it. You couldn't see it? Then how did the candyfloss stay there? What shall I say, it was a trick, in the end all this was nothing but a film, and films are all the same, everythings's the same, optical illusions, make an effort, imagine the scene, with the scriptwriter eating salami, the director on his chair, the sound engineers, nymphomaniac assistants, with off-centre navels, dazed editors, glossy actors, at least on screen, with all the usual problems, troubles with mothers, sisters, fathers who've broken out of prison, exterminator children, wives, fiancées of leading male actors, partners' lovers, disabled relatives, Hollywood, fabulous houses on the coast that slide straight down into the ocean overnight, a younger brother who goes around with a 45 pistol and fires it at waitresses, and they always have to get him out of a scrape, cars that go out of fashion every month, photo-reporters, make-up artists, the star's tyrannical sex organ, a sex organ that is ultimately treacherous, tiny, almost a child, that many squeeze between their legs, or wrap in an orthopaedic bandage, only when she appears things change. All fidgeting, looking, smiling... What do you mean she? Eleonora. Well, I don't see the connection between the story with Eleonora and the film that I've just... There is a connection, when Eleonora appears, birch trees rise up out of the blue, cranes fly, you hear music, the sand, crawling, with fingers tickling you along your spine, you can make out her face even with sea shells over your eyes, because, you see, the young man on Fall of the Bastille Street was right, the women of this species have curves and breasts that you can sleep on until the month of December, the month of presents, when everything comes to an end... *Attention, doors opening! Attention I said, the doors have opened! How about making yourselves scarce?* Has the driver gone mad? I don't know, but I think it would be better to get off.

And now that we're out, what will we do? 'Cause the trams have stopped too. Wouldn't you like to have a hot dog? A what? One of those sausages, with mustard. All right, if it doesn't cost too much. So, he cut her head off, stuck it in suitcase, the police came and he shot them one by one, there were five of them, but the lieutenant, a black man with a drooping moustache who went after him covered in blood, got out of the window, it was night, and went to the cemetery, to her mother. Is this really a hot dog, 'cause it tastes like rubber? Take the cellophane off it. Ah, why didn't you say so, they must have thought I wanted it to take home if they gave it to me wrapped, and her mother rose up from the crypt and that boy still going 'Where are you, Eleonora?', and pulling the wire grille sideways, and then wait for it! Tell me. It wasn't her mother. And then it was all over, they caught him. For which reason I changed the channel and watched *Michael the Brave* for the seventh time.

Let's take another train, madam, from Obor. There's no point in staying here any longer, it's too hot. As you say, let's head off, maybe we'll be lucky enough not to land with another cracked railwayman.

I see the escalator is broken in this station too. What platform are you going to? It doesn't matter to me, 'cause I'm enjoying the conversation. It's just a pity I've dirtied my dress with mustard. It comes out with detergent, don't you worry. You're always ready with a joke, aren't you, and as I was saying, the mustard really is very hot, against a wonderful soundtrack come the fights, Michael's on his horse, shouting, roaring, bombs going off, flags on heads, pitchforks, swords, knights fall in the mud, one ends up with a broken hand, another gets his eyes poked out with a lance… *Attention, doors closing! The next station is Dristor.* Oops! If the next station is always the same, no matter which train it is, how about getting to the point? The point? Yes, not meaning the tapered end of a tool or weapon, or as you were probably thinking, the prongs of a deer's antlers, but in the sense of the essential element. The key to the story. Who Eleonora actually is. Who she is in reality, not what someone or other said about her. Because I can see that you know what you're talking about where films are concerned. I know because I've been a married woman. It's true, I don't sew much any more, my eyes are failing me, but I've become a block caretaker, I've got responsibilities, I collect the rent, give the change, get mixed up sometimes and folk never have the right amount, keep tabs on who's hanging around the building, but

I don't take any risks. 'Cause I had an operation for a cerebral aneurysm, you see, one of my eyelids keeps dropping. But it doesn't droop all the time, it droops when I least expect it, and everyone says poor thing, she's blind in one eye!... Ah, the Romanian film was also a beautiful one, and I cried at it too, from beginning to end, 'cause I thought Michael was nice. The girl too. I was all trembling when they stuck a spear in his back... Talking about that, don't you get the impression this metro is shaking us about a bit? Yes, it's going too fast. Perhaps it doesn't stop. Oh yes, it stops, look, the accordionist has got on. When in God's name did he get on? And where? At the last station. Next it will be the one-armed man, the spastic, the blind man, at Timpuri Noi it will be the child that crawls on all fours, and then the dumb child. The Gypsy man hasn't been for about a week. However, the burned Gypsy woman will be there, with the orphan. But how come you know them all? I go by metro, don't I? The funny thing is that once you pass a certain station, I can never remember which one, they all show up again, in the very same order. I don't believe it's the same ones, madam. Because if it was, that would mean that they can walk faster than the metro, or they take another metro, parallel to ours, but at a much higher speed. That's the only way they could come into the carriage in exactly the same sequence. Could they go above ground? I hadn't thought of that. Listen, tell me honestly, aren't you a writer? No, madam, I'm a newspaper seller. And do you sell many? It depends. Enough, if I may say so. Then let me explain to you what the point of the story is. I'm listening. There was this girl, in a hospital bed, with lots of needles stuck in her arms...

After a short time I was somewhat shaken up, the train slowed down and I again had the sensation that I could hear something that sounded familiar. In normal terms this is called auditory hallucination. All the same, I pricked up my ears, partly because I don't believe in normal terms. I closed my eyes and tried to concentrate, through the changing fortunes of the girl in hospital who had ended up on the oxygen machine again. Madam, stop for a moment... Listen, please! Can't you hear it too? Of course she could. All the travellers were listening, now there could be no shred of doubt. Someone was calling out in desperation, probably in the next carriage, 'Where are you, Eleonora?' And shaking the automatic doors with all his might.

Translator's notes

The unnamed film involving a railway and an episode of violence is *The Re-enactment* (*Reconstituirea*), a 1968 film by Lucian Pintilie, in which a prosecutor forces two petty delinquents to re-enact a drunken fight in front of a film crew, with tragic results. The film's exposure of the brutally oppressive character of the communist state caused it to be withdrawn after only a few sporadic showings, and it was only after the revolution of 1989 that it became available for public viewing again.

ASE (pronounced *a-se*) is the acronym of the Academy of Economic Studies, a prestigious institution of higher education in economics and business.

Militari and *Pantelimon* are districts of Bucharest, on the west and east sides of the city respectively.

The *golden hen and her chicks*, or Treasure of Pietroasa, is a collection of fourth-century gold objects discovered in 1837. Ten of the 22 pieces originally discovered have since been lost, in the course of a history involving theft, fire and a period of nearly 40 years in the Soviet Union. The remaining 12 are now among the treasures of the National History Museum in Bucharest.

Dristor and *Timpuri Noi* ('New times') are stations on the Bucharest Metro.

Michael the Brave (*Mihai Viteazulul*) is a historical film of 1970, directed by Sergiu Nicolaescu and starring Amza Pellea as the Wallachian ruler whose brief unification of the principalities of Wallachia, Moldavia and Transylvania in 1600 has been seen since the nineteenth century as prefiguring the creation of modern Romania.

Flash

It was on a Thursday, around six. I had gone out with my dog, an English setter with a black patch over his left eye, because he needed to pee. It's not a time that I usually pee, but it's nice in the park, the leaves fall, the birds fly, buds appear, other times it snows, you are, so to speak, in the middle of nature, which says nothing. And just when I felt myself most at peace with nature, with man's hair-shedding friend, with people, contemplating with an abulic air the grass growing through the cracks in the paths, the dog picked up a piece of paper, and sometimes they're smeared with poison by people that hate dogs or simply feel good spreading poison on something. I snatched it violently from between his teeth, and before throwing it away, I gave it a passing glance. It was me. In semi-profile, on raster paper, 13 x 18 format, with a basketball in my hand.

I looked at the dog without any expression and handed him back the photograph.

He swallowed it.

About two days, I think, went by. I was in the centre of the capital, the city of my childhood gone wrong, lots of commotion, coloured cars, lights, adverts, phones, humming sounds, puddles of ice-cream, some people were looking intently at big houses, sort of villas with battlements and pagoda-style roofs, surrounded by green electric fences, behind which guards with hermetic features stood motionless, others were queuing for newspapers, lottery tickets, sea shells and toilet paper, which comes in various different types, I, for example, never use the kind that is extra-fine, porous, in shades of pink, except in an emergency, as a handkerchief, otherwise it tears in the middle and you can have the most unpleasant surprises, a few people were sipping soft drinks with their eyes tragically directed upwards, and several compact groups were eating *mititei*. I bought four, took one bite, and was about to fling the rest in the litter bin when I saw something in the orange metal box, a photograph. I don't know what made me lift it out. In fact I do know. It was me again. On glossy paper this time, taken from above, you could see the beginnings of baldness, beside a little bear. I was laughing, in the mountains.

I felt slightly uncomfortable.

I tried to set fire to the bear, the lighter wouldn't spark; finally it caught light behind the travel agents across the road from the Intercontinental.

On Friday evening, Ioana, my wife, told me she had found two photos of me at the hairdresser's. They were lying on the concrete, not far from the cash desk. Some ladies on their way to the hood dryer had pierced one of my cheeks and my right eye with their heels. I asked her what she had done with them. She replied calmly that she had given them to the girls. As I know that generally hairdressers don't enjoy looking at photographs, especially photographs of me, I hoped that they had thrown them in the bin in the end, together with their clients' hair. I was left in a rather uneasy state, however. That evening I drank a very strong sedative tea, St John's wort. The next morning, Ioana told me St John's wort isn't a sedative, lime blossom is.

Perhaps that explains the fact that two hours later, in the middle of the night, I dreamed that someone was photographing me naked on the beach. At Mamaia.

On Monday, on my way to the trolleybus, my attention was caught by the beggar at the corner of the street – there are lots of beggars at street corners these days, some of them are blind – who, although I have seen him every day for more than five years, has never stimulated my charity, humiliation, shame, feeling of guilt or other feelings of this sort. The truth is that I avoid looking at him as much as I can, because he irritates me. He has gold teeth – which he shows when he's asking for something – hair in his ears and fleshy lips. Not to mention that he is quite well dressed, his grey jacket would suit me perfectly if I was a bit stouter. Now he was selling, somewhat bizarrely, candles for the living and photographs of me. I asked him where he had got them, I mean the photographs, and then I bought the lot. There were 10 of them. Actually 11 to be precise, but the last one was in such an advanced state of crumpling and discolouration that I thought no one would have been able to recognise me. On top of that, it was a pretty old snapshot, I suspect I wasn't more than five at the time. The cadger pressed me to take that one too, saying that his father, who was extremely old, had kept saying for some time that the world was getting smaller. It is getting smaller before our eyes, even fixed on photographic paper, where the phenomenon can be clearly seen. As for where he had found the photos, he confessed that it was in the street, on his way home. Despite the fact that he lived in a half-demolished block, situated at the edge of the district, there was nothing for it but to take a trip out there. I didn't find any more photographs, but the building was pervaded by profound grief. A few hours before, a mother on the ground floor, obese, had sat down after breakfast on her bed, to take a rest, right on top of her own two-month-old child. She had forgotten about him, she was thinking of other things, she hadn't noticed him. On top of that he was tiny, a sweet little kid, and above all, very quiet, unfortunately. She sat on him with her full weight for almost three minutes, sighing, as was asserted later, for which reason there was no more need for a doctor. The little one didn't even manage to say boo, as is customary in more or less similar situations. Or if he did, it was of no importance, because he couldn't be heard under so many kilogrammes of Mother, which, as is well known, is not a good sound conductor. The woman was howling at maximum volume, maddened by despair, and beating herself with her fists on the nose, on the temples. The beggar gave me a summary of his opinion, as he uncovered his head, his hair was dyed indigo, which was that, leaving aside, if possible, the appalling suffering caused by such a drama, one thing had to be acknowledged as obvious and a matter of common sense, namely that it was much easier to bury a little child turned to gelatine by its own mother, as of all human beings this was certainly the one who needed the smallest, and thus the cheapest, funerary accessories. I didn't contradict him, he seemed violent.

The next day I went to a friend who is a professional photographer, I showed him the photos and, to my surprise, he showed no surprise, explaining to me that this sometimes happens, not to worry, it's something to do with the astral body, yoga, and he enlarged them. I had just seen a film by Antonioni about an artist photographer who discovers a murder on a negative with some miming at the end from a short story by Cortázar, 'Las babas del diablo', I think, the name of the film has slipped my mind, only in my case nothing interesting appeared, apart from the extremely poor quality of the images and a veneering hammer whose presence could not be explained. The photographer cleared his throat. All I can tell you is that the photos are taken with the same camera, at night, the details can hardly be made out. They photographed you at short range, with an additional light source. Probably a flash, though I wouldn't stake my life on it, it could have been a spotlight. Then he switched off the red light in his darkroom, we drank a glass of wine together, and he suggested I should keep looking, I might find some that had come out better.

I didn't have to make a special effort. Three weeks later I started finding them all over the place, and it was raining too, spring had come, they were wet, covered in bird droppings, the migrating birds had come back home, and, for all that, my face could still be easily recognised.

I am a journalist. Sometimes I also write short stories.

One day, in the metro, a plump, sociable, difficult lady suddenly started talking to me from the next seat although I had done nothing to encourage her, she said she was a seamstress, she gave me a mass of details about that distinguished profession, perhaps she wanted to initiate me into the secrets of the trade, to make me a tailor before we reached Dristor, where I was waiting with an increasingly pronounced nervous tremor to get off, then she saw my photo on the identity card from which I had taken a receipt to read on the journey and for the next six stations she told me the story of another ill-starred woman, Eleonora. She asked if I was a writer, I avoided giving her an answer, especially as I didn't know what the answer was, in the end I said no, the photo was of my cousin, a well-known sportsman, she was sure to have seen him on TV, whence the confusion, it was just a pity that Eleonora had disappeared, as far as I could understand.

The only photo of me that had appeared in public until recently was one taken with a bellows camera in France, by a friend who is a priest and works in his free time for a religious publication. Behind me was a monastery with a little white flag fluttering from its right-hand tower. I was standing in front of the other tower, so that – the main focus of the picture being the one with the flag – I could hardly be made out. And yet this photograph was not only published with me in the foreground but it also seems to have had some success, perhaps because I was the gravedigger. As the village in the valley was a superstitious place, half Basque, no one was willing to take on such a responsibility, and they asked me. It so happened that someone there had died, an almost volatile old man, but the gravedigger had died the previous day, and in the very moment the shutter was released I was throwing a shovelful of earth over him. As an amateur *fossarius* I acquitted myself tolerably well. The grave rose nicely, in the background was the Loire, and over it stood a leafless pear tree, in which one pear could still be seen.

It was the first photo of me that I was really fond of.

I never found out what happened to it, I never saw it again, not even in the newspaper's collection.

After another month, Ioana took to gathering all the photos found in the street, sticking them tastefully into an album bound in red leather.

Unfortunately, just at the very moment when she was positioning the last portrait, the nanny showed up, she tends to show up like that, right at the last page, the woman is from the country, Ioana stuck it in askew, got annoyed and walked out of the room, and, by the way, I should say that I detest people from the country who have come to the capital to take our flats, to steal the light bulbs on the landing, the washing lines, the washing, even when it isn't dry, the aerial sockets, the mirror in the lift, the doorbell button, to chew sunflower seeds, black ones, and spit the husks all over the place, in the tram, in the living-room, at work, in ministries, with the greatest relish, to talk backwards, to wear hats with ear-flaps, to feel the irresistible need to take their shoes off every time they enter a dwelling-place, and then to sit there in striped socks, hard to forget, to raise thick clouds of dust by continually beating their carpets, to burn leaves in the autumn because that's the done thing, no one has any idea what practical result such a custom has, all anyone knows is that it there is no escaping it, whence too the cough occasioned by the choking, sickly sweet, carcinogenic smoke, to call to one another other from the balcony, sharing thrills and onomatopoeia in connection with the latest episode of *Blood of My Blood*, *Cheated Women*, *Luisa*, *Fernanda*, *Antonela*, *Eleonora*, *Little House on the Prairie* and *The Rich Cry Too* while they rinse cabbage leaves, I'm more than certain to get bronchitis from the smoke, or if not from the smoke then from the dust spread everywhere by the plaster stalactites hanging from their ceilings, to thicken their hall walls with plaster too, but this time with geometrical, village designs, or to put up wallpaper imitating tree bark, so as to be elegant, like in the forest, and stick it on permanently with wood glue, so that no one can get it off without bringing their neighbour's wall down at the same time, to sit for days on end on iron benches in front of the block, so as to see who comes in and above all who goes out, to plant tomatoes and onions in the little park right beside the block and then throw empty *ţuică* bottles on the vegetables from the upper storeys, so as to make them stink, to stink beyond good and evil, and, concomitantly, to pour litres of eau-de-Cologne over their heads that I wouldn't splash my dog with even in jest – all right, so the nanny showed up and explained to my son, who apart from the fact that he is a very obedient child is also very naïve, to say the least, that the best thing for him to do that morning would be to shove the dog into the stove.

He didn't go in easily, but with their combined efforts they managed in the end to squeeze him in. When I got home, I detected an unaccustomed smell of burning, luckily my son clarified matters, he came running and said Dad, the doggy's been sitting in the stove for an hour and he's not barking any more.

I forgot to say that as well as the setter they had incinerated Dante, the 1932 edition, edited by Ramiro Ortiz and printed on granulated vellum paper, because they couldn't get the fire going.

As I couldn't beat my nanny, not even in theory, because she's head and shoulders taller than me, I beat the child, even though my perfidious, abject, Freudian desire was to sit him on top of the *Divine Comedy*. But that would have been pointless. The fire had already gone out.

All I could recover of the dog was the skeleton, which I buried among the tomatoes, and as for the nanny, I didn't even dismiss her, for the simple reason that as well as having paralysing hips she also has connections in the Ministry of Culture. Connections who make up for all her initiatives. On top of that, when we have guests, she always puts on very tight dresses. Which creates a pleasant ambience, especially when she leans over the tray. On top of that, the muffled swinging of her wet-nurse's chest, like something emerging from our troubled history, often sublimates these intimate states, transforming the pleasant ambience into a solemn atmosphere. Ethnographic.

When more than five months had passed since the last incident, I began to ask discreetly, around magazines, notaries' offices, artists' studios, in all sorts of editorial offices and watering-holes, if anyone knew how my photos were appearing in the street. I was answered with a shrugging of the shoulders so expressive that I could have made a drawing of it.

I didn't though.

On the other hand, I think it was another Thursday, I caught the nanny adding pen and ink moustaches to one of the nicest photos, the one where I'm wearing a pilot's helmet, which turned up recently in Amzei Market. At the same time, exasperated by the fact that it kept jumping off its rails, Ioana had set about dismantling with pliers the electric train set that I, with all my love, had given my darling little boy as a Christmas present. He himself was at the table, calmly breaking walnuts with his forehead. I felt I was getting old, so I put on my coat and went out. It had turned cold. I stopped for a moment by the gutter and came across another photograph. In this one I had been snapped eating maize snacks, at a wedding.

I took to writing again.

Before long, the publishers returned my manuscripts together with a number of photos of me, slightly touched up, which I had never sent them.

I started to become suspicious, to look more carefully where I was stepping, in case the odd photo got stuck to my sole. In November, still walking along suspiciously, I inadvertently stepped on an old dear's bunion. She fell in a heap, with a sad look in her eyes. By now I generally walked next to the wall, with my collar raised. I had come to be known in all the districts. And for my part, I knew the coils of wire sticking out of their paving slabs, the depth of their potholes, the heaps of rubble, cans, waste paper, the broken glass sprinkled deceptively over their pavements, their bushes. One time, a little boy held out to me a photo that might have come straight from the developing tray, saying that it looked like me. Of course it looked like me, given that it was me, but to this day I haven't been able to understand why I slapped the little boy.

After nine increasingly oppressive months, we reached the point of divorce. In court Ioana declared that she could no longer bear seeing my face all the time, day and night, no matter where she went, like an eternal election poster, she had had enough, she was fed up with seeing my photographs scattered all over the city, or having them brought to her every day by neighbours, relatives who then stayed for dinner, and ate everything, malicious cousins, look, dear, how well he's come out in this one, passers-by, postmen, dustmen who went on to ask for money for them and for the funeral of a colleague who had perished in an industrial accident, the rubbish compactor had chopped him up every time, wandering photographers, the odd policeman with a blank look, Albanians, street children, fire-fighters, street sweepers, Father Christmas, in a panic, on the intercom, getting the season wrong, the district mayor, feverish teenage girls in search of their idols, and even athletic strangers with nylon stockings over their heads. She had accumulated around 2,000 photos, some of them quite well done. They all had one thing in common, they had been taken at night, as my friend had suspected, all that was different was the quality of the paper and the size of the aperture. The judge spent more than four hours looking at them, she chose four, then she smiled at me.

Ioana was left with the house, the child, the nanny and maintenance payments.

I found myself a studio flat in the end in Drumul Taberei, with a view over the plain and walls of cracked breeze-blocks, which I have completely covered with photos. Some of them are stuck with Poxipol, others are pinned up with drawing-pins, nailed in place or set into the wall. Unfortunately, not one is in colour.

Very seldom, I still go out in the evening through the city and look for more.

Translator's notes

Mititei are a popular Romanian dish, consisting of grilled rolls of minced meat mixed with herbs and spices.

The *Intercontinental* Hotel has 25 floors and is one of the tallest buildings in Bucharest and a city centre landmark.

Mamaia is a popular resort on the Black Sea, with numerous hotels lining a long beach.

Candles for the living and for the dead, lit and placed by the faithful to accompany their prayers, are a common sight in and outside Orthodox churches in Romania.

Ţuică: see note to 'Chance'.

Amzei Market is the most central of Bucharest's open markets.

Drumul Taberei ('The road of the camp') is a district on the west side of Bucharest, created in the urban expansion of the communist period. Its name recalls the events of 1821, when the army of the revolutionary leader Tudor Vladimirescu camped there.

Playing Jesus

Perhaps I overdid it with the make-up. One eye came out blue and the other orange. My mouth, on the other hand, was acknowledged by everyone to be a masterpiece. I made it black. It couldn't even be distinguished from the beard of Michael the Brave that they gave me from the props room, it was the only one they could find. When the lights came on, the director entered, with a bit of a cold, he sat down on a chair somewhere in the hall, there was no one else in the hall, it was beautiful though, and I began to play Jesus. I was Jesus, because I'm the right age, and I have an olive complexion and a gentle air. The hairdresser tried to accentuate the gentle air, with scissors, while he was arranging my sideburns. In the course of the operation he clipped my right ear. It was extremely painful. I bore it without a murmur, because ever since I was a child I have been committed to an artistic career. It is true that sometimes I shed tears in the morning at *Bugs Bunny*. In the *Art of the Fugue* too, when the oboe comes in. And it nearly always does, especially in slow movements, wrapping its spirals around them and bringing to mind for some inexplicable reason fields of flowers, white flowers, marguerites, which Gypsies gather, weave into garlands and sell the next day in the market with a perfidious smile. Now I have let my hair grow long, as Jesus wore it, especially in his youth, and my face has taken on a profoundly religious look. When I appear in the street, everyone greets me with a deep bow. Sometimes their hats fall off and I pick them up. When they perform their bows in the middle of crossroads, the people risk their lives, there are cars that drive into them, or, if they are luckier, pass over them, scraping their spines with the axle shaft, an accident that leaves some of them stammering. I continue, however, to pick up the hats scattered on the tarmac, I respond to their greetings with an imperceptible inclination of my head, cross on red and dress in a white raincoat, with no collar. It seems that all this makes an impression. It doesn't impress the director, though, who told me one evening that a more pathetic interpretation than mine he had never seen in his life. Still, it helps me to get under the skin of the character to the point where it becomes unconscious. He is such a simple character that I have had to read several books about him. I've been to the university too, I've studied icons, I've been to residents' meetings, to church.

I rehearse a lot, in front of the fixed mirror in the wardrobe door, just as I have heard the great actors do. I don't have problems with the text, I have problems with the facial expression, as my physiognomy is incredibly immobile. It doesn't even change when I cut myself shaving. With indescribable efforts, I frown, laugh, suffer, apply ointment for herpes, on my upper lip, it stings, I become thoughtful, I get angry, howl, beat my fists on the table, on the walls, on the door, break plates or fall into the blackest despair, lifting my forearm to my forehead, the way it was when the phone engineer found me one Saturday morning and he wouldn't install the phone any more.

I've seen the films of Zeffirelli, Pasolini and Scorsese – and I can understand very well the last-mentioned's intention of presenting the character in a state of crisis, exemplified by all the rolling in the dust and close-ups, it was extremely suggestive, I mean it suggested epilepsy, Prince Myshkin, or just schizophrenia, like Prince Myshkin's, in the end, as my director is old-fashioned and on top of that not in the best of health, he never dreamed of forcing me to play an invalid, and explained to me that if I was still tempted by such an idea I had better not imagine that I had any chance of getting any more sick-leave, because I had taken quite enough as it was. On the other hand I would be uncomfortable pretending. Because the last time I pretended a lady from production started crying and brought me camomile compresses. I've also seen *Jesus Christ Superstar* several times, I liked the music, especially Mary Magdalene's aria, I learned the score of the principal singer by heart, only I have a bass voice and he sings with a high-pitched voice, a sort of tenor towards soprano, probably that's how they told him to do it on the set, or how he saw the role, or he couldn't do it any other way. After numerous exercises I managed, one February night, around two in the morning, to sing high-pitched, accompanying myself on the kitchen pans. That was because I had sold my piano, it had a cracked bronze plaque and an insufficient number of black keys. The white ones were all present. The neighbours calmed me down, with the help of some friendly individuals, fine connoisseurs of music, who quietly led me to the ambulance where there was a jacket waiting for me on the seat, a straight one. I put it on myself, it was just my size. I don't remember exactly how, but in the end I managed to leave with it, and when I undid the arms to go on set, the stitching came undone.

One time, in a pub with a mauve neon sign, while I was going over the scene with the wine one more time, I drank so much that I fell on my back in an uncomfortable position, complete with the chair and tablecloth. A gentleman in a narrow tie, who wasn't playing in the film, helped me to get up. I thanked him, I got up, and in return I gave him my mini cassette player, a Panasonic with equaliser. The gentleman in the minuscule tie thanked me too and went away with the Panasonic, perhaps for fear he would identify me. But he had identified me. Indeed it was only normal, on the set I keep having problems, which rapidly become known all over town. And I have problems because, from the first hours of the morning, when I haven't even turned up yet, there appear failed directors, hysterical actresses, half undressed... (I haven't turned up yet, because as well as rehearsing at home I have to do the cleaning, to invent new recipes, to make improvements on some of the lines, confronting them with the Gospels, to repair the door handle, to do sport. I train myself every day, for example, to hold my breath as long as possible underwater, in the sink. My record is one minute and 10 seconds. More than that I can't do. Maybe because of the chlorine)... screenwriters in search of inspiration, no one can stand them, because most of the time they try, with destructive enthusiasm, to take a share in the composition of the film, they're usually obscure writers hankering after glory or just starving, they stuff themselves at the canteen, never stop modifying the text, make jokes, change each others' dialogues, decompose them, pester them, one says "Lama sabachtani," another says no, here it's "Lazarus, come forth," and a third proposes phlegmatically, when he sees me, that I should begin with the line about Barabbas, and just when I'm about to utter the name Barabbas, the set secretary goes past with her note pad in her hand and a pitifully short skirt, so I forget, I look at her year zero thighs, bursting with health, and I try to think of something else. For example, how to settle the small misunderstandings with the grips, the camera operators, who are never satisfied with the light, there isn't enough of it no matter where you film, the stunt men (I've got one to double for me in the dangerous scenes, which haven't been shot in the end, I've only seen him once so far, walking about with a hammer in his hand), the choir, the other actors, and, once again, dialogue writers who cut lines, cut cables, and don't put new ones in their place. On Thursday I combined the words that some of them had suggested, and no one laughed apart from me. Still, I had an inspired air. Inspired or not, my air always leaves the producer cold, he never stops asking – apropos of my exercises at staying immersed as long as possible – why I don't walk on water, but how could I walk on water when there is no water, the tap is out of order, the basement plumbing has packed in and the mechanic died a few days ago of water on the lungs, and I can't repair them, a little later came the scene with John the Baptist, where not only was there no actor willing to cut his head off, because he was the director's nephew, but the boy wouldn't agree to stay either, even though the episode was historically authenticated, muttering that, authenticated or not, it sucked anyway, all he should have had to do was to bathe himself – no one was very sure where – to baptise and to recognise Jesus, he didn't recognise me, anything else he refused categorically to interpret, at the end of the day he hadn't accepted this role just to be decapitated at the first rehearsal, he was still young with his whole life ahead of him, he wanted to get married, in the end his uncle convinced him by promising him a Japanese motorcycle, a Honda, and they chopped him with a Japanese meat cleaver, there wasn't much blood, but the image came out splendidly. You could clearly see, in the finest detail, the carotid sectioned, the trachea likewise, two cervical vertebra smashed, the jugular deflated, the eyes upturned and the mouth twisted in a horrible rictus, and that's the most you can expect from a period scene. The water of the Jordan was added by montage, for live filming they used the Dâmbovița, beyond whose waves Unification Square and the Bank of Religions could be made out at one point.

After that came my scourging. I didn't deserve it. I shaved at the crack of dawn and let myself be scourged. All I remember is that, unexpectedly, just when I felt I was really getting into the role, the left spotlight exploded. After that I couldn't make things out clearly any more, it was as if a kind of mist had descended. All the same I can't forget that, even though I had filled his wallet with plenty of money so he wouldn't hit too hard, I mean on no account like in the screenplay where it says "with all his might", the bastard of an extra who was playing the role of the executioner not only whacked me with all his might but did it with real hatred, managing to slice my back in about 30 places, and that's not even in the Bible. But it will be from now on, if the film comes out. I still have wounds on my back, when I lie down it's as if I'm on a hot grill, like Joan of Arc, my flesh catches fire, I clench my teeth and endure it, an actor has to endure. De Niro, great as he is, worked as a taxi-driver for six months, everyone knows that, for the sake of a run-of-the-mill movie, later he studied Lucifer for several years in order to play him for less than 10 minutes in another horror picture, Marlene Dietrich agreed to have all her molars taken out just so that she could acquire a shadow under her cheek-bones, full of mystery, Greta Garbo stoically bore the torment of wearing shoes in key scenes, when she had enormous soles, flat feet and depression, and even though no pair ever fitted her she put them on, a Roman officer's horse let itself be shoved over the edge of a gorge at the height of a battle with the Dacians, Meryl Streep asked to be hosed with cold water in the middle of winter, so as to be able to die convincingly in a film about beggars, Maia Morgenstern likewise, others get slapped for real without warning, some are sick and come on set like that, lying on stretchers, the examples could go on. I haven't attained such a level. All I am doing is playing the Son of God around the district. I imitate his gestures down to the smallest detail. His way of speaking. His simplicity. I've got so simple that I can't even buy myself bread any more. And since I started dressing in white and wearing blue glasses, I've realised that, little by little, people have started to respect me, I'm not allowed to pick up their hats any more, and the respect has taken a spectacular leap forward since it became obvious that I was determined to take my role very seriously. I bought a little cross, not too expensive, but one that I carry almost all day on my back, from morning until afternoon, around five, when the sun sets and the wind picks up, because then it's not heavy although it's made of oak, the drivers toot their horns at me, put on their headlights, I really like that, I can see better where I'm stepping, and I walk with the cross all over the place, as far as the main boulevards, it's worse with the crown of thorns, because my ears hurt. An old ear, nose and throat specialist advised me to rest it on one eyebrow, so as not to get earache. In the end I did that, one Tuesday, and since then I've been going about with cotton wool in my ears, sometimes in my nose too, just in case, I speak with a baritone voice and I can hardly understand the director's orders any more, luckily he's got hold of a megaphone.

It's worth the sacrifice, because I've never had so many smiles directed towards me, not even when I was a child. Even the shop assistant at the corner tobacconist's smiles at me and offers me a Carpaţi cigarette for free, the policeman looks in the air when I cross the road on red or amber, the tram driver makes room for me on the seat beside him, in the cabin, lets me play with the little bell, ticket inspectors salute me, the barman gives me a small brandy, also for free, once every three months, at the cinema I haven't bought a ticket for ages, I go in by the back door, followed by my cross, I don't put it down even in the dark and I spread myself however I please, the people around me disappear rapidly in concentric circles, the ophthalmologist got me plastic frames for my glasses, green ones, out of his own salary, I asked him why and he answered that he liked the colour, that it suited me, for several months I've been receiving the visits of some high-class girls, who listen to me preaching my sermon on the Mount of Olives standing on the kitchen chair, cook for me, sometimes come with their mothers, they're of marriageable age, and with one thing and another, they have a lot of troubles, who doesn't? the butcher, for example, despite the fact that he chooses the best cuts of meat for me, without the least bit of bone, saves me the tongue, tongue with olives is my favourite dish, the tailor brings me the occasional old jacket and doesn't ask a penny for it, and many, in fact more and more individuals offer their services as impresarios or butlers, I've thought of that, but a butler in a two-room flat is a bit over-the-top, even the screenwriters are nice, they ask my opinion, it's true they don't take any notice of it, the assistant director murmurs in my ear that my interpretation is brilliant, it's just a pity I don't have a voice, I sing too high, former schoolmates pat me on the shoulder, hard, and give me the odd kind word, I wonder what the matter is with them, it's true that a month ago I won a billion on the lottery, but that doesn't mean anything, in the end all I'm doing is playing my role as well as I can. In the play or the film, because it's no longer all that clear what it is, anyway, even a theatre play would be welcome, and if that too becomes obscure, perhaps I'll set about writing a book.

My eyebrows have grown, my beard, my eyes, my eyes have taken on a bizarre shape and a distinctive colour, cobalt blue, old, like 2,000 years ago, as my neighbour on the landing keeps telling me with a smile, he's a policeman and he knows. Under the old régime he was a militiaman, he takes a long look at me, through his eyelashes, he has thin eyelashes, asking me, when I arrive home late, why I have blue eyes at present. Unfortunately I can't answer him, because he's not a cinema lover. Yesterday, on my way to the studio (it keeps transforming, now it's become very large, easily holds 5,000 for the scene with the loaves and fishes) I saved a cat from death. Its mistress had thrown it in the sewer, I got it out, I took it in my palms, stroked it and in the end it started to miaow, for joy I think. A few seconds later it bit me. I carefully placed it on the platform of the number 42 tram stop, with a feeling of profound satisfaction. A feeling that was cancelled out a short time later by the Virgin Mary, when she said to me, as she tidied her black robe, that I ought somehow to experience in reality the pain that the nails driven into my palms are supposed to produce, because the way I play it nobody's fooled. That set me thinking.

Last week we filmed some scenes somewhere on the coast, because that's the only place where you can find sand. Because of some sort of water worm, with wings, it was impossible to go into the water, they bit. The holiday-makers played an unplanned role in our project, because almost miraculously they had exactly the expression the director was looking for, all irritated, impatient, dead-beat, all wanting something or other, in most cases to be somewhere else, many sick, with flu and meningitis, in short extremely expressive, the cameraman recorded their blackened faces on film, he's going to use them for the crowd scenes. In the evening there followed the Last Supper, which didn't turn out well because of Judas. The next day, with great skill, at one go, I changed the two fish and five loaves into a seven-figure number – I had been practising a lot at home. Not only could the trick not be seen, there wasn't any trick, playing naturally is everything. As proof of that, after a talkative extra revealed to the crowd what scene we were preparing, a huge queue formed on the beach, there were over 5,000.

Mary Magdalene is very beautiful. I watched her going into the waves, immune to worms, and I'm watching her now too, in her dressing-room, She is dressed with questionable taste, for the evening, she is wearing some brass jewellery and she has put on aggressive make-up. She is putting the final touches to her hairdo in front of the mirror. She looks at herself attentively, from the front, in profile, in three-quarter view, pouts her lips, lifts her hair, lets it fall, her hair falls out, she's left bald, she picks up a lock from the carpet, thoughtfully winds it round her index finger, unwinds it, tries its resistance by pulling it hard, several times, breaks it, throws it away, hiccups, cries, then puts on Superb No. 22 lipstick. Every 10 seconds she cries out sharply: "Fortuna–ta!" The shots in the Garden of Gethsemane have been taken in the IOR Park. You can make out the boat *Mugurel*, transformed into a two-star restaurant. The most complicated scene is the one with the blind man today, with the historical consultant maintaining that in reality there were two blind men or if not in reality, at least according to Matthew. In the end, one is selected by competition, the other is left for another day, and I find myself face to face with the happy winner, blind as the night, while the microphone boom swings over our heads. It needs at least 20 takes, we aren't at all natural, neither me nor him, I can't find the right tone, and when I find it I forget my lines. The next day I heal the blind man at the first attempt, I do the same with the others, the deaf man, the mute, the lunatic, the woman with an issue of blood, the multitude are astounded, Lazarus comes merrily out of his vault, Mary Magdalene applies the myrrh parsimoniously, I try to ask her out, she refuses, she refuses the producer too and goes quietly to her dressing-room where we hear her again crying out rhythmically: "Fortuna–ta!" When I get back home I don't find the cat on the platform any more. I look at the sky. In my flat I stop looking at the sky, partly because through the window all you can see is the back court, and start reading a book about mysteries and unusual healings. It's got pictures.

It all started with the daughter of a neighbour on the fifth floor. She has a completely withered arm, the right one, motor impotence, it's remained that way as a result of a riding accident. And she's deaf as a snake. Her mother can hear well, she usually keeps her hands clasped on her chest, and she has breasts stuffed with silicone. I started to play with the little girl out of boredom, out of loneliness, it's of no importance, out of curiosity. The first days she couldn't understand anything of what I said to her, so I had the idea of expressing myself through dance. We would dance for hours on end, following Béjart plans spread out on the parquet, until the upstairs neighbour showed up. Then, with her dolls, with her teddy bear, we got closer to one another. The little girl had tapeworms. One day I explained to her – how I managed, how I got the idea, I don't know – *Muzikalisches Opfer*, suggesting that she sit down at the piano without fear, she had a Steinway, and just be careful not to press too hard on the right pedal, the mechanism was faulty, a lever had given way. She looked at me with her large, shiny, violet eyes, she had always looked feverish to me, then she went towards the stool, sat down, and played *Canones diversi super thema regium* without a slip, closing with *Fuga canonica in epidiapente*, which knocked me out. We parted, since then we blow each other kisses on the stair, her mother told me what miracles the surgeons had done and an ear, nose and throat specialist when she wasn't at home, her breasts seemed to have lifted even more, maybe she had put in some more silicone, for joy, I asked her for a laugh if she didn't want me to help her about the flat, to sweep the floor, for example, because I'm good at that, I've got a new broom, however she cottoned on pretty quickly and said no. Maybe also because I wear glasses.

Then there was the episode with the paralysed old lady, pinned down in her bed in front of the TV without the power to get away and for so long that she had forgotten by whom. She was terrorised. She had to put up with the whole schedule, she had no way of turning the set off, she couldn't switch to another channel, sometimes it switched of its own accord, and the power didn't come and go the way it used to do, so she heard and saw everything, culture in the world, Chinese chopped up and thrown in the sewers, which they blocked, the national air transport company stolen by a director with a gold watch, the president of the country moving around like a ballerina and writing 10 books, jerking his shoulders, smiling continuously and showing his uvula at every teleconference, in tragic close-up, the speaker of the chamber of deputies getting fatter from one broadcast to the next, solemnly denying that he was stealing houses or was sexually disordered, after all he had two children with his wife, who was a housewife, arranging his sentences in a little feminine mouth, like a cherry buried in his soft chin, declaring that he was a music lover, listened to Wagner in his free time standing barefoot on the ground, so as to feel the German soil of the homeland, was an admirer of the Nibelungs, so there was no way he could be homosexual, Brünnhilde was the proof, agitated people, haloes, a numbing pile of haloes televised by maniacs, paranoiacs, senile people, kleptomaniacs, drugged adolescents, competitions at sitting on poles, tango, freedom, prisons, Europe, detergents, the reconstruction of history, Tampax, I feel dry and clean, vibrators, national dignity, talking hamsters, they press a red button with their snouts and a plate of food comes out through a little door, the opinions about evolution of the educated man in the street, who has been watching *Santa Barbara* for a decade and is going to keep on watching it, car races where one turns over, wheels fly off, the driver jumps out, the fire-fighters arrive, a real UFO frightening the sergeant, Mr Marian, who has also done some courses for veterinary assistants, what the devil!, where are you Mr Marian, cried a security guard from the ditch where he was observing the natural phenomena when he saw the object floating by the front of the police headquarters, brain surgery, an American got a transplant of a baboon's head, lived for an hour, didn't say anything, secret agents filmed live, ghosts in Scotland, on a loch, whirling golden leaves over the grave of death, rubbish, Gypsies among the ruins, crowns of dark kings with chrome steel incisors, scientific documentaries with ovules penetrated the modern way, with a needle, sunken churches, feverish priests splashing holy water by surprise, at the corner of the street, the film about Jesus abridged, films where people's fingers get cut off, with crocodiles, cyborgs, elephant people or just immortals, with ninja swords, Koreans, bombardments, blood, low wages, money, no one's got any, Mercedes cars with alarm sirens, yellow pills for cancer, guaranteed in Congo, magnetic passes, AIDS, how to get accustomed to dying, summer course, death is something natural, it's much less natural to live, witches, fights in parliament, the international exhibition of coffins in Frankfurt, the unimaginable desires of married women, children, lots of them, human rights, tear-gas bombs, incendiary bombs, the end of the world and of literature with a key, how to vote, you stamp the paper and then blow on it to dry the ink, why young people are leaving for New Guinea, why they aren't leaving, secret Dacia at lunch-time, around two, Burebista resuscitated, with his cap, a health minister in a state of putrefaction, cholera, meetings, tuberculosis, Serbians, smuggling, the government selling the merchant fleet, helicopters crash, in the year 2000 there will be a cosmic catastrophe, the temperature will go down to 50 degrees below zero and the sun won't appear any more, it will be pitch-dark, we'll freeze, even though people talk with difficulty as it is, in maximum 200 words and those pronounced badly, the Arabs do deals with biscuits and wear ladies' stockings over their faces, ladies don't, surveys about sex, the PANDA Romanian-Chinese friendship association, the miner, the trouser stripe, Pascal and the thinking baton, robberies, rapes in the twilight, live, boils, investments, wondering individuals with perfect features, chronic patients, euthanasia, it should be done to them, it would be best if it was done to them immediately after birth, rap music, metal, trash, banks going bust, computerised games of chance, the midnight phone with men with yellow ties and pointed beards, who sort out dilemmas, misfortunes, my fiancée has left me, how can I go on living now, how old are you?, 19 and I want to commit suicide, ah, no, first you should express yourself, find a formula for reformulating the deep ego, the phone rings and the psychologists solve on the spot the most acute existential problems, of love and mothers-in-law, when the programme continues it is morning and someone is drafting wills with the new spelling, there are now eternal resting places closer to the centre, Archbishop Lucian of Tomis blesses nuclear reactor number three, sprinkling it with heavy water, from a censer, Chick Rasino is condemned to death on the electric chair, live – a humdrum serial killer, then he cut off their breasts, serial but fat – he wishes the people happy holidays, it was December and they pulled the handle, the cosmonaut who was Soviet when he set off round the earth and came back Russian, and found himself obliged to change his identity papers, because he didn't live in Leningrad any more, he lived in Saint Petersburg, history rushes on, respecting speed limits in the rural districts and villages of the homeland, Chernobyl, Hiroshima, India, the paranormal, bent forks, overturned glasses, sad billionaires, because they've got problems too, for example alcoholic wives, ugly orphans, TV programmes for senior citizens, with cemeteries, for parents, for children, for cretins, for millionaires at midnight, with peasants, evening events, murders, he killed his father-in-law with a schnitzel beater, his son with a cross-head screwdriver, and he threw his wife in the well, it was spring, Olympics, Knights Templars, the Holy Grail proving to be in reality the womb of Mary Magdalene, she had a child with Jesus, then she came to France and the Cathars carefully preserved the divine bloodline, the Inquisition burned them, and the last descendant didn't want to say *pentagon*, didn't want to say anything in general, he was French, handicapped people with haircuts, inexplicable healings, insolation, interviews, erotic scenes, the muscular black man pumping away with his eyes turned upwards, perspiring and, who knows why, laughing, with overlapping teeth, you can see his tongue, pink, the woman is panting, she is white, if they had made the film in the heyday of the Ku Klux Klan no one would have been laughing any more, in the middle ground are leaves, the inevitable vegetation that suggests combating racism by coupling, by greenery, the implacable star sign, the idiots' zodiac, mutants that have been appearing for a time among kitchen cockroaches, they are bigger, have almost indestructible chitin, there's no more writing-paper, the street-spraying machine passes softly through the district, parliamentary motions, heroin, it's quiet, no more checks on wealth, and a host of intellectuals at round tables are demonstrating their irresistible urge to beat about the bush, they've got a bush, that's their business, but why do they have to beat about it in front of us? asks the moderator, because that's what they do, *The Twilight Zone*, *Star Trek*, the boy and the dog that he eats in the end, how to protect ourselves from the apocalypse, shorts about fashion, dramas, South American serials proving how useless the efforts of all those dictators have been, reportage with apparently simple people who don't want privatisation because they are honest, illegalists, they want Venus, the mons pubis, want the Moon, want Molière, the first edition, to read it at work, in the knacker's yard, in the break between two actions, the first action consisting of collecting stray dogs in a hemp sack, strong, or a jute one, and the second being definable in terms of two dog catchers hitting the sack full of dogs with samurai crowbars, the fabric becomes coloured, dark patches appear, red-mauve-chestnut, blood, it seems, dogs' blood, the PANDA association is closed down, they've discovered life on Mars, a bacterium. Twenty-four hours out of 24, because the broadcasting schedule has been extended. And all the schedules keep being extended, until reality comes to a stop. It doesn't even trickle. It remains stunned, outside itself, like a sort of silence. Of subterfuge.

The old lady was gasping with her eyes coming out of their sockets, at the end of her endurance, She confessed to me that her nose bled at films with karate and she wet herself at the news. She had called me to help her because she had heard what had happened with the little girl, she didn't want me to teach her to play the piano, just to be able to walk. I sat down on a flimsy chair, I fell on the floor, I sat down again and looked at her. She was, indeed, very old, she looked like a quince. Wrinkles, deep and filled with a sort of juice, furrowed her face in all directions, she didn't resemble a quince so much as a windscreen at which a stone has just been thrown. I looked at the TV too for a few seconds, it seemed to be a tragedy, with a man waving his shroud, he said it was Christ's, then some individuals in national costume turned up, wearing dark glasses, who said it wasn't Christ's shroud at all, no way, it was theirs. Then I made a sign with my head, like this. The old lady got up straight away and asked for a glass of cherry liqueur from the cupboard. I brought it to her, the neighbours who had entered the studio flat with me didn't notice the movement, they were caught up by the images, changing the channels. After she had drunk all the cherry liqueur, the old dear made her way with small but rapid steps to the wardrobe, took the iron and flung it with all her strength at the screen, hitting a squirrel on Discovery Channel. Then she picked up her bed and walked out. I quickly made myself scarce too. Since that day I keep seeing her in the entrance hall, she says hello and climbs to the fifth floor. From where the *Musical Offering* can be heard uninterrupted, played with four hands.

The filming is progressing, I have bought myself a shroud, the oak cross is polished with so much carrying. The same with rehearsals for the theatre play. One June evening I invited a few actors to my place. I don't know what got into me. We had caviar and egg mayonnaise. Mary Magdalene was among them. I danced a blues with her, *Body and Soul*, everyone drank, without the slightest moderation, ate, fortunately not too much, the eggs were heavy on the stomach, around 11 someone slashed the table runner my mother gave me, he didn't like the design, I did, a colleague with an important role in the film inadvertently pulled the shower from the wall, the water gushed out for an hour, the guests had a lot of fun, it was warm, and around 12 a guest I didn't know threw herself from the balcony. Man is a marvellous being, she said as she climbed over the balustrade, gracefully holding her silk dress. She fluttered down to the ground. I live on the sixth floor, it was lucky she didn't fall on some passer-by, it would have been a disaster, as the woman weighed over 80 kilos or at least had done two minutes before she took flight, she had weighed herself on my Pobeda scales, with a magnet, I put on my white raincoat, I went downstairs and put my hand under her bleeding head. She recovered there and then and asked me if I was cross with her. It's a free country, I said, everyone does what they want. She got up, climbed back up the stairs, the lift wasn't working, and threw herself off the balcony again.

Even the second time, no witness saw what I did, down there, in the street.

And there's no way I can tell anyone, no one would believe me.

It's strange, but there isn't a single person in the whole town who knows the truth. Although once, in a metro station, Semănătoarea, I spotted a tiny poster, about 15 x 15, on which was written in red *Friday 9 September Jesus Christ Heals 4 P.M.* I peeled it off the wall and stuck it in my pocket. Then someone stole my winter coat from the cloakroom, complete with the poster. About two months ago our director became ill with cancer. He couldn't breath, he kept looking at the manometer that showed if the oxygen was working, usually it wasn't, he suffocated, he perspired, he now weighed only 40 kilos and fainted when he went to the toilet, so that he had given up going, one day I told him that Jesus healed on Friday at 4 p.m., and he had a fit of coughing. It was only normal, his wife had dragged him round lots of doctors, some had taken blood off him, two test-tubes, then 11, many had performed punctures on him, others X-rays, CT scans, one had tried to cut off his leg, everyone was really desperate, one elderly professor said he only had one more month to live, at the best, so in the end I came to the hospital one Sunday, asked the great man to keep quiet so that I could concentrate and put my left palm on his forehead. It was cold. After a few seconds he sat bolt upright, he gave me a fright too, he threw the bedpan out of the way and exploded in a fit of laughing. Your acting's as bad as ever, he said between bursts of laughter. But never mind, I see it works. He was laughing himself to tears. Then a nurse came and gave him an injection to make him stop laughing.

A few days ago, a puppy run over by a car, a four-wheel-drive Nissan, died in my arms. I scratched it gently behind the blood-filled ear. It breathed deeply, a few times, and looked at me with moist, warm, human eyes. It had come back to life.

Perhaps I overdid it with the make-up. One eye came out blue and the other orange. I went down into the street and I saw again, standing motionless at his observation point in front of the block across the road, the individual who has been following me for several days. By the way he is shaved on top of his head he can only be a secret agent. I hurried my pace and when I turned the corner towards the boulevard I met, as I do every morning, a beggar I think I have spoken about already, to whom I never give anything. I feel a strange, inexplicable antipathy towards him, possibly because of his white stick, which he holds arrogantly pointed upwards. Apart from that he also has a slight, but appreciable, air of condescension, which reminds me, by who knows what association of ideas, of the time when I was a child and I used to play with those kites that never flew, they generally just dragged along the ground and the handicraft teacher would come and step on them. I greeted him as usual and suddenly, without any motive or warning sign, he smiled at me. Now, to have a blind man smiling at you out of the blue, on Murgului Way, is, somehow, unpleasant. I held out a coin to him. He winked, gave me an amused look, he had a cobalt blue gaze, and asked me how I was doing. It was only then that I recognised him, he was the blind man I had healed in the film.

And so I decided to go to the police. My identity card had expired anyway. There they asked me all sorts of things, insisting on my childhood illnesses, then they got me to fill in a lot of A4 forms. I filled them in until my ballpoint ran out. I asked them to give me another. They didn't have one. So I went to buy one. At the bookshop, to my surprise, the sales assistant, a splendid blonde of about 20, asked me in a somewhat disconcerted tone: What, you of all people don't have a ball-point pen? Here's a black one. Maybe you'll give me your autograph.

Translator's notes

Michael the Brave was a ruler of Wallachia at the end of the sixteenth century who briefly brought together the principalities of Wallachia, Moldavia and Transylvania – territories largely populated by Romanians – in 1600, in a unification that has been seen since the nineteenth century as prefiguring the creation of modern Romania. The image of his bearded face is familiar to Romanians from statues, coins, etc., not to mention his portrayal by Amza Pellea in the 1970 film (mentioned in 'Where are You, Eleonora?').

The River *Dâmbovița* flows through the centre of Bucharest, nowadays reduced to a concrete-lined canal, with its flow regulated by an accumulation lake. *Unification Square* (*Piața Unirii*) is a large square in the centre of Bucharest. The *International Bank of Religions* was one of the numerous banks that emerged in Romania after the revolution of 1989. It went bankrupt in 2000.

The Dacians (*Dacii*) is a historical drama of 1967 directed by Sergiu Nicolaescu, about the wars between the Dacian king Decebalus and the Romans at the end of the first century AD.

Carpați cigarettes are a Romanian brand, named after the Carpathian mountains.

The *IOR Park* (now called the Titan Park) is one of the largest parks in Bucharest, situated on the east side of the city. Its name, pronounced *ee-oh-ray*, was the acronym of Intreprinderea Optică Română (Romanian Optical Enterprise).

Burebista was the first-century BC ruler of an extensive territory centred in what is now Romania. He was celebrated under the national communist regime of Nicolae Ceaușescu as a precursor of the unity and centralisation of the modern Romanian state. In visual representations he is shown wearing the tall cap worn by the Dacians on Trajan's Column.

Dacia, the ancient territory of the Dacians, later a Roman province including large parts of modern Romania, represents the ancient roots of the modern country.

'Illegalists' was the term used in the communist period of those who had been (or were claimed to have been) members of the Romanian Communist Party before the Second World War, when it was a small illegal organisation.

A *militiaman* was a member of the communist-period police force, which, following the Soviet model, was known as the Militia (*Miliția*); the older term *poliție* was restored when the Militia was replaced by the Romanian Police (*Poliția Română*) in 1990.

One Friday Afternoon

Father is dead. He was a quiet man, a bit mystical, with two deep furrows on either side of his nose, sometimes melancholic, and on Sundays, at lunch, he was in the habit of playing jokes. He would throw his soup-spoon up in the direction of the chandelier and then try to catch it. He didn't catch it. Sometimes he broke the chandelier, at other times the soup bowl. The soup would spread thick and yellow not just over the tablecloth, but also on his pressed trousers, and finally even on the Persian carpet, where it became extremely visible and stable. I laughed until tears ran down my face, Mother didn't. I am still laughing, as I look at the Order of Labour 3rd Class that Father was awarded around '68. It's a nice box, dark red in colour, with a pleasant feel to it, and inside there is a silver badge, a red ribbon and Father. The badge shows the national coat of arms, with rays.

The truth is that he never persecuted anybody, not even a neighbour. On the contrary, he helped them all, as far as he could. For example, a chap wanted to leave for Venezuela one spring and Father obtained for him, at enormous cost, an astrolabe. Unfortunately, the man didn't know where to put it and he didn't even make it to the airport, he headed off through the woods, at a hurried pace, so they shot him from a watch-tower, right between the eyes. They brought him to us in the evening to be identified. Apart from his face, which looked like something by Kandinsky (Wassily), he was the same piano teacher we had all known in the block, but yellower than usual, and dressed in a very expressive black suit, buttoned up to the neck. I remember the cleaning lady muttered something, along the lines of how he stank, although no one had invited her to the identification. Or to the wake for that matter, because he stayed for two days in the hall, for everyone to see him.

Father was a jovial man, he wore braces. The only one, in the whole block, who knew how to enjoy himself. He had drilled holes in the entrance door and installed three peep-holes with green lenses, which he looked through on Sundays in particular, keeping a note of who went up and down the stairs in a black notebook. When he didn't know the name of the person who passed, he scratched a little x on the panelling, about the level of the chain.

Searching one day through the papers of a suspiciously elderly neighbour

(I was always urged to do this, lock pick in hand), I came across a more unusual record, entitled *Epistle*, written in a deliberately infantile hand and signed Gabriel, from which I quote a short fragment: "A well-known illusionist (received with a standing ovation in Madrid and Stockholm according to the poster) appeared one afternoon in the ring of our village circus. We all crowded to see the show, expecting wonderful things. And it came as no small surprise to us when we discovered, quickly enough, that not only did the man find it impossible to juggle with little balls of white plastic, or red as the case might be, continually dropping them on the ground and running this way and that after them, sometimes slipping on the sand, and not only did he give off a sort of bluish smoke, which smelled of diabetic's urine, he was utterly incapable of shouting anything witty, some riddle for example, something that everyone could understand or at least the children, who got bored and took a hacksaw blade to the central pillar of the tent, which fell with a crash on top of a few old dears, causing them to cry out, understandably enough, that the end of the world had come, and he couldn't even manage a simple somersault, not because of his impressive wings, magician's ones made of plywood – in reality he looked more like an aeroplane than anything else – but because of the surprising dimensions of his head, which was covered with locks of astral hair, as a peasant remarked, exaggerating like all peasants, in fact just some mean wisps, dyed, twisted round curlers at night and soused with brilliantine during the day, wisps which, I admit, might have passed for the model of distant constellations, at that age or only if you lived in such a village, with no electric light or historic monuments to remember, you could easily be deceived in matters of hairiness, and after all, most sensations depended on the place where you found yourself, if you were sitting in the front rows, you would soon realise that that enormous head really upset the balance of the acrobatic illusionist, however it was not earth-coloured, as we would have expected, it was not pear-shaped, bore no signs of mutilation, didn't bleed and didn't even stare, that way, with grinning teeth, to make us laugh. It was the head of an angel. After two hours we managed to take him to the village bar, where we got him blind drunk."

Sometimes, when darkness fell, we played at spies. More precisely, I was the spy and Father would go after me on all fours, as far as the bathroom. There he caught me, with admirable regularity, and squeezed my fingers in a vice of his own craftsmanship, which had big wooden screws, meticulously carved. It hurt, but I had to scream with pleasure.

A little later, when I was 16, I discovered my father in his workshop – where he had all sorts of microphones, firecrackers, objects difficult to identify but electrocuting, cameras, funnels and headphones with which he listened to the central-heating pipes – delicately drawing a neighbour in the nude. The neighbour, although she was very beautiful, was groaning. Perhaps partly due to the fact that she had been tied to the lamp stand, with wire. I only ever saw her a couple of times after that, she seemed changed, but even now I still keep the drawing, above my bed, in fact it's a gouache that renders very well both her breasts and the lamp stand.

And yet, I repeat, Father was a good man. I stand firmly by this statement, in full knowledge of the facts and in spite of the fact that recently it has been alleged increasingly vehemently that he sent hundreds of people to the seaside. Where it has been found that they were tortured horribly. It's not true. All they had to do was to build, to the best of their ability, one small sandcastle every day, no one ever asked them to make it too big. The only tricky aspect was the beachcombing, for they felt obliged, if not out of decency then for reasons of an aesthetic nature – in order somehow to pay for their free board and lodging – to gather iridescent sea shells, the sort known as *mermaids' nails*, which they then stuck on top of the sandcastles. Some of them, more easygoing, more elderly, more enigmatic, preferred to pull out their own nails, usually from their fingers, with pliers, but in certain cases also from their toes, and to place them on the tallest tower of sand, which was thus coloured with a little blood too, attempting by this method to deceive Father, when he came to inspect their work. Of course they couldn't deceive him. And they were, naturally enough, punished. Unfortunately, they can no longer bear witness, because they died when the tide came in.

The piano was Mother's. I think I was about five when I was surprised at the violence with which Father decreed, with his head under the chandelier, that I ought to learn to play. Mother objected that I was too young, and that anyway she couldn't see what use it would be to me. Especially as I hadn't even started to speak yet. That's of no importance, said Father, it's time he did something intelligent. In our house, which was situated in the centre of town, no one had ever played. Not even Mother. As for the neighbours, there is nothing I can say, not one of them even dared to jump over the barbed wire fence. It was only three years later, when we moved into a flat, that things began to look different. And so a teacher appeared. He was thin, he wore round-rimmed glasses, and he was terribly frightened of Father. For all that, in the two hours that the weekly piano lesson lasted, we played, the teacher and I, with the miniature puppet theatre or made figures in modelling clay. I was tone-deaf. But when Father came, it wasn't me that had to show him what I had studied that day, but the teacher. He sat on a stool with his back bent, his hands visibly trembling and stained with red-yellow-green modelling clay, and timidly interpreted a Chopin sonata, always the same one, in B-flat minor opus 35, then, to the delight of the family sunk deep in their armchairs, the donkeys' waltz, which ended up putting everyone to sleep, even the maid who had just put sugar in the *ciulama* a second time. Instead of salt. The teacher put up with the sugared *ciulama* and Father's observations of a musical character for almost six months, until, one morning, he came into the house wearing a woollen hood over his head, hit the piano keyboard with hatred, at the bass end, shut himself in the storeroom, confessed that he was an enemy of the people and I was mentally retarded and he couldn't take any more – he said the bit about not being able to take any more in a high-pitched tone – asking in closing if I wouldn't like us to make together in modelling clay, he had brought a box, the head of Garibaldi on his deathbed. We made it, and quite good it was too, with blue moustaches, only the next day the teacher didn't reappear. I, for one, never saw him again except that one time, in the evening, when they brought him to us dressed in black. Father threw away the head of Garibaldi, and I broke the bronze plaque on the piano, and then pulled off a pedal. Later on I found the pedal fitted the tricycle with which I entered a county tricycle competition. I didn't win, in fact I came last, to the despair of my parents. My dream was to become an artist. My whole being was directed towards such a goal. About 10 or 20 years later, I managed to achieve something in that line, when I was selected, after a telegenicity test, to play in a religious film whose title I have forgotten, apparently I had the leading role, or to be more exact, I was stand-in for the main protagonist and together we made the blind see, the lame walk, and the lepers laugh. But I never really liked the film world. Even though I still exchange greetings in the street with the blind man that I healed. And in my childhood, despite my obvious aspirations, I had to learn all sorts of nonsense, to skate, to run the 100 metres, to play leap-frog, to shin up ropes, and I couldn't do it, the games teacher, an old bore with just a year to go until his pension, told Father on me, and so both ropes and teacher disappeared. History was more than I could manage, all I liked about chemistry was the acids I used to splash on the girls' skirts, they didn't find it funny, women have no sense of humour, in Romanian I was useless. But I did have a talent when it came to drawing. I was constantly drawing, feverishly and with my tongue sticking out of my mouth, tiny people, like an infant Bosch. I used to play a lot in the cemetery. I pulled the wings of flies, shoved moths into the oven, cut worms in two, stuck round-headed pins in the eyes of mice. I was a mature child. On the days, usually at weekends, when I could hear unbearable screams coming from the attic, where Father did his work, I would do a watercolour and run quickly to Mother, who would be sitting with stereo headphones over her ears and a black mask on her face. I couldn't show her the watercolour because I couldn't take her mask off. I had a difficult childhood, I couldn't find comfort anywhere. And Father was working. Working all the time. I couldn't disturb him on those occasions, he would have been annoyed. He had got it into his head to purify the district. To clean it up. The skylight, on the other hand, was always covered with dust.

In any case, I must admit that he almost never encouraged me to paint. He used to say it was a job for women. A man should be out digging. Firing guns. On top of that, he claimed that I wasn't capable of drawing people in movement, or even easily recognisable. Take a better look through the peep-hole. Learn to make sketches, he advised me. I did all I could in the way of sketches, but I never saw him satisfied. He didn't approve of my interests and I couldn't understand why, after all he had got me a piano teacher, and that was in a similar line, if not exactly the same as what I liked. Only one time, up at Babele, did I manage to arouse his interest. To his delight, I fired two suction-tipped darts at the sun with a toy pistol. I never found the projectiles again. I cried for a whole day, I didn't even touch my drawing pad. Then Father promised me I would have a real pistol, when I got bigger. When I got bigger, he enrolled me in a parallelepiped-shaped school for the children of officers like him. There were lots of us in the building, a grey building. The teachers acted strangely, rigidly, wore uniforms. Some had the habit of flinging the register from the classroom door right onto the teacher's desk. They told me I had too many dreams, too colourful, too unnatural. On an orienteering exercise I went off in the wrong direction, stumbled, and found a red mushroom. The same mushroom was discovered by the instructor, who explained to me that it was a lower plant, one without chlorophyll, which lives as a parasite or saprophyte, and multiplies by means of spores. Then he reeled off the names of several poisonous mushrooms: common stinkhorn (*Phallus impudicus*), fly agaric (*Amanita muscaria*), *Boletus satanas*, *Russula emetica*, suphur tuft (*Hypholoma fasciculare*). This, he went on, snatching the plant from my hand, is a *Lactarius deliciosus*. It's also known as saffron milk cap. And to demonstrate to me how delicious saffron milk cap was, he ate it. One minute later he went into a coma.

Then there was shooting. A sergeant who knew Father saluted me, a corporal kissed me on both cheeks, when I wasn't looking. The problem was how to load an automatic rifle and then shoot with the thing too. At first I asked why I had to shoot, but as no one gave me an answer, I took aim at the nearest tree. It was an oak. I hit it twice in the crown, to the applause of my classmates. A handful of birds took to their wings chirping. I was ordered to fire again. At a hare. Although I couldn't see it, I shot it to bits. Some Gypsies, whose houses were close to the eastern wall of the barracks, were playing music, it was a wedding. I don't know what got into me and I fired at them. I hit the vocalist in the foot. There were screams. To put a stop to them, I fired three more times. The violinist died on the spot. They buried him in a great hurry beside the hare. Not right next to it, though. And that was the end of the whole business, no charges were pressed, Father had connections, I had hallucinations, that's what everyone claimed, apparently I had them even in my sleep, and the fiddler had been a man of modest means with no family. Since then I haven't had any more dreams. Four years later I finished the class. Then I ended up in hospital.

I still remember with pleasure the long shady footpaths along which I walked in the cool spring mornings, in my flannel dressing-gown, trying to guess from which window Father was watching me. I knew he observed my every movement, he had been admitted at the same time as me. I felt good in the hospital, perhaps for the first time in my life, even though I had been told I was on a mission. I had been placed in a wing for neuroses of varying degrees of severity, some swallowed forks, others ran after birds, in any case, the majority were a pretty quiet bunch of little autistics and manic-depressives. The rest consisted of colleagues of mine, likewise on a mission. We knocked together a sort of team in our six-bed ward, we helped each other to clean our teeth, we ate together the packages our relatives brought, the relatives were crying, we shared everything, medicines, soap, cockroach spray. The hospital cockroaches were innumerable, agile, red and black, it seems they liked it in the hospital, because we saw them everywhere, on bedside tables, in beds, even though to stop us seeing them they gave us lots of oily injections, after which we couldn't even walk for a while. The nurses were without exception blonde, I think they were former handball players, sort of feminine – but not very – descendants of William Tell, the unanimous opinion, expressed in a whisper as we played backgammon in the hall, being that between a crossbow and a syringe there is, practically speaking, no difference, not even regarding the distance from which they are fired. The time passed. Sometimes I threw a double six.

I noticed bizarre individuals among the usual characters who did nothing but wander round the yard in pyjamas and slippers. Right from the beginning I got talking to a painter, an interesting guy who had tried to kill himself by injecting industrial solvent into a vein, he hadn't succeeded and now he was without one hand, Bordea I think he was called, and he spent all his time sitting with his ear pressed to an old radio. One time I asked him to give it to me so I could listen too and he said there was nothing to hear, because he never switched it on. And he couldn't switch it on either, because almost all the parts were missing. Another one, a dentist, commanded me on two occasions to open my mouth, and then asked me if I had ever seen ghosts. He had seen them, near the Cişmigiu Park, coming from Brezoianu Street. The strange thing was that they were wearing hats. On top of that, he seemed to be homosexual, both times, at the end of the tale about the ghosts, he invited me in a melancholy manner to pay him a visit after we were discharged – he had been in hospital for 10 years – he had a little jewel of a studio flat somewhere near the Aviators' Statue, he had forgotten exactly where, I replied gently that I couldn't. Although he seemed convincing, one time I was in the dining hall, and I was just watching a Mozart violin concerto, with Oistrakh, who had been dead for four years, apropos of ghosts. And kind of in connection with this, I remember that my parents came to visit us very conscientiously every Sunday. They brought us juice, tubes of paint, socks. Now I was painting compasses, in the manner of Braque. Father didn't like Braque, on the other hand I noticed one winter that he did like a woman who worked in the bread factory. She was in a different building, in a women's ward. And it was cold, snowing like out of a flute, the bread factory woman walked barefoot through the snow. About the same time I got to know a new fellow patient, a grumpy guy of around

60. His problem was that he couldn't sleep, and he would walk for hours up and down the corridor, from one end to the other, smoking all the time, advancing with measured steps, perfectly equal, for which reason he came to be known as *the train set*. One December afternoon he made an unscheduled halt in the stairwell and, with an impeccable last-minute pirouette, fell down the stairs head first, as far as the floor below. So he at least was one that I didn't have to keep an eye on any more. Still, I made quite a good portrait of him, with one eye bruised and the base of his skull smashed, as they took him to the morgue on a heavy stretcher.

When I was discharged I received detailed instructions from a gentleman well wrapped up in a checked blanket, about the proper way to follow and denounce citizens who showed deviant behaviour in society. I admired his blanket and followed his guidance as best I could. However, I was always exposed and, curiously, they all offered me a vanilla ice-cream. Back at home, Father would study the cornet that I had taken care to bring to him intact, under the microscope. Then he would demonstrate to me what parallax is, he would point out to me a paramecium wriggling about under the lens, or he would try to explain to me the workings of a video camera, a plug socket, or the satellite that passed every evening over our house. I think the mere fact of adjusting the eyepiece awoke nostalgia in him, because he would then start telling me over again, in parallel with brief clarifications regarding the life of infusoria in fresh water, the history of his family, his mother had been a beautiful woman, who suffered from tuberculosis and at that time there wasn't any hydrazide, so she took paracetamol, she cut her hair short, and took care, in spite of the fact that she was continually spitting blood, of her violent husband and two children, his sister had become an engineer on a construction site, where, in a cabin, she had met her future husband, a dynamite expert who was to end up a consul, and his father, the patron of this small world, in other words my grandfather, had already reached the rank of general when he bought the first motor car with a bulb horn in town, with which he ran over the grocer. It seems he was a well-built man, distant, who knew two foreign languages and spoke them fluently in front of the bathroom mirror, and who later kept an intimate diary full of rich detail, in which he made a note of the names and vices of all his neighbours and, up until an hour before he died, the way he divided up his pension: one leu on gas for the lamp, three lei on bread, 10 bani on matches, 900 on țuică. Father used to say to me, smiling ambiguously, that my grandfather would represent a splendid model of the way we live, if he were still alive. Negligent. Infantile. Or rather thoughtless, wasting his time on trifles. As a living example he took myself. He knew I wanted to be a painter, even though he had hoped I would become an illusionist. Especially after the school episode. In life you don't get to do what you like, he would say, and he would say it often, perhaps he liked the way it sounded, and then you need to try and do something in the service of others, who are helpless, of society, which is eternal, and do it while you still can, for we have before our eyes all the time an image of limit, you know it, although some might say you don't get that much help from your brain, because I saw for myself the waves on your ECG, it was as if they were from a notebook of lined paper, the cemetery, that's the measuring rod, the ultimate representation, on some crosses it says Ionescu, on others it doesn't, we will never forget you, here lies Father, or our beloved Daughter, for a long time, the grave's in a hell of a state, it's subsided because of the rain, shocking how much it rains around here, when I was little I used to steal mulberries from the trees that grew out of the bellies, buttocks and cheeks of those reconciled beneath the ground, if they can be reconciled, vitamins and worms together, in the mulberry, worms being rich in proteins and mulberries in vitamins, and as I munched them I looked at the inscriptions done by real artists, at the figures, dates of birth and death, often engraved wrong, but it didn't matter any more, in marble or wood. And sometimes a photograph. He in the army, she at high school or in the old folks' home, in an old snapshot, shining in sepia, behind a little cracked window. The majority doing nothing during their squalid lives apart from struggling to get out of squalor, failing to understand, the poor imbeciles, that poverty helped them to be closer to the sun at which you fired the suction-tipped darts, to ponder, to perspire and to pass away without regrets into the ether. People are dangerous, that's the truth, there never was and never is anything to be done with them. You even need a few minutes to make out their names on the monuments.

Father had a hammer. Twenty years ago, it was Wednesday, after I saw that tool covered with clotted blood and strands of hair, it started to rain. I do not understand why it had taken so long, but it was only then that it occurred to me that Father was murdering people with his hammer, in the garden. A lot of suspicious mounds had appeared among the vegetables.

And he did what he did, I am absolutely convinced, with the consent, if not actually at the urging of my aunts, who had remained unmarried, having disturbing feet, with triple soles, I could spot them through the keyhole of their bedroom with its starched curtains, somewhat peculiar ladies when it came down to it, who pretended they were going to church when they were actually just going to the toilet at the bottom of the garden, where I had placed a huge spider. But a stupid one, because in two years it never even stopped them doing their business, not to mention frightening them. It was so gentle, the poor thing. It couldn't even eat a fly, let alone two aunts. I think they were the cause of all the evil, because, among other things, they undressed in front of the mirror and then said the *Our Father* in the nude. And if they irritated me they could drive Father out of his mind, especially as he was starting to be in bad health and, no matter how calm you might be, just listening to them would still be enough to make you capable of murder in the end. Seeing how they combed their thin hair in the sink and forgot to wash it or, if they did wash it, blocked the drainpipe, how they hummed unsettling folk melodies with the window open, how they talked to themselves, wandering all through the house, how they reproached Mother for not putting nourishing ingredients in the soup, as they did, unpeeled potatoes, because the skin contains tocopherols, how they looked at the factory workers, panting like in *To the Left, Three Hammer Strokes*, a famous song of the time, how they took possession of the bathroom in the morning and how they did pull-ups on the carpet-beating frame. Well, that day it rained, I looked at the birds. There were a few blackbirds, a crow and two tits. They had eaten a lot, someone had left a whole loaf of bread soaked in water for them on the doorstep, or perhaps they had soaked it in something else, perhaps a little spirit, and they had finished it off in two hours. At a certain moment the crow fell as if struck by lightning. One of the tits hit its head against the window repeatedly, and the other birds were sick until about nine o'clock in the evening. They kept hiccupping, some of them fell off the phone wire. Fortunately the yard wasn't tarmacked.

That was when I started to understand.

I still didn't know very well what. But I kept thinking with unfading emotion about the crow. About our life that passes.

Some time later, the priest, caught up with reading, got in a muddle and, instead of throwing earth onto the coffin, threw it on me instead. And I had a cold that day too. I wiped the earth from my nose with a corner of the ribbon on which was written eternal regrets. As the ink was still wet, the regrets came away and all that was left was eternal. From the block of flats beside the cemetery came the sound of Mussorgsky's *Pictures at an Exhibition*.

Don't let me tell you how many problems I had with the coffin. I went into lots of shops or whatever they call themselves, and everywhere it was explained to me in a sticky, auburn and anguished tone, rather religious too, that flowed softly from individuals who were polite, auburn-haired and had extremely small eyes, very close together, that there are considerable differences in price among the objects in question, because some are lighter, made of poplar, while others are made of oak or beech, indeed there are also some with an aerodynamic form, made of aluminium, for special occasions, and in any case a coffin with carved ornament is more expensive than one without. I looked at a few examples on display, which, fortunately, were empty. And I also found out, on the same occasion, that the carved ornament represents without exception a range of specifically Japanese flowers, it was true, I observed that they were carved with a patience in keeping with Japanese fanaticism, in such a manner that I presume that even newborn worms despise them, that is if they do not find them amusing, at least for a while.

Then there was the problem of the handles. One brass handle costs you an arm and a leg, putting you in the situation of suddenly hating it, bitterly, wanting to pull it off, to trample on it, to melt it down, not to mention four of them. So in the end I opted for a simple little unplaned coffin, without padding and without handles. I felt that after all we could carry it on our shoulders.

But since only three people attended the funeral, and two of them were women, I had to drag it.

Father looked askance.

If I remember well, that look was also among the things that irritated me so much that Friday afternoon when, after he had looked dispassionately at my latest painting, it was of a train set, and he told me I didn't have the slightest talent, Father tried to make me understand what talent is. Work. Vocation. Devotion. Do you know what vocation means? he asked. Look! And he showed me his medallion, the silver badge with the national coat of arms, awarded 'for exceptional services in the defence of social and state order'. Then he played me a tape recording. It was an Agfa tape. I heard a woman's voice asking for water. I asked him to let the tape run. After a few moments of silence I could make out the same voice, but now it sounded more poetic. Probably no one had given her water. What the people there did to the woman was not recorded. I looked sideways at my father. For the defence of state order, he repeated as he straightened the curtain, which for some reason was flapping. Then he confessed to me that he had been working in that trade for 18 years, a trade that was almost musical, if indeed it is not pure music, for only in such a profession can you listen every week to someone asking for water with burning eyes or crying out in B-flat, as in the Chopin sonata that he used to like so much when he was peacefully eating *ciulama* with sugar, and he concluded his tirade with his eye pressed to the peep-hole, saying that he was proud. I asked what of. He couldn't answer, especially as a lady in a hat was passing. After pausing to let the lady pass, I asked him to give me a B-flat. He couldn't manage that either. So I hit him with the hammer, just once. He had a very soft head.

Translator's notes

Ciulama is a traditional Romanian dish, consisting of meat or mushrooms in white sauce.

Babele is an area on the plateau of the Bucegi mountains, above the popular resorts of the Prahova valley. It takes its name, meaning 'the old women', from a group of strangely shaped rocks.

Cişmigiu Park is one of Bucharest's oldest parks, originally laid out in 1847, and taking the form of gardens around a central lake.

Ţuică: is a traditional Romanian spirit, distilled from plums or other fruit, similar to slivovitz or schnapps.

Wedding Photographs

Exactly two weeks before I was due to get married, my upstairs neighbour left his kitchen tap on. As a result of the flood, an abstract design of large dimensions and predominantly green in colour appeared on my ceiling. The plaster swelled. I had to repaint the room. Just when I was right in the middle of preparations for the wedding. The unfortunate neighbour offered to help me, but as he was permanently drunk, and I was too tired to be more attentive, he painted the wrong room. The bedroom. Walnut wardrobe included. With just three days to go until the happiest event in my life, the flat looked a sight. I went to sleep with a paper hat on my head and a paintbrush in one hand. I had forgotten to put out the cigarette in my other hand. As was only to be expected, it fell. The carpet caught fire. I got off with mild disfigurement, but they had to take my neighbour to hospital, where the doctors shook their heads. They didn't think he would make it to my wedding. The day before I was to get married my mother and father came and you should have seen their faces when they saw the state of the house. Mother had a fit. Then they helped me, to the best of their abilities, to move some shelves, managing to break the bedroom window in the process.

When the big day came, I woke up half an hour later than I should have, with my hair all over the place, deep shadows under my eyes, and a curious desire to do mischief. I looked at the alarm clock. It had stopped. I calmed down, wound it up until its spring snapped, and went into the living room. Mother had carefully arranged my suit on a chair. Father, nervously looking at his watch all the time and urging me to hurry, sat down with all his weight. Father is very fat. The chair fell apart, and so did the suit. Mother tried to sew what could be sewn, but the stain I made on the left lapel when I dropped my coffee-cup was impossible to remove.

The two friends I had sent to buy flowers couldn't find any. The florists' shops were closed, and the Gypsy flower sellers had mysteriously disappeared. In the end, they picked some from a little park – I don't know what they were called, but they were yellow – and one of them managed to steal two carnations from a cemetery. The watchman gave rapid chase. When they arrived covered in blood, Mother was on the verge of another fit, Father was weeping at having destroyed my suit, and I was trying to convince the caretaker of the block of flats that the cries he could hear were shouts of joy. I convinced him, and he shouted too, but not for joy. When he had gone, slamming the door so hard that the peep-hole jumped out, I frantically shoved under the bed a good part of the papers I had covered the furniture with during the painting. With them went the wedding present, which broke. I left the wardrobe as it was. It was starting to dry.

We were already two hours late. I went down to the street and I couldn't find a taxi. One of my friends threw a little stone at an empty taxi that wouldn't stop, at which the driver pulled up, got out, and gave Father a beating. In the end I managed to hitch a lift. It was a nice car, shaped like a hearse, a '70s Mercedes with no windscreen, and it had a puncture at the crossing of Baba Novac and Brezhnev Streets. Fortunately it also had a spare tyre, smaller than the others to tell the truth, but it did the job. My friends got into a van that took them in a different direction. On the way we met a funeral party, who managed to get ahead of us, so we had to follow them all the way home, which was the way they were going. For some reason the band was playing *Let Me Show You Bucharest by Night*. We saw Bucharest all right, including the cemetery my carnations had come from. At the cemetery they asked us to put on black armbands.

When we finally reached the Sector 3 town hall, on Perfume Street, the doors in the back, where my parents were sitting, wouldn't open. I was sitting in front, with the bride's foul-smelling bouquet in my hand, and I didn't particularly want to get out again. I had to, though, because the driver's door wouldn't open either. After the extraction of the driver, who ended up on the tarmac with a cut to his head, the two of us set about opening the rear doors. Other people who were eagerly waiting to get married came to our aid. The only result of our combined efforts was that a door handle got pulled off. Mother and Father had no option but to climb out over the front seats. Father demolished the death seat on the way. Without murmuring, I gave the driver almost a quarter of what he had paid for the car in the first place, and we finally entered the courtyard. My future mother-in-law grabbed the bride's bouquet and made as if to slap me across the face with it. I ducked just in time and my flies came undone. I couldn't do them up again, though I tried for about three minutes, in the town hall toilets, assisted by my cousin, who was a sportsman and very strong. His strength didn't do him much good, however, because in our hurry we had gone into the Ladies, from whence we were ejected with screams, undeserved labelling as 'pigs' and 'homosexuals', and a rain of blows from heavy handbags with metal clasps. An incisor flew over our heads and landed with a light thud in a vacant cubicle. It was my incisor. My cousin tried to recuperate it, and ended up on the receiving end of another blow, this time well aimed, which smashed his shock proof watch to smithereens. Then someone scratched both our faces. We emerged in an unsettled state. Mariana was waiting for me calmly in the courtyard. She was calm because she hadn't recognised me. We had missed the time that we had been scheduled for, so we were the last to go in. I was uncomfortable because of the business with my flies, not to mention the fact that my future wife wasn't wearing a bra, while her dress was completely see-through. The guys waiting in the courtyard had stared until they broke out in a sweat, and looked as if they now wanted to unite their destinies with Mariana for ever, or at least for a short while. I whispered to her to put a handkerchief over her cleavage, and then found a transparent excuse and hid in among the bushes to escape my embarrassment. Especially as my future mother-in-law was looking for me, probably intending to finish me off.

It was five to three by the time our turn came round. We entered the registry office trembling with fear. People were talking with lowered voices. The registrar had already had one too many, and was smiling from ear to ear at no one in particular. When the clock on the wall struck, the man fumbled for a while with his tricolour sash and finally put it on upside-down. Those who had come to attend the ceremony waited with bated breath. He started to recite the text in a squeaky voice, until he stopped at the words "in our country the family is…" He had forgotten what the family was. He asked the secretary, but she couldn't remember either. To stimulate her memory, the woman nibbled a pastry left over from an earlier wedding. She still couldn't remember. However, she choked on the pastry. She was carried from the room red in the face and with her legs flailing in the air. All this time I was standing still, hiding my flies with one hand. Our godfather was taking colour pictures for us. When he wanted to change the film he discovered that he hadn't had any film in the camera. Father turned on the cassette player, but no music came, and for all that he thumped it, shook it, and plugged and unplugged it repeatedly, nothing could be heard. He had forgotten to press *play*. It was only after he got home that he remembered, surreptitiously wiping away a tear, and wiping the whole cassette too, as he pressed the *record* button at the same time. I had thought ahead, however, and had brought a second cassette player. It had seen better days, and the speed of the motor was unpredictable, but anyway it worked. I signalled to an uncle of Mariana's, who immediately put the object in question, a first-generation Philips, into operation. A lively *Wedding March* resounded through the room, at a speed considerably faster than usual. Everybody's gestures adapted to the tempo, and became feverish. We took two steps forward and nervously signed the marriage register. Mariana signed in her maiden name by mistake. When my turn came, I dropped the pen and my father-in-law stepped on it. It was a Pelikan. Then there was the distribution of sweets and glasses of champagne. The registrar knocked back two and started to laugh loudly. I did a quick count in my head: two multiplied by 14 weddings, 28 glasses. He was pissed. He collapsed over his desk, trying at the last moment to grab hold of the godmother's dress. The godmother took offence, and, in spite of her years, she ripped his tricolour sash in a single movement. Meanwhile dissension had broken out over the sweets. "I mean, why does he only give me one, and it's one without chocolate, when that girl in green gets three?" a soprano voice was heard to say. "Just be thankful, because I haven't even got one," replied a contralto. It was like a signal. Immediately they started pushing and shoving and throwing sweets at each other. One got me right in the eye. I can't tell you how good it tasted, but it was hard. When everyone had settled down again for lack of ammunition and my father-in-law had promised me a new pen, a plastic one, we went out into the courtyard at the back of the town hall. Here we had the official photographs. The town hall photographer took them for us, with a big black Hasselblad. The only thing that was disconcerting about it was that it didn't give off smoke. It made a big bang, though. The old people of both families had a good laugh. We smiled, we stood up straight, we froze. It was terribly cold. The photographer asked for an exorbitant sum, about as much as I earned in five months, telling us that he would give us the photos ready framed. He showed us the frames. However, for all that he was clearly a professional, one of the group photos came out blurred, because the very moment he shouted "Watch the birdie!" someone started beating their carpets on the neighbouring waste ground, and everyone's eyes turned that way. A child holding two paper windmills above his head skipped across in front of us and fell into a pothole. We got him out with difficulty, because he had got caught on some wire, and we got covered in whitewash, and shit too, I think, fortunately frozen. As soon as the child was out of the pothole, he started to scream, while his windmills rotated in a dizzying manner. His mother appeared, a distinguished woman, who wished us "house of stone" with unrepeatable oaths. We hurriedly took our leave, with more kisses, some pinching each other viciously, remembering the sweets and other things, and we went out into the street to look for a taxi. This time we were lucky. We put the flowers and presents in the boot and by the time we had waved to everyone the taxi had gone off without us. So we took the trolleybus. After just one stop its trolleys came off the wire. The driver got them on again, cursing vigorously, in about three-quarters of an hour. Unfortunately we only went another two stops, because a dynamic-looking housewife took one look at Mariana's dress, let out a severe sound, and charged us in the name of morality to get off at once. We got off, but not all of us, because my mother-in-law stayed behind to fight with the housewife. On foot, through the snow, we made it home in just two and a half hours. In front of the block I slipped on the ice and dislocated a finger.

After about three hours we managed to get everyone together in the flat, tired and starving. However, the cooker was now unusable. The gas had been stopped. So we ate cold sausages, with Portuguese pickles. An aunt got indigestion and brought up an unexpected quantity of sausages, after which she forgot to flush the toilet, thus bringing on an identical attack in the only high-society family that we had managed to invite. We drank. We sang. The heater hissed. Around midnight, with a bandaged finger and an ashen face, I went to get some rest. I didn't rest, though, because Mariana woke me up a few minutes later. Our godfather had got drunk, and was writing obscenities on the walls. My freshly painted walls! I let out a hoarse shriek. When I went into the living-room, determined to sort things out, it was too late to do anything. It seemed that the game had appealed to everyone. It reminded them of their childhood. They were all writing on the walls now, with felt-tip pens, red, green and blue ball-point pens, pencils and forks. Only one was fast asleep, wrapped up in a blanket.

Not to mention that we listened for hours on end to Mozart's *Requiem* at maximum volume. A classical music freak kept putting it back to the beginning, standing guard over the record-player with a vicious look in his face. At first some tried to protest, to change the record, but they gave up in the face of physical aggression from the music lover, and ended up dancing to the *Dies Irae*.

The wedding night was nothing to write home about. We were shivering all the time, as it was minus 10 outside and, like I said, my parents had broken the bedroom window. We put some cellophane across the frame, but it ripped in the strong wind. Then after a thorough discussion we decided to try something fitting to the occasion, something that would remain imprinted in our memories for the rest of our lives. However, we couldn't manage a by-the-book performance of the *babarishkrata*, that amorous position in which both partners have to stand on their heads, with their eyes closed, their arms twisted behind them, their spines bent so as to be able to touch the navel with the tip of the nose, and their legs entwined in the air with the toes spread out. Maybe part of the reason we couldn't get the posture right was because we still had our outdoor coats on. After more than forty minutes in which we failed to get together as husband and wife, Mariana got cramp and I got a stiff back. We decided the Indian text must have been translated wrongly, and went to sleep with our toes still spread out. In the morning we were woken up very early by a neighbour banging on the water-pipes. We banged back. Then there was the burned neighbour, who had come from hospital, nearly carbonised as he was, to wish us a house of wood and a big fire. We were completely frozen, so we thought his greeting didn't sound so bad. We even asked him to take a picture of us.

It is cold now too. I'll never find out why they don't bury us with coats on in the winter. With my teeth chattering I look at the wedding photographs, one by one, and I am touched by the faded colours and departed faces, by their air of theatricality, which is accentuated by the quasi-absent and somewhat inner light. I supplement them with non-existent photograms, caught before and after the moment the shutter release was pressed, inconvenienced only by my perfectly horizontal position and by the fact that I can barely move my hands. It was a lovely wedding, when I think about it, and hard to forget, the best proof of that being that I am still thinking of it now, in the dark, although so many years have passed. Here where I am now, I have observed an interesting phenomenon, namely that the worms don't come from the earth, from outside, to colonise you. It is the exact opposite. They form in your own body and burst through to the outside, piercing the wood. For the first few days, you feel them like tiny explosions under your skin, and the itching is intense. Then it passes, together with your skin. In my case, decay began a long time ago, and, although I have no belief in the afterlife, I suspect that Mariana is somewhere beside me, close by, or that when she does come, we might manage to touch hands, somehow, with just a slight effort.

Translator's note

'*House of stone!*' ('Casă de piatră!') is the traditional Romanian greeting to a newly married couple.

October Letter

In the first place I like the way you sleep. You sleep as if the world did not exist, you lie as if the leaves and the sky would not change their colours at the same moment, you sleep as if God had made people sleeping, in a late moment of tenderness or supreme tiredness, or perhaps so as not to see the word *despair* except in sleep, in the dark, the blinding table lamp lit at the weekend illuminating to the point of incandescence this vocable especially, the rest remaining more or less in darkness, with your hair spread across my nose, smelling of orange, on the sheet, over the whole bed, as far as the first floor, where it scares the cleaning lady, you sleep with one hand emerging from under the bed cover in a freeze-frame of slender fingers, white and threatened by the imitation mahogany frame of the bed, a subtle and tragic dance stalked by all the wooden bed frames in the world, I am painfully startled when I see your hands, wrinkled and fragile as an autumn morning, when I watch the way you lie with your head hidden under the pillow, you sleep deeply, as if you were a submarine with its ballast tanks emptied, a seal cub skating in the month of January, an exotic fish with its dorsal fins painted with varnish the colour of the sea, in a perfect camouflage, so as not to be observed from the evil ship that they throw grenades from against any submersible, even if it is imaginary, you sleep peacefully – even when I'm beginning to convince myself that it is all just a dream, perhaps yours, and then a neighbour starts running about in his flat – you sleep relaxed or tensed, you sleep happily, sometimes you even smile, and you growl, who knows how many abandoned dogs are passing under your eyelashes, and you stroke them, and you talk to them, you scratch them, you sleep deeply, like a drunk, face down, breathing inaudibly, you sleep like someone/ something that is not yet entered in the dictionary of synonyms, but keeps falling from the Great Bear into my bed and only the 10 toes on your feet bring me back to reality, no, it is not an angel, not even one that might, with its pathetic breasts, feature on the Christmas tree, nor is it a rare hypostasis of Hermes, seen from behind, with Italian sandals, because, all the same, 10 toes cannot replace two wings, so you sleep as graciously as a snow ballerina, indifferent to the music of the world played on the cymbals, unfortunately no choreographer has ever managed to present a show on this theme, quite simply the subject has never crossed any of their minds, a beautiful woman sleeping, without snoring, without trills, leaps, or other sudden movements that scare the white rabbits in other dreams, dancing slowly to the rhythm of the night and no more, her music being nothing but the definitive sadness of magic, of the block opposite, or perhaps the masters of ballet have felt intimidated by the floorboards of the stage on which usually nothing happens but on the other hand they creak horribly, imitating, at best, the death of an unimportant character in Act Two, with percussion accompaniment, you sleep, it seems, quite differently to how a really-and-truly-dead-person would sleep, even though you will die, my love, for real, you sleep, finally, so elegantly and calmly, like a sailing ship advancing on a friendly ocean, with imperial seagulls to starboard and white whales pushing the prow with their snouts, you sleep like a sailor on his watch who instead of crying out with all the air in his lungs *Land ahoy!* turns the other way with a smile, no sign of land, it is all just water, 92 percent, or so it says in books of navigation and treatises of anatomy, probably the whole universe is the same, water, you sleep like an astronaut who does not see the clouds covering the horizon, cool white, with a threatening air, in which our minds will dissolve in the end, because such a person lacks gravity and the right to beatification, cosmonauts cannot in any way become saints, anyway their aluminium helmets, with parabolic antennae, are sufficient for them, you sleep, when all is said and done, like God himself, the trouble is that you do it on my pillow. Not to mention that sometimes you stick your fingers in my ears.

And if you should fall asleep for ever, I will set fire to the bed covers, the flat, the block and the poplar tree outside, where two woodpigeons have made their nest and lots of sparrows that you have fattened beyond measure by constantly putting plates full of dry breadcrumbs out for them on the window-sill. And I will turn myself into a sparrow and I will come, flying like an idiot and without any noise, to you. In the constellation Orion, let us say.

Jazz

I was on my way to buy soda water. I was thinking of my childhood and I hadn't the slightest inclination to buy soda water. However, I had hitched my Walkman onto my belt. The brown belt of my dead father. Which he only ever wore once, in Prague, the place where a famous clock turns time, but not lovers, back. The hands go round backwards, it seems like an optical illusion, but it isn't. A beautiful city. Stopping for a little in the old Staré Město district, I remembered that it was my birthday. Probably that was why I was going for soda water. I had put on a really cool cassette, *Ragas and Sagas*, in which I could hardly understand anything, even though I had put the volume up to maximum. Right in the middle of my head, Garbarek's saxophone, soprano and tenor, depending on my stepping with my left foot, when I stepped with my right I seemed to hear a sort of flute, or perhaps it was still the same instrument, Ustad Fateh Ali Khan voice, Ustad Shaukat Hussain tabla, Ustad Nazim Ali Khan sarangi, Deepita Ustad Thathaal also voice, it was like a disease, they were all called Ustad, and, if it wasn't a disease, in any case it was something to do with far off maternity, overwhelming another continent, mothers screaming in Arabic, Arabs, tousled, gynaecologists in turbans, in short overalls, looking at mothers screaming and smoking the pipe of peace or whatever they smoke over there, while the hospital hut fills pyramidically with the echoes of Egyptian uteruses, Manu Katche drums, the drums resounding in both my cerebral hemispheres, compressing them, and, a bit further on, the wonderful smell of rubbish uncollected for 100 years being collected, making two or three sticky volutes and a Picasso drawing, not very successful but in the sky, gushing impetuously from the rusted bins, leaning to one side, battered, and when I had got to *Raga III* straining my power of penetration because I can't hear very well, although I have very large ears, when I'm not attentive they even move, and when I had got to where I said I had got to I saw stretched out on the tarmac like a greenish woman that greenish tinge, indolently winding, I don't even know why she is greenish, but that's how she is, especially when she lies down on the pathway improvising ancient Indian positions, sacred positions, delighting the eye, she shyly leaves the rubbish and stinks worse than the deodorant that hairdressers put on at the weekend, in the bathroom, in the dark, you hold your breath, the blood no longer rises up as it should towards thought, you fall into a sort of olfactory trance, and you would like to say something to someone, anything, the year of death, for example, the trouble is that there's no one in the street, and I think there's no one in general, I mean that there might be no one in the whole city, a city that when all's said and done is just as photogenic as an abandoned rubbish bin, from which any trace of intelligent life has disappeared with the exception of one small dirty man, in a small dirty room, born there long ago, straight on the carpet, a woollen carpet, worn, transparent, with fringes eaten away by time or animals, on which his mother who was past her second youth cried out in amazement, and he sits and let's say he writes the story of his life or of the district, a novel, on pink paper, he can't understand why he writes, but write he does in blue ball-point pen with a yellow cap, and all of a sudden you feel like throwing up because of the fundamental stench between the blocks, some mornings you actually do, with your eyes swollen like onions, in a corner sheltered from the wind so as not to spray yourself with your own gastric juices mixed with remains of food, tomatoes, as a rule, on your overcoat, trembling like a worn out animal, with whiskers, saying respectfully and how do you do good morning when an elderly neighbour sees you, 'cause that lot can see you no matter where you hide, wishing him health between two retches, two convulsions, long life to you, I see you're not well, he says to you as he departs with a distinguished air, because it has never happened to him to vomit, he has a cast-iron stomach and a mind in perfect working order, his air becomes a little perplexed only if he has observed the earphones with something trailing from them, whatever it is, however there are days when you lend them to him unfortunately I don't know how it is that right then you can hear Olivier Messiaen, *Le merle noir*, and, poor thing, he drops his bottles of milk on the tarmac, and the milk mixes with that greenish overflow and the drops of rain. It is October, the trees have changed colour, the soda water shop is closed.

Fortunately I know another soda water place, about 11 bins further on, at the end of the street. I smile slightly, the thought that there is another soda water place makes me smile, feel good, stroke a pregnant cat in passing. After a few steps a reddish-yellow leaf falls on my shoulder, a beautiful one, looking at it closely I would say that it has no edges. I stick it to my forehead with spit, I can hear the big drum pounding in my brain, I change my mood and viciously crush a caterpillar, with the point of my shoe. The caterpillar dies with a tiny sigh and without pain, stretching out its hairy legs in an unstudied position, which might even be amorous. VERMIGAL. Synonyms: Molevac, Vanquin. Oral suspension containing 1% pyrvinium pamoate. Therapeutic action: active antihelmintic against oxyurids and strongyloides. Where are the strongyloides, why don't they come? About caterpillars, not a word. The preparation has no contraindications. I take a short cut across the school playground which seems deserted, like a penitentiary the way it's armour-plated, with wire fences that are sure to be carrying high voltage electric current, and steel bars in the windows, so the pigs of children won't break the glass, 'cause they do break it, on top of being irremediably ugly specimens, and little, and with no prospects. This lot don't even grow up any more. At last I pass the building, I see the tree in the playground where they raised the flag when the pioneers used to sing, and I remember the father of one of them with whom I was friends up until fifth grade, when we broke up over a woman, a very calm gentleman, he had an operation one winter for a brain tumour and he's still alive, he gets potatoes from the market, calmly swears at the country folk, listens to music, although his left temple is concave, that's where they took out the tumour and who knows what else and they took it to the museum or wherever they keep tumours, after they had hollowed out his temporal bone with a fork, a high-performance Zass fork, no chance of other surgical instruments in a poor country, so you use the fork both for interventions on the brain and for eating, if you have anything to eat, it was situated in the Turkish saddle, the excrescence, perhaps they pulled out the saddle too, for medical reasons or out of patriotism, from the old antipathy towards the Turks who've come now to make bread, as if we didn't have any, and that after blighting our history by stealing our wheat, our rushes, our headscarves, the chimney timbers and our kids who they did that to as well, from behind, on the Turkish saddle, eating olives, until our ancestors were left with a fixed stare, and now it seems normal, the father of my former friend, he still loves his wife, after 100 years of life, *La Sonate en fa majeur K. 533 ne naquit pas – comme le démontrent indeed les deux numéros de l'index Köchel – d'un seul coup.* When I listen to jazz I talk in French. *Le Rondo provient du 10 juin 1786 et les deux premiers mouvements – Allegro et Andante – ont vu le jour le 3 janvier 1788,* and now I've found soda water. I'm happy.

Happily, I also pass by the shoemaker's. The old man, who never seems completely real, nothing ever does, is wearing his huge glasses as usual, like a diver's mask, with solid frames, screws you can see from the door, he's breathing heavily, cancer, I suspect, or a head cold. He trembles continuously and greets me as if he were looking at me through a periscope of minus 10 dioptres, in fact perhaps he really did look at me through a periscope, from a great distance, with his head hidden in the waves, as Father used to do when he swam, he didn't give the impression of a contented man, with money in the bank and grandchildren to be proud of, the waves were green and miniature, at one point a dolphin appeared on whose back I could see some fluorescent ulcerations, such as dolphins have, it slashed through the water with a gracious movement, perfect, as if shot from a bow, and the old man smiled, he has adjusted now, he has got accustomed to the almost 10 kilometres that have separated us for so long, while between us, or more precisely behind him, lies that choleric heap of footwear. Walking boots, galoshes, shoes of all designs, with laces, zips, buttons, buckles, elastic, with and without heels, knee boots lascivious or heroic, ballerinas, slippers. Mostly dark in colour. Squashed, burst. With the heels coming off, crushed against each other. How many navigators might have worn those size 46 heavy duty boots, which are passed down from father to son, down to the last father, after which Mother wears them, hobbling with interest, how many beautiful women might have walked about in those Spanish sandals with ankle straps, pushed out of shape by the big toe, how many weddings, torments, births and journeys have been borne by all those diaphanous creatures, with calouses? There is no way of knowing. And even though they are piled on top of each other, it is as if the shoes were still walking, were floating on water, all that is missing is the feet, while around them there is nothing but an endless maritime loneliness. Anyway, with one single exception – the shoes you never take off – all footwear makes at least one stop here.

Sighing, the shoemaker took off his artificial leg with difficulty, polished it for a long time until it began to shine like a wedding ring, then started playing with a shoemaker's last, throwing it with one hand and catching it in the other. Stretched over the last was a very elegant little lady's boot, a red one. The lady was in the next room, she was weeping. I couldn't understand why she was weeping, I switched off my Walkman, and I heard on the old man's battered radio that our mosquitoes are going to be taken to America to be studied. They're going to be taken there because the Americans can determine the clinical form of the meningitis whose virus they carry, in their proboscis, buzzing around as far as India, this provided a motive for her distress, perhaps she was suffering from meningitis, or she had a love-child, or she was weeping because she had lost the other little boot, where else if not at the cinema? The Gloria Cinema, at the matinée, after a suspense-packed film with octopuses and intergalactic trucks. When I asked the shoemaker why she was so upset, he answered that he didn't know, but if he were in her place he would suffer because of the other little boot, with studs, which she had indeed lost. She had lost others too. Like any woman. The moment she appeared in his workshop, with red eyelids and no knickers, I was just telling the old man that *il paraît vraisemblable que l'inspiration des deux mouvements soit venue après la naissance du quatrième enfant de Mozart, de la fille Thérèse*, he made no comment, he wasn't interested in Thérèse or he was thinking about something else, and causing me a fit of coughing because he was tickling my heel, forgetting that I had taken my shoe off, it was on his table. I drew his attention to this, he laughed, apologised, and set to work. When he tried to grip the pincers, he dropped the nails that he was holding between his teeth, hicupped twice, went purple in the face and rolled his eyes in a very peculiar manner. He had fainted or perhaps something worse had happened to him. Because he was stock-still, with the whites of his eyes directed at the ceiling. Tall, brunette, barefoot, the woman I was talking about stayed in the workshop to wonder, I took my beige shoe unstitched round the edge and left, lifting my handkerchief to my nose, but not before admiring the wonder of the lady.

After *Ragas* the next recording was *The Upper Room*. I don't know who recorded it, it doesn't matter. I'm singing myself now, together with Mahalia.

A few minutes later I arrive in Negro spiritual rhythm at the chemist's, which is one – superb – block further on. I buy a pencil with a soft lead, a bottle of juice and a jar of face-cream, still *talking with the Lord*, singing along. The pharmacist praises my way of dancing, she likes gospel too, although she can't hear it, she especially appreciates my hand movements and my navy blue cap, with NIKE written on it. I take it off, I hold it out to her, I let her feel it, turn it over, tug the pompom, then I open the lid of the jar, Pond's, the cream I think my first love used to rub on her face or wherever she rubbed it, around the end of fourth grade, she was called Viorica, she sat on the second bench from the front and I looked at her white stockinged feet every time they called me out to the blackboard, I drew on the blackboard the breasts that she should have had in another couple of years, she was blonde, with abyssal blue eyes and a rather tatty school bag.

It was a total love, for as long as it lasted, not very long, because five months later she died, no one found out what of, not even the mathematics teacher, we went to the funeral, a lot of people had come and they were all crying and she lay there, in the Red Flag van, a van much too big for such a small coffin, so fragile, with sails, it seemed to me, and the van was not only wide but also tall, you could only see Viorica if you lifted yourself up on tiptoe or climbed onto a stone, but there were no stones to be found, you had to bring them from home, from the closet, where we all keep them, in the end a stranger lifted me up in his arms, to see her, to make her a sign, I saw her, she was lying motionless. She was extremely calm. Even the driver was calm. He was stroking my aunt on the thigh. My aunt had amazingly beautiful legs, they're amputated now, but then they had dimples and cream garters. She probably let him stroke her as a result of the pain caused by the event and so the van ran into a post, followed shortly after by the entire funeral convoy out of which the priest fell.

Several years later.

I'm still at the chemist's. I ask for an aspirin. In spite of those several years later.

I was playing guitar at Doi Mai, in a room that instead of a door had some strips of cellophane soaked in a sort of gum arabic so that it would stick to the landing-gear of the flies, which did get stuck, regardless of what was happening inside. There was nobody else in the room with flaking plaster on the walls, a sixty-watt bulb and a rug with jellyfish or hunters, hard to say what they actually were, it really was, riding horses on the wall, with a great orange moon shining over the horses, nobody apart from me and Cristina, blonde too but lying on one side, on the bed, there was a miniature bed there, for blondes, and she was watching me through misty irises, I thought it was because of the subtle emotions aroused by the music, *Death is Not the End* (Dylan). *A piece in the main tonality, a graceful minuet, which is within the context of this work perceived as a symbol of wisdom and calm world outlook, appears in the capacity of the final variation. The conclusion of the piece is serene and, at the same time, highly optimistic*, only that in the pause between the two melodies I had also managed to deliver for her benefit an elevated, ramified speech, there was erotic darkening round her eyes, her desire was obvious, about Kierkegaard, death, arrows, umbrellas and other such things, all rather Danish. *Theme. Variation I–XX*. And when I was caught up with the execution of the *Passacaglia* which went wonderfully with old Sören, see *Musical Erotic* or *The Aesthetic Validity of Marriage*, the tonal colour was perfect, I got all the chords right, I had a left hand like a spider, bloodshot eyes and a soul astounded by the fact that I had managed not only to win my admirer but even to leave her struck dumb in the face of so much culture, it was impossible for her not to be overwhelmed, her and the whole village, cliffs, tourists, dogs and all, two or three hours had already gone by and I was mentally preparing myself, surreptitiously, to abandon my instrument and get to the point, and caress Cristina with the same refined fingers that had picked out so many difficult, unforgettable notes, the girl seemed on fire, she was giving off ultra violet rays, when, quite unexpectedly, a good friend turned up in the doorway, he's been away in France for 20 years now, where he has a car on the driveway, two children and a villa, he is sad, he comes in, he sits down on her bed and without a word, of introduction, of greeting, of Fichte, he throws her down between the pillows and starts to finger her, to paw her, to kiss her, to get one of her breasts, suntanned, stiffened by my chords, out of her blouse, the blonde had no need for a road through the *levels of existence* so she didn't refuse a single gesture, and she carried out the whole performance, groans included, as something fully and totally natural, in a cloud of dust and murmurs, right before my eyes when I lifted them for a few seconds from the finger-board, while the flies continued to get their feet stuck on those rustling strips that stood in for a door. I don't even know any more when I left, the chemist's I mean.

So here I am walking all this time through the district to fill the soda water bottles that I have indeed filled. When I saw what was going on, stupefied at the crass uselessness of what I had imagined was an elegant manner of courting a girl of 18, with Kierkegaard and the *Passacaglia* (by Bach), which I had been confident had bowled her over, it hadn't bowled her over at all, it had bored her to death, but she was quite prepared if only out of irritation to take in her arms a hero who would get quickly into action, so when I saw how things stood, I left my guitar, adopted a contemptuous air, almost philosophical, went out to the only restaurant in the village, the Dobrogeanu, bought four bottles of champagne, returned with them to the room – those two had finished what they had to finish, now they were at the stage of smoking with their eyes on the ceiling – I poured them, the bottles, into the bucket from which we all drank water, with a changed expression, in that serene moment, and I began to take little sips of the warm champagne from the bucket that smelled of rust and earth. At night, around eleven o'clock, I went for a pee, but I took the wrong path and nearly ended up relieving myself in the fountain. And not just because I had lost my way, but because I had seen an aeroplane there, on the ground, reflected in the eye of water, signalling with its red lights. After I had been convinced – with difficulty – by some friends that it wasn't the done thing to urinate on aeroplanes, the more so when they were flying to Istanbul, I gave everyone the sensation that they were falling asleep by singing *Blue in Green* (Davis). I think all this was about 30 years ago. Next I tried to throw myself in the same fountain, one hour later. It inspired me. Even though I couldn't see any more aeroplanes. I still thought that another one ought to go by, pretty soon, and I would be able to catch it without delay, from the fountain. But nothing else went by.

First thing the next morning, about half past four, it was still dark and I had a sore head, I found another girl, chestnut-haired and alone, in any case there was no adversary to be seen in the vicinity, everybody was asleep, and I took her to the shore, to catch the sunrise. The beach was completely deserted. And Daisy, that's what she was called, was melancholic, she had never seen the sun rising out of the water before, she had dressed nicely, we were young and idiotic, and as such we dressed nicely, we stood on the sand trembling slightly and the sun didn't appear. Or it did so somewhere else, but in any case not out of the sea in front of us. So I was struck again by poetry, by the imperious desire to show how many lines I knew by heart, so as to move on then to obscene embraces, I can't remember what I recited because after two or three stanzas my stomach started to ache. The previous night's champagne was churning on my gastric mucosa. I was obliged to find an excuse and a Furazolidon, indication for acute diarrhoea, derivative of nitrofuran, adverse reactions vomiting, in the form of tablets of 100 mg, keep in a dry place, protect from light, I got up tense and protected from light, recalling what a torment it was with the violin or cello too, I got the impression that the more I grew the bigger the stringed instrument got too, sometimes I broke the strings, Father forced me to learn to play, I was the son of an intellectual, now I'm not any more, Father is no more, I even studied the piano too, and to cap it all I had to say I liked it, I had no way out and Father had his belt, although I could see from the window the other children in the block who did have a way out, playing leap-frog while I was scattering solfeggios on the linoleum, and all to get where, all to do what, in life and at five o'clock on the wet sand, it was necessary to lie hurriedly to Daisy too, to tell her that the sun wasn't going to appear any more, if not actually never, then in any case not that morning.

I've covered a few more metres in the meantime. At one point I started holding out my hands in front of me, while at the same time feeling my way on the paving with dragging steps. I don't know why, I just felt like it. Pretending I was blind. And just when I'm managing the act better – an old lady even helped me to get round a manhole that I actually hadn't seen – I come upon this curious car. A white Dacia.

Curious because it seems to be in good condition but its doors have fallen off.

It has turned cloudy.

The Hilliard Ensemble, *Officium*, on the other side of the cassette, with a saxophone behind the voices, serene and grave, like any tenor saxophone, working its way in from the background and encompassing the voices from the side, surrounding them, lifting them, *parce mihi domine*, locking them in a net of candid brass, appearing for a few seconds in front, in the full light of day, hitting you in the face with a G-sharp, only to disappear discreetly, through the church. Leaving you with your mouth open, and a bee flies in.

There are certain flies, which I would call cemetery flies, that have a special, unusual body, they are more elongated than the usual ones that settle on your food, they have shorter wings, a large head, attentive eyes and, in general, a distinctive air, impenetrable or distant, insects that are waiting for the ceremony to be over and done with, for the family photographs to be taken, with parents, children, cousins, passers-by, sometimes even laid-back drivers of the minibuses that carry the dead at high speed through cleared streets, you sit on the seat stunned into silence and you see that he's moving, the deceased, a shirt button is coming undone, his eyelid jumps, they wait with implacable patience for the end of the individual photographs, by the graveside, and only when the moment comes for the coffin to be lowered into the ground do they become – almost imperceptibly – a little irritable, they buzz abruptly and try to settle on the face of the pomaded deceased, with the black shoes that he has never worn, they're brand new, never mind, he's wearing them now, they have immaculate soles and laces tied in a big bow. A perfect one. And, even though most of the time no one in the family or in the hospital has requested it, they have embalmed him (I once saw a prosector's little daughter, she was five years old and she was calmly playing with the big toe of a cold old man, she said she liked dead people, her eyelashes were long, her eyes like almonds and she had put leaves in her hair, and a few minutes later she jumped over the rope around the morgue to wait for the van coming for the old man), they have injected formaldehyde into his thorax and abdomen, lots of it, look at the brownish trickle around the corner of his mouth, and in the end they go into the grave together with him, the flies I mean, it's probably a matter of destiny, their destiny as funerary fruit flies, they are shut up of their own free will in the wooden box on the face of the one who is still sleeping, while his wife fans the air over the black lumps of earth, with her handkerchief, trying to drive them away, and the ropes are pulled out.

I've got soda water bottles again.

I notice that I've been getting more and more soda water, recently. I take one out of my shopping bag and try to make it fizz over. Nothing happens. Nothing but a very mild whistle... Felicia. She was well developed, cuddly, I used to put my palms on her breasts in the school playground, the one with the fruit-tree. She had musical breasts, they sounded like a gong when you pinched them. Probably because her father was a butcher. When he got into his car, an oblique, green car, I could see how it went down on one side with a metallic sigh, because the butcher weighed over a 100 kilos, I imagine he ate everything he saw on his plate, he didn't leave anything for the abattoir, a wrecked abattoir, although it still gives off fetid smells even now, I don't know what materials are the cause, he would even swallow the tails, ears, eyes of an ox. He had a moustache. Sometimes he shaved it, when he went to conferences.

I've no idea what has become of her. Of Felicia. Since she weighed about as much as her dad in seventh grade, I imagine by now she can't even get into bed. Still less into the lift. That's because we live in a country with tight lifts, with no room even for a memory, let alone a coat rack that you've just bought and you want to take upstairs, *te voglio disperato*, with chipped mirrors and missing buttons, to get to the sixth you have to press eight, sometimes even that is absent or blocked, and then you just stay where you are, in the lift. And what rosy thighs, like telegraph poles, Felicia had, I would stroke them by portions, perplexed, when we played kissing forfeits. Just them, her thighs, and they cancelled out the horrible mathematics lessons. In the other subjects I could manage all right, I learned everything by heart, I had a photographic memory. But there's no way even a normal child could make anything of mathematics. One time I even asked the teacher, what, for example, are plus and minus infinity? I stood absolutely still, with an angelic expression and my hair falling over my eyes. After a pause, no one had ever asked him such a question, infinity is just something self-explanatory, unless you're an ass, he drew a line on the board and put a sideways eight at both ends, that's all, and as his recreational thinking was prolonged, I promised him that if he would explain to us what it meant, not the convention, but infinity itself, if it existed, what it represented, I would be willing to put a zero in the middle, on the abscissa. Or on the ordinate, since I wasn't very sure either – *e la vita che finisce* – why they were called by those names. And I still said nothing about the obvious fact that zero didn't exist either.

A jack in flames, with I-don't-know-why car doors instead of arms, that's what you resemble, like in the playing cards, a neighbour managed to say over his shoulder as he rushed past me, to get to the lift first, he is the neighbour who repairs all our letter-boxes. A few more steps and he started coughing.

I sit down calmly at the wheel. And I adjust the rear-view mirror of this bizarre abandoned car.

I turn the wheel, to the right, to the left. Then out loud, because no one can hear me, I go *vroom, vroom*. I press down the accelerator. I overtake.

It's strange how you managed to lift the doors. And to put them on your shoulders too. 'Cause you look feeble. Won't you sell them? I would. If you have them anyway – *una furtiva lagrima* – it's a pity not to try, the neighbour continued. After a minute in which he stared at me and shook his head, he disappeared in the direction of the block. The same direction in which we all disappear.

It was only in the tenth grade that I discovered her. The girl the whole school slept with, including the staff, maybe a bit on the short side. She was easygoing, plump, but with a certain charm, a plump charm, she put on lipstick, at a time when no one was allowed to put on lipstick, not even mothers, let alone children, she wore a mauve skirt. I truanted from the third class, the one from 10 to 11, physics, one overcast autumn day I saw a horse in the playground, not too young, not too sturdy, but at the peak of arousal, perhaps by the grills on our windows, perhaps by the fruit-tree with the flag, who knows, right down to the ground, like any male being planted in some place with no escape like a school playground, and the physics teacher noticed that we were craning our necks towards the window and she went herself to look out, through the teacher's window, she saw the indisputable ornament almost touching the tarmac, they blushed, she and the ornament alike, and then she brought her hands together behind her back (a flat back, pierced by her shoulder-blades) and explained a theorem to us with chalk, she was ugly, poor woman, all she had ever played with in her life was chalk, the hypotenuse – I had organised everything, down to the smallest detail, Rothmans cigarettes, a bottle of Drobeta brandy, clean sheets, only that in my nervousness when I found myself in bed with her in reality, she waiting with an inviting smile for me to rush in, to occupy, to lay waste, and I feverishly seeking rescue, I discovered in the fridge a bottle of Pasinal, which I knew calms you, relaxes you, my sister used to take it, and I swallowed two big soup-spoonfuls, not of soup but of that last-minute solution, and only after an hour of constantly growing confusion, the hour of preamble, did it dawn on me that something wasn't right, the most important something of all, I got out of the bed where the mystery, the magic hadn't happened the way I had imagined, and it occurred to me to read what it said on the label, it said bromide, then I lit a cigarette with the precise gestures of a great smoker, coughed for three minutes, and began to tell her, with the look of a man with no future, how unhappy I was, how isolated, making myself weep, in the end, especially after I had confessed that I was seriously ill, I had tuberculosis, and, to add force to my words I played the girl whose name I've forgotten a Gregorian chant on the tape recorder, a Tesla, that was just what she needed, she left at top speed, left in a Gregorian manner, even forgetting her striped stockings in her annoyance, by tram, and to this day I've never found out where she ended up, I hope she didn't have an accident. Because I never saw her again. Anyway she left behind her a smell of mandarins. And a red lighter.

I have managed, at long last, to lift the car doors. I hoist them with great effort onto my shoulders and set off along a dirty lane, just like all the other lanes, pushing my way between the blocks of flats, trying not to notice the passers-by who can barely pass by me. I'm sure I must have cut a memorable figure in those moments, winged not so much because of the scrap metal I was carrying on my arms lifted at right angles to my body, as because of the soda water bottles which kept falling out of my hands, between fingers busy with the car doors, about once every 10 paces. They gave a dry pop, sometimes not even that. Rolling away without any noise. They remained on the path, opaque, out of place. I only had 20, or let's say 30 metres to go to the door of the block, when I felt an increasingly intense heat in my armpits. At first I wanted to scratch myself. But there was no way I could. I pulled myself together, I saw the steps at the entrance and just when I least expected it, I smelled burning. I raised my arms up. And I caught fire.

Translator's notes

Red Flag ('Steagul Roşu') was the name of the truck and bus manufacturing plant at Braşov during the communist period. (In 1990 it was reorganised as SC Roman S.A.).

Doi Mai ('2 May') is a small resort at the southern end of Romania's Black Sea coast.

The Dacia 1300 (later 1310), based on the Renault 12, was produced from 1969 to 2004, and was for a long time by far the most commonly seen car on Romanian roads.

Quotidian

It was a normal day, I was going to work. In my black briefcase I had two cheese sandwiches. I was in a hurry. However, I was stopped by a neighbour with big flat ears, because he says he used to do boxing, I have my doubts, I could thump him any time even over the ears, who started complaining to me in vivid detail about the fact that a woman on the eighth floor was throwing chicken bones onto his car, right on the door, with maddening precision. I asked him politely, looking at his snub nose, how he could explain the trajectory. I mean from the eighth floor, through the poplars, to throw those chicken bones, and why at his car? I even gave him a short lecture about the theory of gravitation, and then, when I saw that he wasn't getting it, I also expounded to him the theory of relativity. At this point he seemed to become a bit more attentive. And he gave me an astounding answer. The chicken bones describe a sort of arc of a circle, almost perfect, thus avoiding the trees, and then fall on the car door. He showed me the marks. Can you see them? You can't say I made them up. They were marks of chicken bones just as surely as they could have been marks of anything else. I took my leave of him with much deference and set off for the metro. As I turned onto the main footpath, I met another neighbour, with Sony headphones stuffed into his auricular pavilions. He was dancing to the rhythm of the music, alongside an abandoned Dacia. It seemed to be jazz. I unwisely accelerated my pace and, a few metres further on, two dogs emerging from the eternal cemetery tried to bite me. One managed to stick its teeth into my left boot. I kicked it on the snout aggressively. Just at the moment when a very fine deceased was leaving or entering the cemetery. He had flowers on his chest, around 50 years old, eyes closed and a splendid pallor, which went wonderfully with his blue, striped suit. He looked like a piano teacher. Only he didn't have his hands clasped on his chest, but along the sides of his body, and when I say along the sides, that's just a manner of speaking, because somebody, I don't think it was the priest, had crossed them right over his genital organs. Or over what was left of them. I lifted my eyes. A hang-glider was passing above the block. White with dark red patches. I took a deep breath. I continued on my way in an unclear state of mind and when I had become somehow dreamy, I bumped into a spiv who was warming his rubber hand in the sun. It was a fragile sun. The man was wearing a Bartsons overcoat and leaning on a coquettish, Suzuki motorcycle, with nickel plating. He leaned towards me and chanted in an alert whisper marks, dollars and something else. I thanked him, I said no. I've got a piano too, he continued in the same breath, I got it from an actor. I don't know how to play the piano, I confessed. What about pounds sterling? he asked with a gleam of hope in his eye. I shook my head with a downcast air, but that of a man who appreciates things the way they are. Consequently he held out a 100 franc note to me. I took it.

Down below, in the station, I watched for a few seconds the young man with sensitive features who was quietly playing with a yo-yo. Without realising why, I recalled the scene the previous night. I had been watching a piece of modern theatre on Arte. The actors were beautifully painted, with violet predominating, nude, close shaven or with crests of hair, some were wearing feathers, horns and foetuses, others chains, some of the actresses had thick pubic hair, and they were all beating with probably justifiable fury on some majestic-sounding pots, while at the same time miming lovemaking and roaring out their lines such as they were, three of them, with bulging eyes. It was a classic text. While I sat stunned in the armchair in the hall, I heard some suspicious noises coming from behind the door of the flat. I pricked up my ears. They seemed to be sighs, a rustling, groans, like the sounds of someone twisting and turning in bed, unable to sleep. After lying in wait for about a quarter of an hour I opened the door suddenly, with a T-square in my hand, and I saw a woman dressed in a polyester suit, with a burgundy headscarf, who was stretched out asleep on the landing, on my doormat. What are you doing here? I'm sleeping, she said to me. Aha! And I shut the door softly.

As usual, it was crowded in the metro. At a certain moment, someone hit me with something on my Achilles tendon. I turned round more as a reflex and not because I wanted to demand an explanation. The man behind me was holding a wooden box between his feet. He looked me straight in the face and unexpectedly stuck out his tongue at me. On his tongue he had a white pill. I couldn't tell what it was and I gave him a friendly smile. As he didn't stick his tongue back in his mouth, I smiled at him again.

The metro stops on time at Victory Square. I rush out with the force and speed of a piston, irresistibly pushed forward by a group of ladies. I regain my balance and make for the exit. I take a look at the steps of the escalator, which are striking one by one, at slow tempo, against the torn body, caught under the metal threshold, of a rat. I jump over it and enter (or emerge) again into the hazy light of day. The sun has dissolved into a cold milky spot. I make my way as usual towards the newspaper kiosk. Beside it, on a stall, several boxes of small eggs are placed in superposed layers. An individual in front of me, with a respectable-looking hat, makes a sudden halt, strikes the first layer of eggs, twice, with his elbow and goes on his way with a preoccupied air. The vendor is silent. Egg yolk drips slowly onto the tarmac. When it comes to crossing the street to the bus-stop, pondering a little, with my eyes half shut, on these times we live in, I see a Daewoo Cielo coming in the wrong direction, which knocks smack into me, fortunately not very painfully. I get up covered in blood, open the driver's door with the intention of giving him a beating and I see a beautiful woman, with superb legs, blonde, who looks at me with slightly startled eyes. I apologise, wipe the blood from my nose and arrive limping at the editorial office.

Here there was a lot of celebrating going on. Someone had just had his sixtieth birthday or had died before he could reach it, I couldn't understand very well, but everyone had got to the stage of Cinzano with ice-cubes. I took a cube too. Then the potato salad made me feel ill and I went to the toilet. In the toilet someone had relieved himself on the seat, and then written on the walls, with shit, BEBE + GICA = LOVE. I felt nauseous and threw up over GICA. I rinsed my mouth out, washed my eyes, walked out and saw the cleaning woman. Her pleasant appearance was enhanced by her hair being tied on top of her head with a large ribbon, a khaki one. She was sweeping up an omelette that someone had just thrown into the hall. When I opened the door of the editorial office I found them all weeping. Apparently they had seen Jesus at the window. I looked too, but apart from a ladder on which a bricklayer was climbing who could very well have been Jesus, I couldn't see anything. I told them so. They looked. They didn't notice the bricklayer. It occurred to me then that short-sightedness is an infirmity, I ought to change my glasses or my way of being. While I was thinking about this, with my glass in my hand, a girl from distribution came up who wanted to sell me a pullover. The make-up editor made us laugh, I had a coffee, and the girl from distribution managed to sell the pullover to the guy who shifts books around, on a trolley with a wooden wheel. It suited him wonderfully. Apart from that, the colour was pink, the sleeves were too short, but it had a cat on the chest that was included in the price. The cat, of course, was black.

Around two o'clock I enter my office where no one ever cleans and here is what I find waiting for me (in my secretary's handwriting) under the title *Summary*: "We have received at the editorial office about seven years late (exclusively due to the French postal service, which apparently suffers from undermanning or anonymous falls of postmen from trains and aeroplanes) a stirring letter from Samuel (a Jew?) Beckett, dated 22 December 1989, one o'clock in the morning, thus drafted a very short time before he died and before the Romanian revolution started at the Intercontinental Hotel. The epistle contains a desperate appeal addressed to Romanian doctors (!), in whom the dramatist places his last hope, as he witnesses with some amazement the violent manifestations of material indifference displayed by the French doctors – indifference demonstrated in spite of the coincidence by which they all simultaneously possess a Mazda, a villa and a Brueghel the Elder – in the hospital where he was a patient. Apart from that, there was almost no one left, the entire medical staff had gone home to observe Christmas and the Romanian revolution, of which they could understand nothing except for the fact that someone was firing shells at buildings, but they wept at the balcony scene (75%). In spite of his age (83 years) Beckett recalled the year 1920, when he played cricket extremely well, and asked the nurse, a black woman, to bring him a bat, for one last innings. The nurse, who was a fan of Barbara Cartland, said she would give him one, but on the head. In another passage, a very short one, the Irish writer confessed that on the rare occasions when he got to his office on the Rue Arago, he spent almost the whole time looking at the walls of the prison opposite, called La Santé. Which sometimes made him exclaim: *Comme le temps passe quand on s'amuse!* Finally he complains a little about how quiet it is around him (*le silence*), about the inexplicable refusal to bring him even one bottle of whisky, while at the same time recalling that he wore glasses before Joyce (a Jew) did."

I pass over my secretary's comments mixed rather ineptly with those of the Red Cross, and look in front of me. On the coat rack a fly has settled. All I can say, explain (answer?) in this unfortunately post-mortem case is that notwithstanding that it was categorically an *Endgame*, there was no way he could have played cricket with a black intellectual nurse, in a French hospital, at Christmas. While so many tragedies were going on in the world. Only that is not an appropriate solution to a letter to the editor, I have to think of something else.

I don't even get as far as inserting a sheet of paper into my typewriter when a young man with a dazed expression turns up. He approaches my desk, and starts to recite in a squeaky voice, raising his arms at the same time: "The ray of sun…" I try to interrupt him. He raises his voice: 'Comes gently, / And caressingly, / Leaps livelily / On the little tree.' That's from Carmen Sylva, I say. Never mind, he says, I have others, my own. He bows, goes back, still bowing, towards the door, lifts the tattered briefcase he had left in the doorway and takes from it a thick folder. From the folder, he takes a manuscript, half of whose pages fall out and spreading themselves all over my office. The poet fishes out a pale blue page from the bundle left in his hand and makes as if to continue. I immediately start typing. Then he tells me that he is, in reality, an engineer. He even has his degree in the briefcase, a degree with the serial number 226385. If I don't believe him, I can check with the Principal's office at the Polytechnic. He gets to the phone before I can, and holds the receiver out to me. I can hear the dialling tone. From the other editorial office comes the sound of trash music. The young man keeps looking at me tensely. I'm a musician too, you know, to be more precise I compose, he says, throwing back his hair with an abrupt movement. I move the chariot of Olympia. Look, I've brought a score, read it! He lays it on my typewriter, over the keyboard. I glance at the stave, C C, G F B, then below the stave: "A bit-ter frost has bro-ken all the lin-den bows." A bit further down I read what further effects the frost has had: "But you, lit-tle girl, what would you like to be? Me? I want to be a mo-ther." I turn the page with the little girl mechanically and on the other side I see a petition. "To the Sector 3 District Court. I the undersigned (name of the poet) bring to your attention the fact that my upstairs neighbour (name of the neighbour) is in illegal possession of an aquarium and an air rifle… batrachians… damp on the ceiling… shoots fish… yesterday I was threatened… damages… with respect." I admit to the young man, with a face like stone, that the poems and the music are very good, but he should go down a floor, to *Evenimentul Zilei*, they are sure to publish them. For the time being, I regret to say, we have no money. As he goes through the door, with tears in his eyes, the poet thanks me and begs me not to divulge to anyone that the lady who inspires him works in TV. This is a secret that must remain between the two of us. I assure him that it will. He can't tell me the name of his muse, but he is eager for me to promise one more time that I won't reveal it to anyone. I promise him again and he goes out. I start going through my correspondence again.

The second letter is from the Colombian Gardeazábal, who asks our opinion concerning the two idiot children he made the mistake of describing in *The Bazaar of the Idiots*. While one of them was performing a miracle – he healed a leper – a blister appeared on his heel. Not only has the blister not disappeared, it is actually growing. Note that the other is now marked with the same papule, as the boys are twins. I draft my response on the spot, on headed paper: "One solution would be not to make the children display their miraculous qualities while standing. Bear in mind that they are at a tender age, when the calcaneus, like other bones, those of the head, for example, is not yet fully formed, and the skin of the heel is exceptionally delicate. Make up some chairs, a bench, a bed, a parapet. On the other hand, if they are pre-school, they should be enjoying their childhood more. Singing, sleeping. Playing. With a little imagination, you can arrange things so that the twins do the healing while bounding across a meadow. Or, if you feel that such proceedings would take away from the solemnity of the miracles, reduce the miracles, or the number of those who come for treatment. The idiots' exhaustion would disappear and so would the blisters. After all, the gift of these two, however great it is, still cannot possibly bring health to the whole world."

I take the paper out of the typewriter, put it in an envelope and take from the left corner of my desk the first folder that I lay my hand on. There, on the left, are the prose works of authors who are unknown, misunderstood, unpublished, who first of all ask your opinion, then become resentful. One time, a novelist I had rejected put a dead bat under my doormat. The same doormat where the woman in polyester slept last night. Out of the folder falls the photograph of the author, 13 x 18, an ugly character, on white filigree card. He is the first who has sent me a photograph. He seems to be eating a steak. The details don't show very well, because the photograph is taken with flash. I read the beginning of the first chapter. It is morning and the principal character is walking his dog, which three lines down is about to die poisoned, but the master saves it on time. I stand up and place the folder on a cupboard, on top of an imposing heap of other folders, files and envelopes. I'm worn out.

In order to relax a bit, I take a bite out of a cheese sandwich and lift from a drawer a book that I received recently, I can't remember who from. It is called *The Third Violet*. Already on the front cover the reader's emotions are impetuously stirred by the photograph of a pair of young lovers. He is smiling at her and she at him, and she is holding her hand to her own cheek for no obvious reason, shyly, against an electric blue background, which suggests the sky. Over the girl's scarf, a red one, a huge violet has been stuck by the modern technique of collage, also blue in colour, but from another photo. I turn over the book and run my eyes over the quotation in a black border on the back cover: "Man's level of culture can be seen from the respect he has towards books." So great is their respect that they have even dropped the diacritics. I don't know why, but I feel like hiccupping.

I put the book back in the drawer and decide to take a nap. And just when I'm about to sit in the armchair, I come upon a black rat (*Rattus rattus*) sleeping so soundly that I don't have the heart to wake it, especially as I recall the one I saw butchered in the metro. I didn't wake it and I lay down on my desk. A few minutes later in came a dramatist who, when he saw me stretched out there, began to weep. Even though I didn't know him, I wept too. It was also because I had just begun to dream about the actors with feathers and the woman on the doormat. Then the girls from the editorial office turned up, they brought champagne, we got merry, I read the newspaper, the light was switched on. About three-quarters of an hour later an old man entered in a wheelchair, holding a manuscript in his teeth. He gave it to me. It was a novel. The others withdrew discreetly, we were left alone, the novel was called *Twilight of the Gods*. In a way, I was expecting it. And on the very first page, I come upon Hawker, loaded with suitcases, descending the steps of the railway carriage. "The easel was swinging uncontrolled knocking against the head of a little boy who had withdrawn back with care." I look at my left hand, the ring finger to be precise. Of course, it isn't a matter of the uncontrolled tenses of the verbs. There is a clinical explanation. The fact that it was swinging and knocking clearly indicates that the easel had already knocked against the undoubtedly hard head of the boy, at least twice, because he had only stepped back once, probably the moment he realised that something was knocking against him. I cough, I look at the photo of my wife, Kodak, it's very beautiful, she's sitting on a camel at Saturn, I skip 10 pages and breathlessly read the following mind-blowing sentence: "The grey father of Hawker entered the room slowly beating his legs." As I was still out of breath, the pencil dropped from my mouth. Together with a long expiration of admiration for the butterfly style in which the grey-haired parent makes his entry, enigmatically beating both his lower limbs at the same time, like Nureyev with his heels stuck together. Or perhaps I am interpreting wrongly, and it is not a father who enters the room, but a bird, the unforeseen reincarnation of the father, which beats its feet because its wings are broken by a shot at short range. And it beats whatever it beats *slowly*, because it is old. I admit that this is an explanation that calms me.

What is this, a translation? I ask in a honeyed tone. We all translate, says the old man. As his reply is profound and there is no colleague to be seen on the horizon, I have no option but to plunge further into this literature typed double spaced, in a small font, and I do so slowly beating my feet, as I can't use my palms, because between them I am holding this book with its high cultural temperature, almost 40 degrees, could be malaria. On page 55, Stanley (Hawker's dog) complicates his existence for no reason, by entering into metaphysics: "Stanley, uniform and dishonoured, got up wagging his tail.' Nowhere can I see, no matter how much I look back, for what reason he is dishonoured, I can only presume it is from birth, all I can understand is that Stanley is uniform. Like all dogs, for that matter. A nice book about animal life, like the other one, on the cupboard. I jump straight to page 91 and peruse a paragraph in which the author (authoress?) explains the painter's manner of working: "Hawker seemed to attack with this picture of his mind something beautiful and wonderful from his life, a possession of his mind, and he did it passionately, unsparingly, formidably." On the next page Florinda made her appearance, Hawker gave her the hots, then there was something about a clump of chestnut trees and it was raining. I gave the old man my assurance that I would read his manuscript with the greatest interest, he should pay the reading fee, only that I didn't know when we would be able to publish it, we were in a very difficult financial situation. He interrupted me saying that he didn't need copyright and he would pay for the book himself. Paper, labour, design, the lot. He would like a print run of about 10,000 copies. Yes, he could rest assured, I would read it by December, I replied, seeing that he was starting to show signs of unease. I don't know why my voice immediately calmed him, he bid me good day, turned his wheelchair around and swished out of the door. There was no one left now in the editorial office. And just when I was feeling safe now that I had got rid of the invalid, Hawker and all the rest, I looked through the window and saw the bricklayer again.

I went home with a suspicious sensation of calm. In the bus, a lady asked me in a tone that brooked no refusal to punch her ticket. I punched it for her, looking at the yellow leaves that had fallen in Herăstrău and were drifting in a slow procession, backwards, outside the window. What, are you an idiot? Can't you see you haven't punched it properly? I haven't punched what? My ticket! Well, you see, I've only been punching for a very short time, I still haven't acquired the necessary skill. Everyone laughed. I got away from the lady with small sideways steps. On my way back from the ticket punch to the seat that a fat woman with an aggressive air had occupied for me, someone knowingly stepped on my toe. I did the same to him, but rather more heavily. There followed a short struggle, in the course of which I ripped off his shirt and he a button of my jacket.

When I got out of the bus, a Volvo splashed us all with diesel from the sprawling puddle beside the pavement. I decided to go for a drink, in a decent pub. In the decent pub there was only one customer, who was swaying dangerously on his chair. In the end he fell, but not before confessing to me that he was a poet. I wouldn't have imagined anything else, I assured him. Then I left the poet lying on the concrete just as he started to recite something about how he had killed his dog, had poisoned it, and I went out into the cold air heading in the direction of the metro. Beside a grocery shop, opposite the Panasonic sign, a young man in jeans was tugging at a wire grille. He asked me if I knew where Eleonora was. I answered that I had no idea and went down to the station. Here there was a row going on. Three kids were singing a mournful song and an old man wanted to murder them with his walking-stick. No one prevented him. He gave them a hiding. Meanwhile we were waiting for the metro. Which came from the opposite direction, we got on, and we arrived in a completely different station. By good luck it was a nice station. Not so nice to my mind was the fact that it was now three minutes past 10 and no trains were circulating any more. I returned home on foot. Outside, I mean in front of the block, I found my neighbour still trying to repair his car door. She's thrown another chicken bone, he said. But how does she manage to hit your car? She's got telescopic sight.

Translator's notes

Dacia: see note to 'Jazz'.

Intercontinental Hotel: see notes to 'Flash'.

Carmen Sylva was the pen-name of Elisabeth of Wied (1843–1916), wife of King Carol I of Romania and the author of a number of volumes of poetry (but not, however, of the lines attributed to her here).

The *Polytechnic* University of Bucharest is Romania's largest and most prestigious institution of higher education in engineering.

Evenimentul Zilei ('The Event of the Day') is one of Romania's leading daily newspapers.

The story of *Hawker* and *Stanley* is indeed, at least as far as the quoted extracts are concerned, a translation (and is now doubly so, though hopefully its derivation from Stephen Crane's original can still be recognised).

The *Herăstrău* Park is an extensive park on the north side of Bucharest.

Small Changes in Attitude

It's a lovely morning. *Il fait beau*. I don't feel like going to work. The birds are singing too. And it's raining. Dreams filter to the surface, I take a large glass of vodka, to give reality a dank tonality. I have to do it, because I've woken up with swollen eyes, like a snail, fawn coloured, that's how gastropods are at dawn, with punctiform pupils, still keeping little ships on their retinas, some extremely small, almost microscopic, in fact little sandalwood boats that burn wonderfully and smell super-erotic, with rigging, sails and oars, heavy, plus a horde of mute slaves, tongues cut out, no more hope, but with powerful thighs and a nose this big down in the hold, the hold is large, about the size of a conference room, against a charcoal blue background and a tiny cloud on the right, covering the Pole Star. Up there, above the mast. Decalibrating the sextant I got from my father. While I was looking at it, it was a beauty of a sextant, with a phosphorescent sight, I was sweating vitamin B in abundance, like now, and the sea suddenly turned into a tiny ocean, where my father was swimming. My father disappeared, doing the crawl. Even though he swam like a fish, like a champion. He had narrow shoulders and a fine head. Roman nose. He was lost in the waves. I had a long discussion about this with Mariana when we woke up two minutes before the alarm went, and when it went, she had just managed to get him up onto the breakwater, and, all at once, death.

I am sure that no one – or almost no one – knows who I am. That hurts me. It gnaws at me every day, it unsettles me, it causes me explosive existential crises. Around the middle of the 1950s, my parents (apostles of medicine) left Bucharest for a placement deep in the mountains whose name suggests the bleating of a goat with three kids, difficult to reproduce in a curriculum vitae. Here I came into the world, in a rural September. I hadn't even cut my teeth, when my mother, worn out by my continuous screaming (which had driven our sheepdog to become melodramatic) had the happy inspiration to read to me from Molière and Cervantes. Thanks to howls of a different tonality (I laughed my head off), I slept like a log, just as any other gifted child would do.

This was my first contact with great literature. After a few years of literary angst in the course of which I managed, despite my tender age, to batter several cats to death, the family returned to the capital. The cats stayed, with the pumpkins in the yard. I refuse to imagine there were no kind-hearted people who would take them into their homes. It is true that they smelled rather strong, but they were still, more or less, cats. From general school I don't remember very much. Apart from the botany teacher who picked plants from their flowerpots, swallowed them when he thought we weren't looking, and gave us long extemporary talks that invariably began with take a sheet of paper. Every since then I have been unable to take a sheet of paper without having a brief nervous tremor. The high school that followed was called 43, and it rose up, white, beside a concrete-mixer. I swallowed plenty of cement powder and I got a lot of first prizes, I still have the little laurel wreaths, somewhere. Unfortunately some of them are now too big for me, I can't wear them any more. And how I would love, sometimes, for example when I go to the Athenaeum, to put them on my head again. Or to parties. Because, I repeat, no one knows who I am.

While I was cleaning my teeth, one fell out, I saw my ugly mug in the mirror, how it gets on your nerves if you're not balanced, with two nasogenian folds inherited from my father wide enough for two columns of ants to go for a Sunday stroll, thinking at the same time that I've given up an honourable profession that gives you the right to wear a pointed cap, and who wouldn't want to wear one, a little hammer for reflexes in your left coat pocket and a stethoscope with a red plastic membrane, whose earpieces used to fall on the green tiles of the hall, and were brought back to me by the cleaner, a woman of a certain age but still appetising, with a long dress and black stockings, moulded on the heel, the blonde nurse, sometimes even the senior nurse, you've dropped the earplugs of your apparatus, they would say, or your little hammer, here you are, thank you very much, if you hadn't found them I wouldn't have been able to hear anything, no extrasystole, no voice from the cosmos, and the other object has, you know, such a useful piece of rubber fixed to the end of the metallic handle with which I strike elbows and kneecaps unnoticed, until I smash them to bits, sometimes I bang the windows at the entrance of the institution too with a similar result but somewhat louder, I usually gather up the shards and stick them in my pocket, I acknowledge that I have frequently had to refrain from proceeding in the same way with the heads of certain patients but above all with the round head of the hospital manager, once I secretly threw it, without anyone seeing, I thought, into the toilet, however, I was tracked down, a patient brought it back to me, perhaps because he only had a month to live, maximum two, cancer, he didn't know, or he didn't want to know, and he brought it just as he had found it, smelling of shit, doctor, you dropped it down the loo, I've wiped it with toilet paper, it's as good as new now, look, you see how the nickel's shining?, it wasn't shining, but I agreed with him, I congratulated him, assuring him that I would be grateful for a month, he didn't get it, in fact he laughed, and this tooth of mine that has fallen out just broke in pieces, for no reason, because I don't even clench my jaws, what would be the point? the man had an ugly death, groaning like a tuba and overturning the bedpan, he called for his mother, but she didn't come, I gave him water and that calmed him a bit, so, taking advantage of the opportunity, I recalled – memories usually come on deathbeds – my second love, she resembled him a little, just as tall, I mean, I had gone to her home for some histopathology lecture notes, because I've never had the patience to attend classes, I get bored, I become agitated, I break my pencil, but the other students go tirelessly to all the lectures, they have pens, glasses, polyvinyl-covered notebooks, they go conscientiously even when classes aren't held, they sit in the lecture theatre, quietly, hoping that in the end they will take notes from what they are taught by professors who talk without commas, without full stops, doing no more than recite what they have copied the previous evening from various specialised books, if they haven't actually got their wives to do the copying for them, they copy too, with their hair in curlers and in university professors' wives' dressing-gowns with mauve flowers, and when they are not reciting, they deliver poems, long ones, by Edgar Allan Poe, I heard one in biophysics, he was smashed, in the shadowy lecture theatre, "And you are gone, sweet miracle," talking about the door handle that he had pulled off with his scientist's determination and couldn't find any more, the hall was closed for a week, until they found another handle, a good one, now I think I've washed myself enough, and she had gigantic breasts, Carmen, the girl I was talking about, they sailed through the room, and just then she had taken to washing, she took showers, caught the hot water, like in films, only that she did it a bit too much, I noticed that for a while people were never done with ablutions, maybe because of the radiation, and suddenly she appeared before my eyes in the one-room flat in Moşilor Way wearing nothing but a little towel, all I wanted was some lecture notes, and the towel covered exactly half of her, the half that remained visible was wet and white, I was stunned, and before you could count to three she opened it too, I saw a burning bush, so

I took the notes, luckily they were on the table, and I was off, a good thing the lift was working, we met again after that, in the end we did that thing, with our eyes shut and her on her back, it was nothing out of the ordinary, it never is, something like the tunnels on the Bumbeşti Livezeni line, a bit off straight, dark and with the locomotive whistling, I was afraid I would never get out again but here I am, I got out, a boil has appeared on my right nostril, I've squeezed it, now a little spirit, that's it, in any case no one ever asks you what you want to be, when I was seven or eight, I liked modelling in clay, I filled the house with gladiators, leaping panthers, the clay dried and became brittle, so the tiger broke and so did the little boy with the goose, the jellyfish, actors, famous nudes, I always got the genital organs wrong though, I made them either too small or too large, so that in the latter circumstance the statuettes lost their balance and landed head first on my father's desk, ships, I spent hours on end playing with pirates, I poked out the eye of one of them. I didn't want to go to kindergarten. They took me there and I got smallpox. It seems that the important thing is to end up a student, even if students aren't interested in clay, or if they are they don't admit it, I need to put more spirit, it's bleeding, to graduate from higher education so that in the end you can rivet onto the door of your flat a brass plate preferably engraved with *Dr*, in capitals, the same on your chest, to go out in town and have people greet you with a humble tilt of their heads, good evening, good day, doctor, with that *d* distinctly audible, how are you, well?, no, thank you, and the doctor's wife?, so-so, how sunny it is outside, it got warmer while I couldn't manage to tell them that I couldn't care less about their sun, good night, I got married.

I picked her with care. At that time she wore yellow shoes, orthopaedic, fashionable then as now, with very high heels, long hair, trousers, that set me thinking, what if she had hairy legs, as many women have, and they splash on aftershave after they've shaved with worn razor-blades, I asked her out to a concert, something highbrow and unbearable, I haven't fidgeted in a chair so much in my life, Bach, or maybe Vivaldi, hard to say, because they transcribed so many of each other's concertos, just changing the solo instrument so that you can't tell who the composer is any more, now I could hear an indisputable lead trumpet, for which reason I put my right hand on the girl's thigh, which she was keeping pressed against mine for musical reasons, I didn't feel anything very special, apparently she didn't either, it was the fault of the concert, to which I nodded along for two hours with the air of a connoisseur, I think I've remained like that ever since, always nodding my head, even in the grocery shop, and those people sell me kabanos sausages that I don't like, but I take them, what am I to do, I just have to hear something pre-classical like the voice of a sales assistant, and it sets my coiffure shaking, on rare occasions, however, I ask them, timidly, if they have heard of me, no one answers and I say thank you, and the truth is that she had a cracking pair of legs, you could walk on them for hours, all the way to Ploieşti, like on the motorway, any speed, there and back, but it took me half a year until I could persuade her to get out of her knickers, and another three months for her bra, I don't know why that was harder, she didn't want to take it off, I got scared at every attempt, imagining some terrible scar on the areola, or a papilloma, in the end she gave in, but only after I had made myself hoarse singing to her with my guitar from Baez, Cohen and Paul Simon, *Congratulations*, until I broke a string, high E, and in the '70s strings were nowhere to be found, which forced me to play a different way, without E, and when she finally took off her bra I realised that I hadn't been singing badly at all, she had cheeky pink breasts that were like a sunrise in the morning. If your block faces east, that is.

The next day I got drunk with joy for the first time in my life, and my father thumped me on the temple with his left hand, with his ring. It may have given me a haematoma, because I get terrible pains when I hit my head against a door, and all the doors in this bloody flat are behind me and open unexpectedly, especially when I'm writing short stories. What with one thing and another, I see I have been shaving for over five hours, it's now evening. Although it's difficult for evening to have come in just five hours, look, it's got dark, perhaps I've been shaving since yesterday, who could say? no one, indeed not even me, if I was asked why I chose this profession, I couldn't find a decent answer. Looking full of concern, with your eyebrows slightly raised, listening to what people tell you, and they tell you their whole life story, pricking them in the buttocks or the soles of the feet, smelling their mouths, and all mouths smell, it hits you, analysing their faeces, their urine under the microscope, pressing their bellies, when you don't feel the least bit like doing such a thing, you press them and they break wind, hammering their backbones, palpating them, some have scabies, they're filthy or sweating with nervousness, or too fat, and the fat comes off, it sticks to your hands, your fingers get greasy, doing genital checks on women who've passed 50, they giggle, and you slip in a word of encouragement, you don't have a fibroma, probing deep with a glove on and a fatal gaze directed upwards, muttering even an abstract term, a technical word that will make them happy, they blush, with emotion, although you still don't cure them, and everyone wants to be cured, on the spot, to live 100 years, or at least another 10, in vain you try to explain to them that it isn't possible in general, and especially in particular, and, if that's the best you can do for them, they want you at least to take their blood. The basin is in the kitchen.

So you have to swallow a painkiller early in the morning, on an empty stomach, and another one an hour later, washed down by a large brandy, and you take their blood. At such moments you no longer feel the smell of village eternalised in the armpits, or however the poet puts it. You no longer feel anything. You take pleasure in the forest, if you live in a forested zone. If not, you don't. But nor are you bothered by their complicated narratives about the weather, sowing, maize flour, what their pig eats, the way something or other ferments, cheese clots or plums and rain fall, because on account of the brandy you can no longer be attentive, you look at them like this, sideways, and smile in the direction of the combine that is just passing, and when the man lying on the couch asks you if he's healthy, you answer, of course, you've got an iron constitution, but still you should take a Decaris in the evening, with a lot of water, isn't that a wonderful combine? it hums, a pity it isn't moving, there are no side-effects, roundworms aren't a problem, the problem is the image, the mirror, yes, this mirror with its oxidised silver that shows me the wrinkles made by too much laughter in the corners of my eyes, because essentially everything is quite ridiculous, the tooth in the wash-hand basin, for example, was beautiful, it's gone, I guess there will be a price, let's pay it, but only until one day, which came a bit later, because I was talking about Mariana, she was wearing a white headscarf knotted under her chin in baroque style, a white coat, looking like she had come out of the hospital, in fact she had just come in and had gathered her superb first-year-student hair with that miserable music-loving hairdresser's rag, the garb was obligatory, she had eyes of wondering grey green and looked at the cadavers laid out on the dissecting table as if they were alive, eyebrows finely arched towards the temples, she smelled of violets, when spring comes one of my nostrils, the left one, quivers with the memory, if I don't put Rinofug drops in it, in physiology we butchered frogs, she the head, I the body, in a perfect lovers' communion, that's how our love began, with the frogs, after we had stuck a syringe needle in their brain stem, so that the vivisection wouldn't hurt, they lay flat out, with a dim look in their eyes, and, I remember, it didn't smell of violets down there, in the little room for recycling cadavers, which were recycled by the classical method, the mummies are taken away after they have been sliced up by flocks of students, reduced to mush, dissected down to the tiniest nerve, sometimes all that's left whole is the optic nerve, which you can play with, pulling it about like a yo-yo, more precisely they are taken away once they have become unusable, and they are shoved, three or four at a time, into a huge tank, with a brass tap, the tap is turned and hot water rushes in, scalding hot, and this at a time when hot water was stopped all over the city, the remains of flesh come loose from the bones, at first it all looks like a soup, a system of pipes creates an underwater current that agitates, turns, whirls around the ingredients and the liquid, the tank boils, you hear a sort of whistling sound, steam rises, and suddenly you may see a hand, coffee-coloured, skinned, an eyeless head, the eyes melt first, a pubis until recently adored, a chalk-like tibia emerging for a moment at the surface, only to sink back again among the bubbles. And so on until there is nothing left but bones, clean, white, which appear as if in an apotheosis, in the form of skeletons destined for study. Pure. Perfect. Smelling, almost imperceptibly, of anatomy. After we had followed this operation with great interest holding hands like two beings destined for one another, in the hours that followed we bent with the same interest over living people. In hospitals. At least they didn't spin around. I think it was in those months of intensive learning that my love for Mariana took shape. She seemed to understand all the incomprehensible suffering of humanity. More than that, she had read Borges. That knocked me down. No one in the faculty had willingly read Borges. He wasn't on the curriculum. The girl in the yellow shoes would have been capable of doing even the dissected cadavers some good, she had a mission, she was determined to cure the whole world, if that was necessary, although it was never necessary. Sometimes, when she finally realised that she had no way of saving the cow or ox stretched out in bed, her eyes moistened. Regardless of how serious their illness was, she spent hours talking with each one, listened to them with the patience of an Egyptian angel, and they talked, they felt all right, they had a bowel movement. I caught her once using a teaspoon to introduce some tea down the bandaged throat of an incurable patient, who had been operated on for cancer of the larynx. The man was looking at her as if she was God, assuming that God would walk around with teaspoonfuls of tea. I followed her for months on end, I wrote some mournful stories too, about dead people, I sent her letters, pressed flowers, despite the fact that the boys all advised me to throw in the towel, not to get in such a state over her, not to press any more plants, because that one never sleeps with anyone, she's got an obsession, not even if you take her out in a Pobeda. I laid her down in Herăstrău, it was winter, I remember we couldn't get her hat off. After we managed, we forgot it there. It was rabbit.

Of course I was bound to cut myself. Probably so that they can all quiz me, why I cut myself, why I got married, why don't you let your beard grow? why have you done so many things you didn't like? but some of them I did like, the malformed foetuses, for example, or the microscopes, none of you know what interesting stuff you can see moving on the slide, under the eyepiece, if you adjust it correctly. Viruses. Gigantic particles of dust. Segmented parasites. It's true that they can't always be seen. You have to be persistent. I am.

And after I fell in love, after I finished my studies – the professors patted me on the head slowly and tenaciously, until I lost my hair, I was a model student – I was thrown together with other innocents into the countryside, to a lithographed dispensary where I discovered an irrigator, I saved a man's life with it, a completely useless action because he died four days later run over by the commuter train, which has four carriages. After a month I got myself a very affectionate grey puppy, which swelled up at an incredible rate – it was full of roundworm – and burst. Then I bought a white rabbit with black patches, I brought it up lovingly, I gave it carrots, I played with it in the cold nights, I watched it jump, it jumped for a few weeks and then went mad. I ate it in wine sauce, like in *The Black Museum*, it was delicious, but unlike the girl in the book it wasn't depression I got, it was diarrhoea. Which reminds me of a day when I went like any other chap to the privy, the privy had no door, it had been explained to me that no one could see any point, it was built on the crest of a hill, and it was damned cold too, and just when I was struggling to get my trousers down I heard an individual with a baritone voice wishing me good morning, doctor. He was passing a little higher up, among the trees, with an axe over his shoulder, and I shat on myself, while at the same time replying to his greeting and suddenly getting a glimpse of the fact that I did not have the vocation of a medical saint, it took some time for me to convince myself, and it happened right there, in the village, in between chaconnes in the mud, as I carried buckets of icy water from the stand pump in the street, that I wasn't cut out for such a profession, because a healer is static and I felt the need of movement.

And so I turned my back on medicine, tore up my degree, gave my blood pressure monitor and sterilising box to some weird people and decided to take up writing. Because through books, it seems, no one expects their paronychia, their tuberculosis to disappear, to be saved. I learned to type by myself, according the Blanche method, 1927. I destroyed the typewriter. I bought myself another one. Now let me write. How to write. Do it in a crisis. As if the world was in a state of siege. As if everything was going to disappear in an hour or tomorrow morning at the latest, including the cactus on the desk that you haven't watered lately, the photograph of your wife on the banks of the lake, the town, the lights and the gravel in your mind. Write in despair. With acute accents on all the vowels, Kierkegaard font, bold, 15 point, and above all with death before your face and behind your back, on the prowl, smiling like any photo model, with time on the table, clanging, keeping up the tension with little white spaces, laced with ellipses, gradually rarefying the text only to crush it then in the vice, smashing its course, making it howl at an accelerated tempo, *allegro molto e vivace*, panting its way to a traumatising crescendo. Don't be soft with your reader, hit him with ideas, send him to hospital, leave marks on his face. Ruthless. Keep pulverising. It doesn't matter what, just pulverise. Gnaw, bite, break pens, break branches, tear sheets of paper, then crumple them into balls and throw them from the balcony onto the heads of children going to school in vain and they look up and swear at you. You swear too, as you aim empty yoghurt jars and pieces of wood at them. Write with grim determination, with fury, with hate. With clenched teeth. Cursing. Giving yourself ulcers, with perforation, digestive haemorrhage, schizophrenia, Spanish flu, haemorrhoids, duodenal tube. In delirium. Write deliriously. And without anyone seeing, write with love, over which you should pour tons of pepper and Hunter ketchup. Write out of pure, intermittent madness, like a hunter. Out of exasperation. Out of despair. Writing. Freezing. Losing sunsets, friends, beautiful women, foreign countries. One time I wanted to throw myself onto something head first, I found a bridge, built by Germans during the war and allowed to fall into ruin by Romanians, and I was saved by a villager with whom I had drunk a bottle of *ţuică* grabbing me by the collar of my sheepskin coat. It tore. And to this day I haven't bought another one.

And my wife who doesn't understand why. Why I burst into tears at old films that no one cries at, why I laugh when there's nothing to laugh about, why I get drunk when the world is so beautiful.

Then, unexpectedly, there came successes. The first book, the first prize. How proud I was at the writers' restaurant. At a certain point I made my way, as a newly enrolled member of the Union, to the toilet reserved for members. And a short man of letters, with a fixed stare, got upset because I didn't open the door when he gave it a kick, from inside. A few minutes later he came to the table where I was sitting nervously, and launched into a fit of swearing at me. Silence fell over the garden full of great writers. My embarrassment was, however, swallowed up by the flood of invective, the man just wouldn't lay off me, he had a goatee, he didn't want to move away, I fascinated him. I should have looked up to him, he was a writer, but after I had listened to him for about a quarter of an hour, trying without success to interrupt him, I punched him in the stomach. He didn't get up again. I left him there, under the table, it's been years since then. Concomitantly with his falling on his back, at a neighbouring table another creator gave a brief hiccup, said something about Croce, and vomited in the plate of ostropel of a colleague of the same generation who was looking at him with admiration.

Then my second book came out. That got a prize too, at Târgoviște, 300 dollars. The organisers took us by coach to the Dealu Monastery, where I saw the head of Michael the Brave. Or, to be more precise, the casket where it is assumed to have lain for 400 years. Mariana had a laugh at the hotel, in bed, the bed was narrow and one of its legs was falling off, saying it wasn't his head. Another year, and I began to feel I had entered definitively into the world of prosaists with a short novel, about identity. I read my own book in the metro, holding it in such a way that I could be easily recognised from the photograph on the cover. A lady in a headscarf recognised me. I smiled at her, I didn't know what to do, whether or not to give her the book with my autograph, so I got off at the next station. Shortly after that, I won the national grand prize for the best theatre play of the year. I was starting to be the slave of competitions, I was winning them like a horse, I had become addicted. Six months later, another prize, also for the best theatre play of the year. The same year. Neither of them was staged.

The other day I went into a bar, I felt lonely, I had no one to talk to and, after two or three gins I revealed to the barman that I had won a literary prize. A very important one. Bravo, he said to me, giving me an understanding look. But have you got your picture in the papers? Yes, I answered, here it is. He looked at it, then at me, and he didn't recognise me. Even though it was a good photograph. He gave me back the newspaper with a smile. For example, you go out in the street, you're a footballer, a member of parliament, or you present the weather on TV, and everyone turns their heads, wants to see you better, to observe the line of your nose, your ears, whispering your name with respect, with envy, with admiration, with drops of saliva. But if you happen to be a writer, nobody notices you. The Colomber monster at the most. Or the policeman. Who threatens you with his finger, preventively. The best you can expect is that the barman will say bravo and wait for you to give him a tip for the word. You give him a tip. It's unbearable. The thing gnaws at you. Any mute country girl, totally illiterate, who can manage to stay still for five seconds on a beam is incomparably better known than me. Any tennis player who has won the Camil Petrescu grand prize. Any boxer whose little brain hangs out. It's indecent.

The moment has come for me to sharpen my razor. It's an art that I picked up from my grandfather on my father's side, he used to sharpen his razor twice a day and then go out into town, on the main street, he would go into a pub and not say a word until the lights went out. Then he woke up. Right, the razor is in my pocket, I can see that my wife is sleeping, assuming that the beautiful woman sleeping in my bed is my wife. I have to go and buy some yoghurt. There is a certain carton of yoghurt that I really like, with a blue cow on the top. And you are obliged to eat. You leave behind two or three books, a wife who sleeps with the bedside lamp switched on, and some night or other you suddenly realise that nothing is really important, and the least important thing of all is your conceptions about the world, cows, destiny, and why am I so irritated by the look of the guy selling yoghurt? He seems very full of himself, what can be the reason? maybe he's an idiot. Yes, it's possible, it's 10 in the evening after all.

I go in.

He's got a lazy eye. As he gives me the change he smiles condescendingly. Perhaps I'm mistaken, but I feel he's looking down on me. I can't understand why. When it comes down to it, I've been to university, I've saved a man from death, and I've published a few books for which I've been awarded eight prizes. He hasn't been awarded a single prize. Still, I talk to him in a civilised way, I have the razor in my pocket, I gently grip the smooth handle. The stupid fool takes a long look at my winter coat. It's old, I know, the collar has come unstitched, I haven't had enough money to buy another one. Everything I've earned from my writing has gone on a bookcase, three paintings and a sofa. And of course even that has a little cut that I didn't notice in the shop. But the shop assistant seems to be in the know, he's a connoisseur, he knows about the cut on the sofa, he's probably laughing inside right now. If he has an inside. I ask him in a whisper, as gently as I can and leaning forward a little, what the time is. Then, after he has given me the correct answer, I ask him an even easier question, namely if he has any idea who I am. I turn my head, for him to see me in profile too. To give him a chance. He looks at me with amusement. I've lost count of the people who keep looking at me with amusement. I hold my breath and ask him again. He looks at me in the same way. And then I cut his throat, with a rapid movement. Almost elegant. And I grab the carton of yoghurt, but not before two or three drops of blood have splashed onto the top.

I'm thinking of leaving my wife for a while. The truth is that she's been lucky, Mariana, there have been nights when I have looked at her throat much more than I should have done. On the other hand, it's in the realm of the absurd to separate, even for a short time, from someone you are so fond of. But when I wake up in the morning, I realise that the light is absurd too, my fallen tooth being the evidence. I needed a lot of papers to sort out my business. The law court. What impressed me in that building was the corridors. Long, high, twisted. Submerged in a semi-darkness stained by the flickering of a few neon lights. Smelling of sweat and cat urine. Which reminded me of my childhood. But whence so much urine? Whence so many cats? They probably come in at night, look at the accused's box with their phosphorus eyes, curled up on the benches where the next day people with hard hats and cotton skirts will be sitting, and mark the place. Then they leave for the dark recesses of other rooms.

We kissed when I left. Without hurrying, gathered a few indispensable things. Nothing much. I haven't accumulated anything to speak of in 40 years. I took my guitar, a checked suitcase that I lost the key of long ago, my cassette player and a pullover. It might be cold over there, especially now, in the winter. In the train I thought again, with bitterness, how nobody knows me. For a while I tried to transform this observation into a sentiment that might be comforting to some extent. But after about half an hour the individual opposite me started to get on my nerves. He was avidly eating cherries out of a jar of compote and spitting the stones on the floor. I said to him warmly, excuse me, wouldn't you like to spit higher, or further, or to slash the back of the seat, we still have a long way to go and everyone does it, it's in fashion, have you seen *Twin Peaks*? Or let's unscrew the mirror and throw the damn thing out of the window, we might hit a railwayman, or we could smash the neon light, it's just the two of us in the compartment, I'll lend you my razor for the seat, what do you say to the idea, it's very sharp, I sharpened it myself, the way my grandfather taught me, on my belt, what do you think? And the man got up without a word and slipped out through the door like cooking oil, nothing creaked in his wake, and that, unfortunately, just two or three seconds before I was going to ask him if he knew me. If he knew who I was. If he actually had done, that would have been something.

For a while I lost the notion of time. Towns pass one after the other. Trains likewise.

At Tulcea I managed with some difficulty, at the hotels they kept saying they had no places available, and there wasn't the shadow of a tourist to be seen, how in God's name can you have no rooms when I can see that no one comes to your shitty town, but the police came and started questioning me, it was lucky that I still had a bottle of whisky bought in Arad, which I drank with the sergeant or whatever he was, for by the morning it had become impossible to make out what he was saying or what his rank was, he was sleeping on the bathroom carpet out of his uniform, but when he woke he lent me his boat. It wasn't great, it took in water and only had one oar.

The Danube Delta is a wonder. Cousteau said that too. Or whoever said it. Smoke, fog, leaves, dust on them, murky waters, green, sticky, you go along all sorts of identical channels and now and then you see the odd wild duck. Or two. Plus a Lipovan. Wiry, red in the face, steaming drunk. Usually stretched out on the bank, waiting. He's not waiting for anything in particular, just sitting there looking at the sky. Otherwise a decent chap, invites you into his mud and bird shit cottage, gives you fish soup prepared according to an ancient recipe, with water from the Danube swarming with all sorts of nasties, especially cholera vibrios, somewhere and at the same time high above us space probes are flying towards Jupiter, towards Saturn, seemingly they have already crossed the borders of the galaxy and, as far as can be seen, their voyaging is not doing humanity much good, these silvery objects are plunging into the universe and the Lipovan doesn't give a shit, and he asks me where I want him to take me in his rowing-boat, to Mila 42, to the boozer, to get ourselves a drink, 'cause it's already morning, he has powerful shoulders, he's burnt by the sun and by his fundamental stupidity, an enduring stupidity, unshaken by the centuries, by Tatars, by floods, no problem standing up to 36 degrees in the shade without a hat, and I ask him, it's become a habit, Vasile, do you know me? What do you say? Do you know who I am, haven't you seen me somewhere? The man is getting on in years and he looks at me with an interesting mixture of curiosity and weariness, where the hell do you want me to know you from? what else can you be but a tourist, although you don't look like one? and then I think he sees something in my eyes because I hear him say, with a changed voice, sorry, maybe I didn't recognise you, it happens sometimes, my memory's not what it used to be, all right, I say, but tell me if you know who I am? Have you really not heard of me? No, son, I really haven't, what did you say your name was? uh-huh, no, not at all, are you maybe from the TV, 'cause now they all come and film us going up and down the channels in our boats, and at that moment I pretend to lean over the water, I delicately pass the fingers of my left hand over the waves and with the right I take out the razor, of course, it comes more easily to me now, I've got used to it with the passage of time, and I sever his carotid, what a lot of blood spurts out, and he falls, slowly, right on the bottom of the boat, which immediately turns into a splendid puddle of red with violet striations, so that I wonder for a moment where so much Pollock-Gaugin liquid has come from. Then I take up the oars, they seem to be made of iron, and row towards the fishing station.

I return to town late.

For a few days I look at the hills. Then I look in my pockets for a coin to make a phone call. I give up.

I have no money left. Still thinking how to solve this problem, one day I pay a visit to the cemetery, the lime trees are in blossom, I sit down on a bench. I am tired. It is, once again, after a long time, a beautiful morning. The birds are singing too. A few minutes pass, perhaps an hour. I notice the caretaker, a very ugly old man who, 10 metres in front of me, is pretending to sweep a path. In fact he has been studying me attentively for about a quarter of an hour, through glasses with powerful lenses and thick black frames. Right beside me stands a very beautiful cross, made of white marble, with a little wrought-iron fence around it. The fence makes an impression. Where the bars cross, the artist has soldered brass studs, shining, someone in the family polishes them every day, that's for sure, the studs hypnotise you, they look like little stars. I get up to get a better look at the photograph fixed to the cross. A superb young woman, I don't know if she's dead, with long chestnut hair, and film-star breasts, reclines on one side in colour. While I was admiring her, I sensed that the caretaker was coming towards me. It was his broom that gave him away, as he dragged it carelessly on the sand. Immediately I felt for the razor in my pocket. I know, it's getting blunt with so much use. All the same, I asked the old man, with the most natural air I could manage, if he knows me. He hasn't answered. He is still approaching, menacingly.

Translator's notes

'The *Goat with Three Kids*' by Ion Creangă (see notes to 'The Crystal Globe') is a tale familiar to generations of Romanian schoolchildren.

Athenaeum: see notes to 'Diary of a Flat-dweller'.

The *Bumbeşti Livezeni* railway line, which follows the Jiu valley in the southern Carpathians, is famous for its series of tunnels.

Herăstrău: see notes to 'Quotidian'.

The '*village eternalised*' is an ironic reference to the idealisation of the Romanian village in the writing of the poet and philosopher Lucian Blaga (1895–1961), one of whose best-known lines is 'I think eternity was born in the village.'

Ţuică: see note to 'Chance'.

Ostropel is a stew of chicken or lamb in an onion and garlic sauce.

The *head of Michael the Brave* (see notes to 'Playing Jesus') is indeed kept at the Dealu Monastery, outside Târgovişte.

Colomber: the name of the monstrous shark in Dino Buzzati's story 'Il colombre'.

Camil Petrescu (1894–1957) was a Romanian novelist and playwright. The Camil Petrescu Grand Prize is awarded for stage writing (not for tennis).

The *Lipovans* are an ethnic community descended from Russian religious dissenters who settled in the area of the Danube Delta in the eighteenth century.

The Author

Born in 1956, Răzvan Petrescu was brought up in Bucharest, where he went on to study at the Medical University, while continuing to pursue an interest in literature. After graduating in 1982, he worked for five years in rural clinics in Dâmbovița county, before finally giving up medicine to devote himself to writing. His first book of short stories, *The Summer Garden*, appeared in 1989. Since 1990, he has worked as an editor for a number of Romanian literary periodicals and publishing houses. His second collection, *Eclipse* was published in 1993, followed by two plays, *The Joke* and *Springtime at the Bar*, developed from stories in *Eclipse*, and a third book of short fiction, *One Friday Afternoon*, in 1997. He currently works for the Bucharest publishers Curtea Veche, and is a frequent contributor to the Romanian literary and cultural press. His latest book, *Foxtrot XX*, a collection of mainly non-fiction prose, was published in 2008. His writing has been highly praised by Romanian critics and his books have attracted numerous national and local literary awards.

The Translator

James Christian Brown was born in Glasgow in 1962, and graduated in Fine Art from the University of Edinburgh in 1984. He has lived in Romania since 1993, and teaches in the English Department of the University of Bucharest. His previous translations include Ana Bârca & Dan Dinescu, *The Wooden Architecture of Maramureş* (Bucureşti: Humanitas, 1997), Gabriel Liiceanu, *The Păltiniş Diary* (Budapest: CEU Press, 2000), Lucian Boia, *History and Myth in Romanian Consciousness* (Budapest: CEU Press, 2001) and Lucian Boia, *Romania: Borderland of Europe* (London: Reaktion Books, 2001). He gained a doctorate from the University of Bucharest in 2007, with a thesis on nineteenth-century British travel writing about the Romanian lands.

Notes on Romanian Spelling and Pronunciation

As the Romanian spelling system is phonetically based and highly regular, it should not be difficult for the reader to achieve a reasonably accurate pronunciation of the various Romanian names and other words that occur in this book, if the following are borne in mind:

Consonants

c – before *e* or *i* as in 'church', otherwise as in 'coat'
ch (before *e* or *i*) – as English *k* in 'king'
g – before *e* or *i* as in 'gem', otherwise as in 'goat'
gh (before *e* or *i*) – as English *g* in 'get'
j – like the sound represented by *s* in 'measure'
r – pronounced in all positions, slightly rolled.
s – as in 'seat' (never as in 'rose')
ş – as English *sh*
ţ – as English *ts*
Other consonants are pronounced much as in English.

Vowels

a, e, i, o, u: similar to Italian pronunciation, apart from the following:
– final *i* is generally almost silent (as in *Bucureşti*, pronounced bookoo<u>resht</u>)
– *i* before another vowel sounds like English *y* (as in the personal name *Ion*, which sounds like 'yon')
– *o* before *a* sounds like English *w* (as in *Timişoara*, pronounced teemee<u>shwara</u>)
ă – like the *a*- in 'about', or the *-er* in 'mother' (but not so weakly stressed).
â or *î* – something like the *i* in 'fill', but with the tongue further back in the mouth

Stress

In general the contrast between stressed and unstressed syllables is not as strong in Romanian as in English. However there is a tendency, especially in longer words, for the last syllable to receive more stress if the word ends in a consonant, and the penultimate if it ends in a vowel.

Hardback edition first published in the United Kingdom in 2011 by University of Plymouth Press, Scott Building, Drake Circus, Plymouth, Devon, PL4 8AA, United Kingdom.

ISBN 978-1-84102-214-7

© 2011 Răzvan Petrescu
© 2011 University of Plymouth Press

A CIP catalogue record of this book is available from the British Library

Translation: James Christian Brown
Publisher: Paul Honeywill
Publishing Assistants: Charlotte Carey
Series Art Director: Sarah Chapman
Romanian Art Consultant: Simona Vilău
Romanian Cultural Institute: Mihaela Ghiţă
Editorial Advisors: Cristina Sandru, Dennis Deletant and Adina Bradeanu

Typeset by University of Plymouth Press in Janson 10/14pt
Printed and bound by Short Run Press, Exeter, EX2 7LW

Visit www.uppress.co.uk/romanian.htm

Published with the support of the Romanian Cultural Institute

20 ROMANIAN WRITERS SERIES

Twenty of Romania's most influential and award-winning authors are launched by UPP in the series 20 Romanian Writers. Romanian arts have long been unknown in the West and this series aims to make a lasting contribution to the canon of Eastern European literature.

These works have been translated into English for the first time; the collection captures Romania's rich cultural diversity and artistic heritage. Selected by an independent Romanian jury of editors, academics and publishers, the series showcases the most notable Romanian novels, essays, poetry, short prose and philosophy of the 20th and 21st centuries.

Each volume is edited and comes with a substantial introduction that contextualises the work not only within Romanian, but Eastern European and Anglo-American traditions. Texts are complemented with a 16-page full-colour supplement provided by some of Romania's leading contemporary visual artists. 20 Romanian Writers is a landmark collection of the very best Romanian writing. The titles published in this series so far are:

The Cinematography Caravan

IOAN GROȘAN

A black comedy set in 1960s Romania: a Stalinist propaganda film truck rumbles into a forgotten Transylvanian village. The occupants of the village believe in the traditional values of Church and God and are in no mood to participate, placing obstacles in the way of the Cinematography Caravan crew. The resultant humour is deliberately provincial as the villagers find their own unique ways of dealing with them while they're in town.

ISBN 978-1-84102-205-5

Lines Poems Poetry

MIRCEA IVĂNESCU

Ivănescu's poetry represents the achievement of a little-known master. Centring on a wide cast of characters including his alter ego 'mopete', Ivănescu's idiosyncratic, lyrical sensibility offers allusive, comic and elegiac meditations on our common lot.

Ivănescu's *Lines Poems Poetry* was shortlisted for the Poetry Society's 2011 Popescu Translation Prize.

ISBN 978-1-84102-217-8

Occurrence in the Immediate Unreality

MAX BLECHER

This autobiographical fiction offers an intimate and unsettling account of Blecher's ideas of self-identity and the body. He explores the 'crisis of unreality' in relation to the human condition and shares his adolescent experiences of physical infirmity, social isolation and sexual awakening.

ISBN 978-1-84102-207-9

Six Maladies of the Contemporary Spirit

CONSTANTIN NOICA

In this unique work, Noica analyses history, culture and the individual in what he describes as the fundamental precariousness of being. 'Maladies' of the spirit are no longer debilitating, but creative for our European interest in change, unity, and diversity.

ISBN 978-1-84102-203-1

The Băiuţ Alley Lads

FILIP AND MATEI FLORIAN

Two brothers, Filip and Matei, are growing up in a totalitarian society. Everyday life is recounted through their young eyes. Their world is filled with characters from children's television, broadcast by the official communist media, alongside magazines and cinema. 'Joe Lemonade', 'Giani Morandi' and 'Brooslee' accentuate the absurdity and grotesqueness of their surroundings.

The brothers become close through a shared love of football, supporting the same team, Dinamo Bucureşti. Ultimately, *The Băiuţ Alley Lads* is a novel about miracles that take place within a nightmare, regardless of whether they occur in an obscure lane in an obscure district of a country kept in obscurity by communist dictatorship.

ISBN 978-1-84102-267-3

No Way Out of Hadesburg and Other Poems

IOAN ES. POP

In Romania under communist rule, forbidden to write but allowed to work as a builder on Ceauşescu's palace, Ioan Es. Pop lived alone in a bachelor block. His poetry is an autobiographical account of this time: a life with no way out. Having originally been a teacher in a village that he later gives the fictional name of Hadesburg, Pop's writing expresses his response to such a life. The world of the poems is a closed, boundless, imaginary space charged with dramatic intensity and tempered by a bitter-sweet, compassionate, existential angst.

ISBN 978-1-84102-209-3

Auntie Varvara's Clients

STELIAN TĂNASE

Stelian Tănase's books explore the politics of the totalitarian state. He is an historical authority on the communist period in Romania. *Auntie Varvara's Clients* brings to life documents discovered in the archives of the pre-communist secret police, the Siguranţă (nicknamed 'Auntie Varvara'). This extensive work reveals a regime reliant on secrecy. The narrative changes tense unannounced, giving a surreal, filmic quality to the writing. Tănase takes us from the early days of illegal membership of the communist underground, at the end of the First World War, to their eventual rise to power and the struggle for supremacy.

ISBN 978-1-84102-221-5

Who Won the World War of Religions?

DANIEL BĂNULESCU

Contemporary madness in its entirety is summarised in Daniel Bănulescu's play, set in an asylum populated with 12 dangerous madmen who are divided as believers of the four major religions. This is theatre in a world governed by insanity; as Dan Stanca remarks, the play could be set anywhere – in Piteşti, in the Siberian Gulag, in a Nazi concentration camp, Maoist or Khmer Rouge extermination camp, and, even, in one of the CIA's secret prisons... This is the principal merit and black humour of the play.

ISBN 978-1-84102-212-3

Small Changes in Attitude
RĂZVAN PETRESCU

Regulars in a village bar chew over rumours of the Chernobyl disaster. The perpetrator of the first murder tries to tell the court his side of the story. A resident in a block of flats is disconcerted to find his neighbours gradually falling victim to a mysterious epidemic. A chance encounter in the Bucharest Metro sparks an explosion of increasingly bizarre storytelling... Rich in invention and stylistic variety, combining sharp observation with playful fantasy, ironic detachment with an underlying sense of tragedy, Răzvan Petrescu's stories offer a series of variations on the human condition in a tragicomic key. *Small Changes in Attitude* contains a selection from his first three books of short stories *The Summer* Garden (1989), *Eclipse* (1993), and *One Friday Afternoon* (1997).

ISBN 978-1-84102-214-7

French Themes
NICOLAE MANOLESCU

Inspired by the combination of political intrigue and love contained within the belles-lettres of the great French novelists, Manolescu uses this recipe to tell the story of a great love. Cristina Chevereşan considers French Themes as 'love declared or merely suggested, patient and durable, arousing the aromas of French perfumes but also a reading in culture and civilization'.

Manolescu has been a member of the Romanian Academy since 1998. He is a critic and literary historian who was elected President of the Writers' Union of Romania in 2005. In 2006 he was appointed Romanian Ambassador to UNESCO.

ISBN 978-1-84102-208-6

The Book of Winter and Other Poems

ION MUREȘAN

There is at once an enigmatic and original character to the poetic language of Ion Mureșan, who concerns himself through this anthology with the political nature of Romanian poetry. Mureșan's poetry draws upon Transylvanian legends to explore the way the communist manipulation and monopoly of truth leaves the individual powerless. By regaining individual thoughts, through his poetry there is a promise of salvation which reflects what it is to be Romanian.

He is one of the poets included in the anthology *12 Ecrivains Roumains*, published by Éditions L'Inventaire on the occasion of Les Belles Étrangeres Programme organised by the Centre National du Livre in 2005. Some of his latest poems, *The Alcohol Book* (2010) have been included in this edition.

ISBN 978-1-84102-213-0

Why We Love Women

MIRCEA CĂRTĂRESCU

Cărtărescu brings together 21 short stories and articles that he wrote mainly for *ELLE* magazine. The protagonist of every story is female, but they are not individual portraits of women – it is a group portrait of womanhood.

His books have received awards from the Romanian Academy, the Writers' Union of Romania, the Moldovan Writers' Union, ASPRO, the Bucharest Association of Writers, the Association of Romanian Publishers, and the *Cuvîntul, Ateneu, Flacăra, Tomis* and *Ziarul de Iași* reviews. In France, he has been nominated for the Médicis, Le Meilleur Livre Étranger, and Prix Union Latine. His novel *Nostalgia* won the Giuseppe Acerbi Prize at Castle Goffredo, Italy, in 2005.

ISBN 978-1-84102-206-2